Doctor Nai... ...the sweetest
doctor I have ever met.

Yearning To Be American

For doctor Nairi Berner,

with love and good health
wishes,

Jacqueline

Yearning To Be American

Jacqueline Jorgensen

Printed in USA
by Bay Port Press
800•994•7737
www.BayPortPress.com

Contents

Many thanks to my editor Bill Greenleaf for his help and encouraging words.

Also, many thanks to Pearl's Friday class, where I read each chapter and was applauded and cheered-on.

And then, there is Bethany Wickwire, my dearest friend who loves to hear me read my writing, even over the phone and long distance. Many thanks, Bethany.

Finally, I want to thank my husband Jim who learned how to prepare some of his meals while I pounded the keyboard.

Prologue

    I probably pounded the keyboard for fifteen minutes before deciding that my brain needed a rest. So I poured myself a cup of coffee and turned on the television set, which had always helped me come up with words and sentences. But what I saw on the screen was a huge fire that brought fear to my mind instead of creative words. I heard the shaky voices of reporters, the emergency sirens, and the yelling and screaming of men and women. A bomb had destroyed a federal building in Oklahoma. I leaned back on my chair and did nothing but stare and wonder why anyone would commit such a terrible crime against our beautiful country.

    Some time later, I heard the sound of the garden blower in my back yard. I wiped away my tears and went outside to give Mr. Tran some instructions. He is a Vietnamese refugee who mows the grass in my neighborhood. He shut off the blower and walked toward me with fear in his eyes.

    "Have you heard the news, Madam?" I was surprised that he had obviously heard about the tragedy before I had.

    "Who do think did it Madam? It had to be somebody from another county, because Americans don't do things like that, right?"

    I stared at the poor man, as old memories unfolded in my mind. "That's exactly what I thought forty years ago," I blurted. "I was in my teens when I came to the States from Puerto Rico. My main reason to come here was to get away from crime, brutality, and gossip. I learned otherwise quickly, but every time I hear some horrific news, I feel the same twisting in my stomach I felt when I heard the first bad news report in the States. And I still ask myself over and over: 'How can anyone commit horrific acts against the best country in the world?'"

    Mr. Tran shook his head and went back to his work. I watched him walk away, then I went back to my computer, where a storm of memories unfolded faster than my fingers could move. I had come here a long time ago, believing that bad things would not take place in the United States. I have learned a great deal since then about crime and human behavior. But I still find it hard to believe that in a country that has abundance of everything, including opportunities for prosperity, ugly crimes that hurt all of us take place. Even more painful to me, is the fact that a lot of the crimes are committed by educated people, who could have a prosperous life if they tried. The crime, the brutality, and gossip I had ran from was nothing in comparison to the crazy and senseless crime in our precious USA.

As the memories flowed from my brain onto the computer screen, I wondered if every refugee who comes to the States looking for prosperity and salvation believed as Mr. Tran and I had. Perhaps I should go out and interview a few thousand refugees. The tales I'd hear could become My Great American Novel. In spite of all the nasty news I hear daily, I still love my United States. And I hurt deeply when some crazy idiot does or says bad things to tarnish the freedom all of us have enjoyed.

Yes, the old memories filled over three hundred pages, and earned the title, <u>Yearning To Be American.</u>

Chapter One

The Day I Met Frank

Love songs blaring from jukeboxes, and blinking lights set the festive mood on both sides of Borinquen Road. A man called me "gorgeous" from one of the bars, but I increased my pace and never looked back. Borinquen Road wasn't a good place for a *señorita* (a virgin girl) to stroll alone, especially from Friday afternoons until midnight on Sundays. That's when the local men had money to spend on whiskey and beer, and when they flirted the most.

Flirting had always been part of the culture of Puerto Rican men, but a decent girl was expected to ignore the flirts. The wife, or lover, of such men might be watching, and she would ruin a girl's reputation with ugly accusations. Still, as I walked on, the bitter memories of the argument I had with my family the previous night came to mind and my stomach tightened into a knot. *How would I feel walking into one of those bars, just to prove that a girl could do things like that and still keep her dignity?*

Shortly after that thought, I turned into the gravel road that led to our house, and from the distance, I saw my fourteen-year-old brother scraping rust off an old bike in our front yard. The feeling in my stomach became a twisting and burning discomfort. I knew that another fight could not be avoided.

"I hope you're going to tell me that someone gave you that piece of junk!" I yelled.

Lorenzo didn't look my way. Instead, he shouted back, "I'm not that lucky. And it's not a piece of junk! It needs repair, but it's a good old bike. I paid three dollars for it, and I deserve it."

The burst of anger pushed me up the walkway and through the gate. "Three dollars! You spent your wages on that rusty old thing? And where is the money you promised me last night?"

"Don't worry. I'll give you some next week."

"Next week? Are you going to eat parts of the bike until then? I got my wages today – fifteen dollars for one week of working eight to four every weekday. Twelve dollars will go for this month's rent, and I'll only have three dollars left to carry me through the next week. Do you think that's fair?" I had walked up the steps, but backed down and kicked the old bike, which landed on its side. "Answer me, Lorenzo! Do you think that's fair?"

He leaped toward me with clenched teeth, his big brown eyes narrowing.

"You! . . ." But before he could take his first swing, our mother's pale face appeared at the window.

"I'm getting sick and tired of you two always fighting."

My anger turned to rage. "You're getting sick and tired! Let me tell you something, Mama. I have been sick and tired for two years, working all day every week, and then having to fight for some help with the expenses around here."

Deep creases formed on Mama's forehead as her dark eyes zoomed in on me. "Nobody asked you to bring us here! So stop your complaining!" With that she moved away from the window, but my fire had been ignited, and I wasn't about to shut up yet.

"That's right, Mama," I yelled. "I brought you here from the mudhole you called home. I wanted to give you and my sisters and brothers a chance to live free from Papa's drunkenness. Now it's clear that I made a big mistake. You'll never see the good in me. I go around in extra-large dresses just because you don't want me to look like a manteaser. Well, Mama, this is 1954, and I'm the only eighteen-year-old girl around here dressing like an older woman to please you. But you'll never appreciate anything I do for you."

Mama didn't return to the window. Obviously she didn't want to continue the fight, but I was still fuming. So, I went into the house, put on a yellow dress, tied a red belt around my waist, colored my lips red, brushed my hair, grabbed my wallet, and headed for Doña Inez's place to pay the rent - but not before walking past a few bars, just to feel bold and free.

The barrio, Borinquen, had earned the nickname *Point Revolution* ten years earlier, when the United States built the nearby Air Force base. People from all over the island had moved to the barrio to find jobs on the base. The locals had predicted prosperity so they built bars and cantinas with jukeboxes and blinking lights on both sides of the road, until the long strip of little businesses stretched all the way from the city of Aguadilla to the main gate of the base. The businesses had customers from early morning to the late hours of the night. But Fridays were paydays for most people, so the entire area became a carnival that lasted until midnight on Sundays.

The owners of the businesses lived on their second floors. Those who lived in single homes on stilts rented out spaces under their houses to men who worked on the base, but lived too far away to go back and forth every day. Those tenants paid to hang a hammock from one stilt to another, which was where they slept every night.

"Hey, over here, sweetheart!" I heard a man say as I walked past a bar.

"Now that's a natural blonde," another man said from the next bar. "No dark roots on that one. I'd give anything to have her in my arms."

I continued on, looking straight ahead. Then I heard a woman's voice. "Hey, blonde! Better stay away from here if you know what's good for you. Next time, I'll throw boiling water on you to scar your face and make your yellow hair fall out."

I briefly looked toward the voice, and saw a woman up on a weathered balcony. She had shaggy black hair, a bulging belly, and two naked little boys clinging to her legs. She was the typical wife, or lover, of the type of man who wasted his flirts on me.

I shook my head and headed to Doña Inez's place. I'd pay the rent and help her around the restaurant, because I didn't want to return home too soon to another argument.

As I walked on, thoughts about my life unfolded in my mind. I had run away from ridicule, brutality, drunkenness, and my father's sharp machete six years earlier.

Fortunately, I had found a compassionate couple who had opened their hearts and home to me. They gave me more in four years than my parents had given me in twelve. When the couple died, I went back to the farm to rescue my siblings and our mother and had spent the past two years teaching them to live free from Papa.

Now they were making my life miserable, and I needed to disappear from them for good. Yet I knew that the only future for a girl those days was as some guy's woman and mother to a houseful of starving children. I had run away from slavery before, and I had no intention of going back to such a miserable lifestyle.

Marrying an American man would be the quickest way out of this situation. Everything I had heard about the American people in the past two years had been good. They were educated, honorable, compassionate, good-looking, and rich. And the best thing was that the local girls who had married American soldiers had not been back to the island complaining about a bad life in the States.

Well, I had been working on the Air Force base for two years, but I had never been introduced to one unmarried American man. I had watched them, through a louvered window at work, as they marched down the street in their crisp khaki uniforms, their shoulders back, their long legs straight, and their steps firm and steady. I knew I wanted to meet one of them, but I didn't know how.

Besides being unsure of myself, I felt stupid and unattractive. My skin was too white, my hair was too light, and my eyebrows and eyelashes were almost white. I didn't use face creams or makeup, and I seldom wore lipstick. I made my own dresses long and wide to hide my figure. At five feet three inches tall, with a twenty-inch waist, slender hips, and a 32B chest, a fitted dress would make me "a man-teaser" according to my mother. The baggy dresses, she believed, would protect me from ugly accusations.

I had seen some of those gorgeous men on bus stops going to and from work, but they had never said more than a quick hello. Later, I learned that because I was a blonde, they thought of me as the young wife or daughter of one of their own. Even the military bus driver who saw me at bus stops pulled up and motioned me in, never asking for an ID. I didn't volunteer information, either. Without realizing it, he saved me ten cents each day, the cost of a ride on the civilian bus to and from work.

Of course at that time, I didn't make any Puerto Rican friends either. The other women who had been waiting with me for the orange-colored civilian bus waved their arms angrily and yelled in Spanish, "Hey, she's Puerto Rican, too!" But the driver smiled and drove on. As those thoughts came to mind, I realized that I enjoyed being thought of as an American. Now my wishes to marry an American man became a strong yearning. Having an American name, along with being a blonde, would solve all my problems. I would marry the first American I met - and I would not look him over twice, either.

Chapter Two

Airman Frank

I often wondered if angels were guiding my way - and on this day I was convinced that they were.

As I reached Doña Inez's kitchen door, she came out from behind the stove with a red face and twinkles in her dark eyes. "Oh, Sabina, I was hoping that you'd come by. There's a great guy I want you to meet – an American!"

I stood frozen for a moment. *I am being guided by angels! This can not be a coincidence.* "Doña Inez," I finally said, "I just came to pay the rent, and I have to hurry back home. Mama is waiting for me to bring some groceries."

"Never mind your mother. Come help me serve the food and take a close look at this guy. He's the one in the yellow shirt, playing the guitar by the window. His name is Frank Wilson, and he is the nicest guy you'll ever meet."

"I'll be happy to help you. I don't want to get home too soon, anyway."

"Oh, you are an angel."

"I wish my mother could think of me as an angel."

"Oh, she probably does. How could she not, after all you've done for her? The poor thing doesn't know how to give praise. Someday, after you move far away, it'll dawn on her how fortunate she was to have you rescue her and the others from the old farm. Most people never realize a good thing until it's gone."

Doña Inez talked and worked at the same time. Her hands, red from dishwashing, reached everywhere in a flash. She grabbed plates, spoons, forks, and knives. She arranged a heap of rice and beans with chunks of pork in the centers of the plates, then crowned the heaps with golden fried plantains.

While I waited, I let my eyes wander across the dining room, and I saw Frank leaning back on a chair near the window, strumming the guitar. His hair matched his yellow shirt, and when he looked up, his eyes gleamed like a mixture of ocean and blue sky.

I carried two plates at a time to the dining room, where men waited with beers in their hands. They looked at me rather than at the plates. "Thank you, gorgeous," some said. Others just stared like hungry dogs at someone eating steak.

When I brought Frank's plate, Doña Inez followed me with a tight smile. She placed a hand on Frank's shoulder and said in almost a whisper, "This is my little friend Sabina, who's helping me today 'cause my helper's sick. Sabina is a good girl . . . a smart girl, and she is beautiful, too, don't you think?" Doña Inez wasn't shy. She mixed Spanish words with English and came out with perfect sentences.

I saw Frank's face turn red as he gazed at Doña Inez, then at me, and I felt as red as he looked. It was an awkward moment, a spooky one for me. Minutes earlier, I had decided to find ways to meet an American man, and now, there he was, looking me over as one would some merchandise. I stood mute, wanting to run, but I didn't want to embarrass my loving friend.

"Oh, darn, I can't help it," she said, slamming her fists on her thighs. "I have been wanting you two to meet for a long time, so don't look at me like that." She covered her face with her hands and laughed, her thick abdomen quivering like Jell-O.

Frank smiled and shook his head.

I didn't know what to do. I didn't even excuse myself, but turned slowly and walked by all of the other tables back into the kitchen with my eyes straight ahead.

Doña Inez was only a few steps behind me. "I'm sorry, angel. I didn't mean to embarrass you."

"Oh, you didn't. It's just that I don't know what to say to a man, especially an American one."

"So, you aren't mad at me, then?" she asked.

"I could never be mad at you. Let me wash some of these dishes, and then I must leave. I have to stop for groceries."

"You know, Sabina, I don't really mean to intrude, but I think it's time you met a man who can take you away from your mother and all of your sisters and brothers. They don't appreciate all that you've done for them. And they will never learn what they can do on their own, as long as you're supporting them.

"Frank is the kind of guy I would want my daughters to marry. But even though they are fifteen and sixteen, they are still too immature for a serious man like Frank. Besides, he likes blondes."

"Doña Inez – did he tell you that?"

"No, but I haven't seen him chasing brunettes, and there are plenty of those around here. The other thing is that I want my girls to graduate from high school. That's why I work so hard to run this business, to keep them in school. I have been doing this since my husband died . . . six years already, bless his heart."

"I think it's wonderful that you love your daughters enough to want the best for them," I said, with a tightness wrapped around my throat. "I didn't get to graduate from high school myself, so I know how handicapped one can be without an education."

"I know that you didn't get to graduate, but you won't need a diploma if you marry an American. He'll give you everything you need, and you won't need to go out looking for a job."

I didn't like to think that I would never finish school, even if I married a rich American who could give me everything I needed. But since Doña Inez seemed so sure of everything she said, I nodded in agreement with her.

As I finished cleaning the pots and cooking utensils, Doña Inez began to bring plates and silverware from the dining room. Consequently, I ended up staying longer than I had intended. And when I left, she took only seven dollars for the rent, and insisted that I keep five. "To help you buy the groceries," she said.

"No, Doña Inez," I protested. "I didn't do the dishes for money. It was to give you a hand. It's no favor if you pay for it."

"Good, I won't pay. I'll give it to you. But don't tell your family about it."

All my life, whenever someone had showed me a little sign of love, tears always filled my eyes, and my throat closed up so that I could never say what I felt. All I could do now is give Doña Inez a long hug and a kiss. When she squeezed me back, I knew that she didn't need to hear my words of gratitude.

I left through the kitchen door, feeling loved by Doña Inez but confused about meeting Frank. Was I supposed to say something to him before leaving? Would we ever meet again? Would Doña Inez tell him how to find me? And the worst thought yet was, *maybe he didn't find me attractive.*

As I hurried toward the grocery store, the thoughts about what my mother had said to me earlier poured into my mind. I turned away from the main road and walked down the graveled path that led to our house. I'd keep the five dollars to buy myself a pair of shoes and fabric for a new dress.

I walked slowly, not wanting to reach home too soon. Then, I heard the sound of gravel crunching behind me and looked over my shoulder. It was Frank.

"Thought I'd walk you home," he said softly.

"No, thank you. I'll walk alone," I said, remembering not to appear anxious, but silently calling myself stupid.

"Where I come from, we don't like to see a girl walking alone at night, especially a beautiful one."

"It's not dark with all those lights back there. And where is it that you come from?" *Beautiful* had sounded great when Doña Inez said it, but something good happened to me when I heard it from Frank.

"I'm from the state of Minnesota. Ever heard of it?"

I stopped. "Minnesota? No, I've never heard of it. But it's okay if you walk with me . . . only part of the way. If my mother and brothers see you, they'll chase you away with rocks, and anything else they can find."

Frank pulled out a cigarette from his shirt pocket, lit it, took a long drag, and blew out the smoke. "I'll run fast if they chase me. Good enough?"

"Yes."

He laughed softly. "Well, uh . . . how many brothers?"

"Four. Ages ten to seventeen."

"No sisters?"

"Oh yes, three. Ages fourteen to twenty-two."

"Well, how about that!" he said. "We have something in common. I have four brothers and three sisters myself. Oh, please tell me your name again."

"My name is Sabina. But it actually should be Joaquina."

"Why Joaquina?"

"Because children are named after saints, and I was born on San Joaquin's day."

"Joaquina. That's Jacqueline in English, isn't it?"

"I don't know. Is it?"

"Yes, and it just so happens that Jacqueline is one of my favorite names. I'd like to call you Jackie. Would you mind?"

"Jackie sounds good." As I said that, my knees began to shake. *An English name*, I thought. *I look American, and with an American name, no one would ever tease me for being so white. This is a miracle.*

"Say, uh, did I say something wrong?" Frank asked. "You kind of disappeared on me. Whatever it was, I'll take it back, honestly."

I stopped walking and stared at him. He sounded so sincere. I felt as if I had known him for a long time. "Oh no, you didn't say anything wrong. But you can't go any farther. That's my house up there."

"Well, I won't go beyond this point, because I don't want to make trouble for you. Can I call you sometime?"

"I don't have a phone."

"I'll call you at work. Doña Inez said that you work at the base laundry, is that right?"

"Yes. But why would you call me?"

"To ask you to a movie. You like movies, don't you?"

"I do," I said. "But you better go back. My mother's probably looking out the window."

"Okay, I'll go back," he said. "I'm very glad to have met you, and I hope to see you again soon . . . perhaps tomorrow?"

"Yes . . . goodbye," I said, feeling stupid as he walked away. I had learned enough English in the past two years, so my lack of words wasn't because of the language. I just didn't know which words would be right for a girl to say to a man. I had heard some girls talking about the mysterious feelings they experienced when standing close to a man they were attracted to. They mentioned the heat, the tingling, and the need to hide their flushed faces. I wondered if my feelings were like those of other girls. *Was I supposed to tell him that I would die if he didn't call? Tomorrow, Frank Wilson, call me tomorrow, please . . .*

Some of my brothers and sisters looked at me from under their brows as I walked past them, but no one said a word. I went straight to the bedroom, grabbed my toothbrush and towel, and went to the bath shack, wishing the night away.

Mama was fidgeting at the stove when I came back in.

"I made some soup, and saved you some," she said. "Or did you eat at Inez's restaurant?"

I shook my head. "No, I did not eat, but I'm not hungry."

Chapter Three

Dreams of Love

I left the bedroom light off and lay on my narrow bed, trying to picture myself living in the United States as Jacqueline Wilson. Fantasizing had been a lifesaver for me before I ran away from home at age twelve. For years before running away, I had curled up in my gunnysack at night and created pictures in my mind that made me smile when I was sad and warmed me when I was cold. It had started shortly after meeting my first-grade teacher, Miss Traverso. She had probably been in her twenties, and had soft white skin, green eyes, and golden brown hair. I gasped the first time I laid eyes on her because I had never before seen anyone so beautiful. She wore red lipstick and red fingernail polish, silk stockings and high-heeled shoes, and dresses of fine fabrics with flowery prints, laces, and colorful buttons.

From that day on, when life with my family seemed unbearable, I looked forward to being alone. I crawled inside of my head while I was pulling weeds in the cornfield, or while trying to sleep at night, and picked up my dreams where I had left off the day or night before. I always saw myself dressed like Miss Traverso, walking back and forth in front of a class, my heels tapping the floor and the hem of my silky dress swaying with my steps.

Each time, I added something new to my dream, like I was adding another page to a book. I imagined a beautiful white horse with a long, smooth, yellow tail and mane, and pictured myself riding it to go visit my family at the bottom of the mountain. I pictured my parents and all of my sisters and brothers looking up to me, envying me for being so rich and gorgeous. In my fantasies, I brought gifts for everyone, just to make them feel guilty for ridiculing me because I was so white. They didn't know that if I had been given the choice, I would have been born with dark skin, brown eyes, and black hair to look like them.

The memories of my family's teasing were still painful, and they hurt even more every time we argued, especially over money. I could not understand why they expected me to pay for everything they consumed, or how they could treat me so badly after I risked my life so that they could live free.

None of them had lifted a finger to help me six years earlier when Papa held a sharp machete to my throat. I would have died, had I not fainted. If I had died, none of them would be here now. It was pure luck that Papa had left me on the floor and gone to beat on the rest of the family. When I awoke, I took off running, promising myself that one day I'd come back to make them regret what they had done to me for so many years. After four years of a better life in the city, I went back to the farm to help my youngest sister and our two youngest brothers. I ended up taking everyone but my father, determined to help them all, just so they would grow to love me.

I faked a deep sleep when my sisters and mother came into the bedroom. Mama and my youngest sister Alicia slept in one bed, and Emilia and Gloria on another. I heard them turning, taking deep breaths, and exhaling hard. Perhaps they felt bad about what had happened earlier, but they didn't say the words I wanted to hear.

My four brothers – José, Lorenzo, Alejandro, and Felipito – slept in hammocks in the next bedroom. I heard their murmuring and whispering, but I couldn't make out their words.

When everyone's breathing became shallow, the memories of my wonderful friend Doña Luisa came to mind. "You'll end up marrying an American man and moving to the United States," she had said when she helped me move to this *barrio*. "With your blonde hair and green eyes, you'll blend in well with the Americans, and your good looks will attract the right man."

I felt a smile on my face with that thought. Then I wondered about the ironies of life, the ups and the downs, and the many unanswered questions. For the first twelve years of my life, I had been teased and ridiculed for the color of my skin, hair, and eyes. Yet those were the features that attracted Doña Luisa when she found me asleep in her storage room. I resembled her only daughter, who had died three years earlier. Of course, at first she didn't want to get involved with a runaway girl, but then her heart softened and she took me to her home, where her husband Don Felipe agreed that I did look like their precious

Teresita.

It had been my hope to reach a city at the west end of the island, where I could make my living sewing gloves. And it had been a miracle that Doña Luisa managed the sewing factory. She and her husband treated me as their daughter, teaching me love and compassion and letting me work in their factory. They even allowed me to attend school. My own parents had deprived me of an education beyond the third grade. Would those people have given me a chance had I been dark, as most children throughout the island were?

Would Frank Wilson like me had I been a brunette?

Chapter Four

The Phone Call

My boss, a fat Puerto Rican man with dark, beady eyes and a shiny bald head, walked into the sewing room and pointed a finger at me. "You got a phone call, but make it snappy. You're getting paid to work, not to talk."

"Yes, sir," I said, then hurried to the phone. My heart was racing with hope.

"It's Frank Wilson. Remember me? We met yesterday."

"I remember," I said, wondering if he really thought that I would forget. "I have a good memory."

"Glad to hear it," he said, then added some words I could not hear because my boss had parked himself at the doorway, his gaze switching from me to the clock on the wall and back.

I managed to understand an invitation to the eight o'clock movie that night, and agreed to meet Frank at the main gate at seven.

As soon as I hung up the phone, my boss said, "Personal phone calls are not permitted here. This is the base laundry, not a place for socializing."

"Yes, sir." I hurried past him and back to my work. Nothing he or anyone else could say would destroy the most wonderful excitement that was building up inside me. It felt like bubbles were dancing in my chest, and I would soon be lifted away from all that had made me feel miserable for years. I worked the rest of the day with one eye on the clock, hoping that time would fly. I would be going to the movies for the first time in my life with a man – not just any man, but an *American*.

I never stopped to think that Frank might not like me once he got to know me better. In my mind, it was all settled. Doña Inez said that Frank was a good man, and that was all I needed to know. She said that he would marry me and take care of me for the rest of my life, and all I had to do was be good to him. What else was there to worry about? I had met the man who would take me to see my first movie, and what-ever people did while courting would happen naturally.

When the clock finally marked five, I covered the sewing machine, put everything in place, punched my time card, and went home to get ready for my first date.

For several years, I had had a regular routine. I would get up in the morning, have my coffee, get dressed, and go to work. After work, I would hurry home to work some more. Every evening, I did some sewing, washing, ironing, or cleaning. If I left the house for a short while, it was to visit the sick, buy groceries, or pay the rent.

But tonight, I would be doing something different. How would I tell my mother that I was going out on my first date? I could just walk in, shower, get dressed, and leave, ignoring my mother and my brothers if they came home early. But that would mean another argument upon returning home close to midnight. Knowing my mother and my brothers, they would be up waiting for me, ready to warn me not to do it again.

Since I was the one who paid the rent, utilities, and most of the groceries, I decided to tell them a lie. The truth had always gotten me in trouble with them before, so what would be the point of honesty this time? My mother would have to believe that I had finally been asked to babysit on base. She would not accuse me of lying, because we knew other women who worked on the base babysitting at night for the extra money, and we needed the money as much as anyone else.

I smelled the aroma of garlic and onion when I neared the house. My mother had spent some of her money and was cooking noodles with potatoes and ham. It smelled delicious, but I would wait to eat. I would-n't have been able to swallow anyway, because the bubbles of excitement had worked their way up to my throat.

I took my towel and bath soap and headed for the bath shack. I scrubbed myself from head to toe, humming and wondering what a girl was supposed to do on a date. Should she let the man hold her hand? I sure didn't want to do anything that might scare Frank away. This was one thing that had to work the right way for me. Doña Inez had said that Frank was a good man, so I wanted to act the right way in order to keep him, but what were the rules of dating? Should a girl appear anxious? Or should she appear uninterested? And how did a girl learn these things?

I felt frustrated not knowing, and for not feeling free to ask my mother. Then again, she had never dated either. Her parents had married her to my father without giving her the opportunity to get to know him.

As I skipped through the kitchen on my way back from the bath shack, my mother said, "Looks like you're leaving again."

"I am. I've been asked to babysit some American kids on the base. I'll get paid fifty cents, which will help me with the expenses around here."

"You scrubbed yourself to babysit?"

"Only because I felt hot and sweaty."

She didn't say anything else, and I felt glad, for I hadn't wanted to start an argument to take away the thrill that was sweeping through me like a storm. I felt as if I had been drowning for a long time, and at last I was coming up for air.

My curly hair had always curled up tighter when I washed it, but I had never stayed in front of the mirror long enough to really see it. That day, the setting sun shone through the window on my shoulders, and I saw my hair as a bouquet of light yellow roses shining like silk thread. For the first time in my life, I felt thrilled to be a blonde.

I put on a pink dress with a white belt around my waist, white sandals, and red lipstick. I looked at myself in the mirror again and noticed that my face had a pink glow I had never seen before, and my eyes sparkled. I felt beautiful.

"Looks more like you're going dancing," my mother said to me as I came out of the bedroom with my little wallet in my hand.

"I know, Mama. It's too bad I don't know how to dance, ah?" With that, I walked out the door, slowly at first, but never looked back to see if my mother was at the window watching me.

Chapter Five

A New Discovery

I saw Frank waiting at the main gate. His blue eyes beamed at me, and my heart skipped a beat. I could not believe this. We had met twenty-four hours earlier, but he didn't look like a stranger to me. *Perfect*, I thought. *Well, almost perfect*. I didn't like the cigarette between his fingers, and he didn't look as good in his khaki uniform as the airmen I had seen through the louvers at work. His shoulders were wide, but his legs were curved, making him look an inch shorter than he would be with straight legs.

"Nice to see you," he said, sincerely.

"I'm happy to see you, too."

"That's good to know. Let's take a taxi to keep the wind off your lovely hair."

No one else had ever protected my hair from the wind before, so never mind the crooked legs and the cigarette. I reasoned with myself that the bent legs weren't his fault, and the smoking was a habit he would give up once we got to know each other better.

Frank flagged a taxi, then held the door open for me. At that moment, I felt equal to the American women I had seen on the base. He motioned me to go in first, and then he slid into the taxi through the same door, sitting so close to me that his right arm touched my left. A tingling feeling shot down my arm and up my leg, and I couldn't find a place to hide my flushed face. *Does this mean love?* I thought, wondering if it would be appropriate to slide over to the other window.

"My boss said that I'm not allowed to receive phone calls at work," I said, to cover the strange sensation.

Frank smiled. "Well, then, this is what we'll do. Every time we see each other, we'll make plans for the next date so I won't need to call anymore. Agreed?"

I nodded, imagining my mother saying, *"A decent girl doesn't sit that close to a man."*

It felt good being that close to Frank, despite the thoughts of my mother. He kept his hands on his lap, which showed that he knew not to touch a *señorita*. Rumors had been flying that some American soldiers with busy fingers had been forced to marry the girl they had touched. According to those who claimed to know, the American soldiers were instructed upon arriving at the island not to touch a *señorita* unless they were willing to marry her.

"Say, Jackie, do you think your family saw us last night, when I walked you halfway home?"

"I don't know. No one said anything."

"So . . . am I allowed to walk you to your door tonight?"

"Maybe, but I'm not sure."

"Well, uh . . . what did your mother say when you told her you had a date?"

"She thinks I'm babysitting."

Frank nodded. "Aha . . ." Then he fell silent.

Oh no, now he'll think I'm a liar. "I don't like to lie, but my mother would yell at me if she knew I was off to a movie with a man."

"Have you dated before?"

"No, never. But I know she would yell, because she says that a girl who goes places with a man is indecent."

He nodded again. "Ah . . . she's old-fashioned."

When the taxi stopped in front of the theater, I opened my wallet for my fifteen cents, but Frank said, "No, I'll get that." I didn't tell him that Mama would not like that, either.

We joined a line of uniformed men, some with wives or girlfriends, and the rest of them single. I had seen the lines before from the bus on my way home from work, but being a civilian, my pass to enter the base was only to work.

When we reached the ticket window, I opened my wallet again. Frank bent to whisper in my ear. "Where I come from, the man pays for everything when he takes a lady out."

I felt my face turn red. "Thank you. I didn't know that."

He smiled and nodded.

I walked through the doors of heaven when we entered the theater. The air was cool, the lights were dim, and the seats were red and velvety. Thoughts of Doña Luisa came to mind: *"With your light skin, blonde hair, and green eyes, you'll fit right in with the Americans."* I wondered if she could see me from up there. I hoped she could.

Watching the movie, *The Glenn Miller Story*, was like looking out a large window at a beautiful world of lights, music, and colors. I suddenly became someone else, totally different from the ragged girl who had run away from the hills.

I discovered love that night. I could see it clearly. It traveled from Jimmy Stewart's eyes to June Allison, who glowed while watching him from a nearby table. He was playing the trumpet on a stage, but his eyes were still on her. I fell in love with him, and with his friend, Harry Morgan, who kept June company. I would make myself a flared skirt like the ones June Allison wore, and I'd be looking forward to many more movies in brilliant colors on big, bright screens in the future.

Frank put his arm over the backrest of my seat, as if to protect me. I loved his arm there, and wanted his hand on my shoulder, just to see what it would feel like to be touched by a man. But I did not tell him that. I didn't tell him that I had never been to a movie before, either.

The movie had a sad ending. Jimmy was killed in a faraway place, which made me feel terrible. My tears spilled onto my lap. Why did such a handsome man have to get killed and leave his beautiful wife alone?

I felt Frank's breath on my ear. "Jackie, don't cry. It's only a movie."

I didn't understand what he meant by saying that it was "only a movie," but I didn't ask. I didn't find out until years later that Jimmy Stewart had not really died. It had just been an act.

Frank insisted on walking me home after the movie. I let him, because I could see from the gravel road that the lights were off at my house. Still, when we reached the pineapple hedge, I said, "You'd better stay on this side of the gate. The night is light enough for my mother to be watching us through some crack in the wall. I don't want her to spoil the good time I had. Thank you very much for the movie."

"Okay," he whispered back. "But I want to see you again. How about a walk on the beach the day after tomorrow? I can meet you outside the laundry and we can go from there. Think your mother will let you go?" His warm breath on my neck gave me bumps on my skin.

"I won't tell her," I said.

"So does that mean you'll go?"

"Yes," I whispered. "Please go back now."

Frank took my hand and kissed it. "I'll see you outside the laundry the day after tomorrow." He bowed and walked away.

I watched him, then walked through the gate and around the house to the latrine. My mother must have believed my story about babysitting, because everyone seemed to be asleep when I walked in through the kitchen door. I tiptoed across the living room and into the bedroom.

I heard one of the beds squeak. "Is that you, Sabina?"

"Yes, Mama."

"Kind of late, isn't it?"

"Yes, Mama, it is. Go back to sleep."

"I wasn't asleep."

I said nothing else, but stretched out on my little bed, where I relived every moment of my very first date ever – the ride in the taxi, the view into a world I had never known, June Allison's skirt, poor Jimmy's death, Frank's arm so close to my shoulders, his warm breath on my ear and neck.

Yes, let the day after tomorrow get here fast, please!

Chapter Six

On Wet Sand

Two days later, when I walked out of the base laundry, I saw Frank leaning against a post. He wore dark jeans and a blue shirt that enhanced his eyes. My heart jolted as he walked toward me, but I had to keep calm and not let him guess my feelings. Deep inside, I felt he was the man who would take me away from all the hard work and misery. If he'd asked me to marry him, I would have said yes without a second thought.

"Good to see you," he said, bright-eyed and smiling.

"I'm happy to see you," I said, falling into step beside him.

"We can walk to the beach from here, if you don't mind walking."

"I don't mind," I told him.

It wasn't far to a beach on the base I hadn't known was there, and I was willing to walk any distance with him. He had a soft voice, which convinced me that he would never scream at me the way my father had screamed at my mother. And his steps were quiet, which meant to me that he wasn't too aggressive.

"It's time to take off our shoes," he said when we stepped from the grassy path onto the sand. He backed up against a coconut tree, rolled up the legs of his trousers, and took off his black shoes and socks, exposing a pair of feet that were even whiter than mine. I heard Doña Luisa's voice in my head: *You'll fit right in with the Americans.*

I unbuckled my shoes and ran toward the water. Frank chuckled and ran after me. We walked on the wet sand, jumping and laughing as the waves crashed against our feet.

"Say, I didn't think you knew how to laugh! Sounds great. I like it."

"Thank you," I said, trying to remember the last time I had laughed.

"Well, I meant that you are so serious," he said.

I stopped to look at him, turning my back to the water because the sun was low and blinding. He did something with his eyebrows that I found cute. He brought one down and raised the other as quick as a flash. "Did I say something wrong?" he asked.

"No," I said, "but I don't think I'm that serious."

"Well, you are, but I like your laugh and want to hear more of it. And I also like your accent."

"My what?"

"Your accent. You know, the way you talk."

"Oh, I like the way you talk, too."

"Good. Mind if I hold your hand?"

I placed my hand in his, and I felt the strange sensation up my arm again. Maybe that was what some girls had referred to as "electricity." However, *I* would never talk about such a thing with anyone.

As I watched the sand slide out from under my feet, Frank suddenly pulled me toward the shore. "Don't want to get your dress wet, do you?"

"No," I said, as a huge wave broke where we had been standing.

"Sorry I was rough, but you would be soaked right now if we hadn't moved."

"You scared me, but thank you for pulling me away."

We walked alongside the water, holding hands and laughing, jumping back when the waves came. It was a great feeling, and there was no mother or sibling to spoil my fun. Walking on the wet sand with a boyfriend had been one of my fantasies.

Still, there was something that bothered me when Frank spoke to me in Spanish. For example, when he said, *"Eres bonita,"* I wanted to hear "pretty" or "beautiful" instead. If I had wanted to hear those special words in Spanish, I would have dated a Spanish-speaking man. But I was afraid that Frank might think I was denying my nationality if I told him to speak only English to me.

"Thank you for inviting me to the beach," I said at last. "I should go home now. My mother will think something happened to me."

"Tell her that I won't let anything happen to you," he said, as if that would make any difference to my mother. "And by the way, Jackie," he went on, "have you ever played bingo?"

"What's bingo?"

"It's a game. I can teach you. Wanna go, say, Friday night?"

"What kind of game?"

He chuckled. "Well, it's a card with numbers on it. As they call out the numbers, you mark them on your card. If the card fills up, you win some money."

"Yes, I'd like to go."

"Great. They start at eight. Should I come to your place to meet you?"

"No. We can meet at Doña Inez's place."

"Good idea. I'll have some rice and beans there. So let's meet there at six. Is that okay with you?"

I agreed. We put on our shoes and started back. The sun had started to fall into the ocean.

"Say, uh, would you like to stop at Inez's now and have supper with me? I really hate to eat alone." He did the cute thing with the eyebrows again, which almost made me say yes. But to avoid a hassle with my family, I declined. I let him walk me down the gravel road until I saw my mother at the window.

"Thanks for walking with me, but go back now. I don't feel like arguing with my mother. She's at the window."

"Well, I don't know what's going on with you and your family, but I'll do as you say. I don't want to make trouble. But . . . well, I'll see you Friday night. Thanks for going to the beach with me. I enjoyed being with you."

I felt lonely as he walked away. As I turned toward the house, I saw my mother back away from the window. Rage crept up my legs. *She's spying on me.* I walked slowly the rest of the way, then went around the house to the bath shack.

I took my time cooling off, hoping that Mama would not start an argument. When I went in, I found Emilia in the kitchen, stirring a pot of beans in a red sauce with chunks of ham.

"Smells good, Emilia. How soon can I have some?"

"It's ready now," she said, her gaze still on the beans. "But Mama is really mad."

"About what?"

"I don't know. She's been pacing the floor and mumbling since she came home from work."

Mama appeared in the doorway between the kitchen and the living room. "Ah, so you finally got home."

"Of course, and don't act surprised. I saw you at the window, spying . . . always spying."

"Not always, but I heard some gossip today."

"Today? There's gossip every day, Mama."

"You left work with some gringo and headed toward the ocean. It didn't sound very pretty."

"Gossip never does, Mama."

"Don't get smart with me, Sabina. You know what I mean."

I turned to face her. "Yes, Mama, I know exactly what you mean. So it's time that you know. I met this really nice guy, and I know he's going to ask me to marry him. I'm ready to say yes and go as far away from here as possible. So you might as well calm down so I can bring him home to meet my family."

"I'm not meeting any gringo, so don't bother bringing him around," she said angrily. "Those people are from another world, and they speak a different language."

My mother walked out of the kitchen. I was too hungry to keep up the fight, so I sat on the kitchen floor with my three sisters and our youngest brothers, Alejandro and Felipito.

"I hope you do marry a gringo," whispered Alicia. She was fourteen now, still small for her age, but as sweet as she had always been. Her big brown eyes lit up when she smiled.

Gloria looked around, making sure Mama wasn't nearby, and with a tight smile said, "Find a gringo for me, too. I don't want to become an old maid."

Emilia's lips quivered. "I'm already an old maid."

A sad feeling shot through me. "No, Emilia. You still have plenty of time to meet someone. You just have to walk away from this kitchen. Get a job where you can meet people."

"I don't want to clean houses on the base. That's the only work I can do."

"Cleaning houses on the base is better than staying here. It'll get you out of the house, and you'll learn things along the way."

When she started to cry, I put my plate down and went to find Mama. She was in the bedroom crying, too.

"Now what?" I asked.

She didn't answer, just shook her head. I grabbed my towel and toothbrush and went to the bath house. There was still too much to do to help this family, but I could not give up the rest of my life for them. They were many, and I was only one. I knew that another confrontation might unfold when José and Lorenzo heard Mama's complaints about my seeing a gringo. But when that happened, I was just going to sit on my bed and read a magazine to avoid the fight. When they went to sleep, I would lie back and think about Frank and the bingo game.

Chapter Seven

Five Dollars!

I wore a lavender dress this time, with a purple ribbon around my waist. I even tied a bow of the same ribbon in my hair. I had managed to go to work and back without getting into a hassle with my mother, but I met her on my way out the door.

"I'll be home around ten," I said. She walked past me without a word. I think I was supposed to guess her feelings and change my plans for her sake.

I didn't even look back to wave at my sisters, who were watching from the balcony. "Don't even stop to talk to Mama or the boys if you see them on your way," Emilia had advised.

"Yeah, just keep going, and be happy," Alicia added. Gloria reminded me to find a gringo for her.

I felt sorry for my sisters, but as I had thought the previous night, there were too many of them, and they all needed more help than I had to offer. I shook the thought of my sisters out of my head and hurried to Doña Inez's place.

"I'm glad you got here before Frank," she said when I arrived at her kitchen door. "I just want you to know that I told him something about your background. He came by the day before yesterday, seeming discouraged because he couldn't walk you to your door. I didn't want you to lose him, so I had to say something. Please don't be mad at me for intruding."

I stretched my arms around her steamy body. "I'll never be mad at you. I know you're trying to help me. But somebody told Mama about Frank, and now she's going around with a long face and muttering to herself."

"Don't you worry about your mother. She'll be just fine. And believe me, Sabina, if you get married and move away, Emilia and Gloria will go to work, too."

"I know you're right, but don't ever tell Mama that you introduced me to Frank. I don't want her and my brothers mad at you. Doña Inez, you seem so sure that Frank will want to marry me. Did he say something to you? We just met."

"He didn't have to say it. I saw it in his eyes. Believe me, that man will propose."

"Thank you, Doña Inez, for telling him about my problems," I said.

Before she could answer, Frank appeared at the door. He wore his khaki uniform, but this time he looked better to me than he had the day we had gone to the movie.

We had our first dinner together at a small table in a corner of the kitchen. "You'll have privacy here," Doña Inez had insisted, reaching for plates and forks.

"At least let me help you serve," I said.

"No, no, you can help another time. Elie and I can handle this. Just eat and talk with Frank."

Frank was glowing in his chair, his eyes traveling from me to Doña Inez, then back.

Doña Inez motioned to me. "Come, come, sit down and eat." She placed two plates of food on our table, and was gone before we could thank her.

"She's a great lady," Frank said with a nod and a wink.

"I know, and I love her," I answered.

Walking into the Airmen's Club was as invigorating as my first movie. Frank and I held hands, which made me feel important and pretty. The place was huge, with bright lights and a shiny floor. All of the men were in uniforms, and there were more men than women, just as there had been at the movie. It wasn't easy for me to walk into that club as if I had been to places like that before. Inside my head, I was shouting to the world that I had found my first step to a better life.

"Let's choose a table," Frank suggested, his eyes twinkling. "Then I'll get us some cards and show you how to play bingo. You might get lucky and win."

I smiled at him, but didn't tell him that I had already been lucky enough to have met him.

"Here, this is a good place," he said. "You can look straight over there and see the man spin that round cage. I'll go get some cards."

As he walked up to the counter, I looked around, overwhelmed by the brightness and lovely appearance of the club. I had seen the building from the bus on my way to work and back, but had never thought that one day I would walk in and sit at a table surrounded by so many American people.

This and the movie must be the highlights of my dreams.

"Now," Frank said, sitting across from me. "This is how bingo is played. When that man up there calls the numbers, you look at your card. If you see the number, mark it like this, then listen for the next number. If you fill out this line of numbers, or this one, or that, you yell, 'Bingo!' I'll help you, but it's really easy."

As Frank explained, I studied his firm hands, the calm look in his eyes, and the cute thing he did with his eyebrows, one up and the other down. I knew I could love him.

When the number-calling began, I busied myself to follow Frank's instructions, but was disappointed when someone yelled "Bingo!" right away. However, after another round began, I felt myself understanding the game. It dawned on me then that for the first time in my life, I was actually playing a game. My life was finally moving in the right direction. If Frank didn't propose marriage, I knew I would find another American man.

Frank went back and got two more cards. My heart jolted when I suddenly realized that I had filled one whole line. "I got one! I got one!" The correct word had gotten lost in my excitement.

Frank raised his hand. "Bingo!"

He stood up and called out the numbers, and the man said, "That's a bingo." I shrank back into my chair, wondering what I should say. I had never won anything in my life, and five dollars was two dollars more than I earned in a day's work.

Frank reached for my hand. "Come on, Jackie, let's go get your prize."

Stay calm, I kept telling myself, for I had no idea what to do. *Am I supposed to clap, cheer, laugh, or what? And will it be right to share the money with Frank? After all, he bought the cards. But what if he does-*

n't take it? Will I owe him? Mama would tell me not to keep the money.

A tall man handed Frank the five dollar bill, and Frank gave it to me. "You won. It's yours."

"You bought the cards."

"Yeah, but you won, so it's yours."

I put the five dollars in my wallet and walked next to Frank back our table, and another game began. The curse on my life had finally lifted. Not only had I been lucky enough to meet a good man, but because of him, I had won five whole dollars!

A while later, a man announced a break. Everybody stood up and began talking so loud and fast they sounded like a lot of chickens cackling at the same time. Still, Frank's brilliant eyes came at me from across the table.

"Say, uh, would you like to go dancing tomorrow night? I know a nice place downtown, Club Borinquen. Have you ever been there?"

I didn't even know that Aguadilla had a club. "I would love to go dancing . . . but I don't know how."

"Well, that's no problem. I can teach you. I'm pretty good at it, if I may say so myself."

All of these surprises were coming at me so fast, I had to keep reminding myself to be careful – not to say yes too soon, hesitate a little, and not act anxious.

"Yes, I would like to go dancing, thank you. But I should go home early tonight, or my mother will give me a hard time about going out again tomorrow."

"Yes, Doña Inez said that your mother is very strict. Is she strict with the other girls, too? Or is she just afraid of losing you?"

"My mother can be very difficult," I said.

We walked out of the building holding hands. Even though staying out later would jeopardize the next date, I didn't feel like going home just yet. Suddenly, the ride in the taxi seemed too short, as well as the walk from the gate to my front yard.

"I'll look forward to seeing you tomorrow," he said, then kissed my hand.

I watched him walk away and felt sad and alone. *There is something really nice about being with that man.*

Chapter Eight

In the Arms of a Man

On Saturday morning, we started our regular routine. José left for work at the base diner; Lorenzo went to the base golf course; Mama sat at the sewing machine; and the girls and I washed clothes in metal tubs behind the kitchen. We had always been able to find things to talk and giggle about. But this time, there was mystery and suspense. We knew that Mama was waiting to start bickering about my new adventure.

"I hate it when Mama goes around with a long, mad face," Emilia whispered.

"She'll probably ruin my dress," Gloria said. "And I'm not even the one with the gringo. Hey, what does he look like? Is he cute?" That brought out a burst of laughter, and I thought of Frank saying that I was too serious.

"I like his deep blue eyes. And I like his hands. And I like that he said I have a pretty laugh."

Mama poked her face out the window, then rolled her eyes and backed away.

"She's dying to know what we're talking about," Emilia said, then laughed so hard that her tears fell into the soapy water. I found myself wishing we could have had more times like that. In the past two years, our lives had been nothing but struggles and arguments over one thing or another, and we all had forgotten how to laugh.

When we finished the washing, I ironed my work dresses, then spent the rest of the afternoon avoiding my mother. I could not let her spoil my coming date. I succeeded, and by seven o'clock I was back at Doña Inez's.

Frank was already there. We had dinner, helped Doña Inez with the dishes, then left. She hugged us and said with her loving smile, "Have a great time, you two."

"How can anyone not love such a lady?" Frank said as we walked away. With teary eyes, I agreed.

We got into the next public station wagon leaving for Aguadilla. Then, holding hands, we walked down one sidewalk and up another until we reached Club Borinquen. It was a wooden, low-ceilinged building with grayish walls, a concrete floor, and dim lights – nothing like the Airmen's club. A heavy-set woman sat on a platform, playing what Frank said was a "piano." The music did nothing for me, for I had known only guitar and radio music.

I saw some American men there, but the rest of the men and women were Puerto Rican. I felt American and beautiful.

"Say, uh, you want to have a drink? Beer? Rum and Coke? Bourbon and 7-up?"

I had seen beer before, but had never tasted it. I would not even look at rum, for that's what had made my father crazy. I had never heard of bourbon. "Plain 7-up would be nice, thank you."

Frank raised his hand, and with his index finger motioned to a waitress. He ordered a bottle of beer and a 7-up. His beer disappeared quickly, and he asked for another, gulped some down, stood up, and reached for my hand. "Ready to try dancing?"

I placed my hand in his and went quietly, as if we were walking into a deep river in which I would soon drown. Many years earlier, when I had been about ten years old, my father had forbidden my sister Emilia to dance. She had said bitterly that dancing was another thing we would not be allowed to learn. Since then, I had been too busy running away and trying to stay alive to even think about learning to dance. Now, as if in a wild dream, I found myself with a man's strong arm around my waist. My left hand rested on his muscular shoulder, and my breast touched his chest.

He whispered in my ear: "A one-two-three, and a one-two-three, and . . ."

I didn't understand why he counted, why his breathing was loud, or why I wasn't feeling happy, sad, nervous, or embarrassed. The only thing going through my mind was: *What would my parents say if they saw me in the arms of a man?*

Frank was still counting: "A one-two-three, and . . ." I felt my feet slightly off the floor, then heard him say, "You're doing fine, just fine."

The smell of tobacco smoke and beer coming from Frank bothered me. However, if I had told him that, he might not have wanted to see me again. Perhaps I was meant to become a nun – an occupation which would allow me to live my life free of men. Yet that very thought gave me a sinking feeling.

We went back to the table when the tune ended. Frank finished his beer and asked for another. "Hey, uh, a little bourbon in that 7-up will help you relax. It's hard to have fun without a little alcohol."

"I don't need bourbon, thank you." I didn't ask what bourbon was, because I didn't want to admit that I lacked a lot of experience. All the years my parents had made me work as an adult back at the old farm had deprived me of learning whatever comes natural during childhood. I would never be able to make up for the parental love and the play times I had missed from day one to age twelve. Then I had run away, and from age twelve I had been working even harder to prove that inside my small frame was a mature, hard-working adult.

Across the floor, I saw an American man waving his arms at a skinny Puerto Rican girl, who looked like a yellow broom with a wide belt around the middle.

"She doesn't know how to dance," Frank said, bringing the bottle to his lips. "But unlike you, she's fighting him."

"Fighting him? She looks scared to me."

"Well, uh, maybe not fighting, but perhaps giving him a hard time, refusing to learn."

Frank emptied the bottle. The waitress brought him another. I wondered if the beer would make him drunk, but I didn't dare ask him. I knew people who got drunk on rum, but I had never heard of anyone getting drunk on beer.

"Say, uh, ready to try again?" He stood up and reached for my hand. I wasn't ready, but I placed my hand in his and went, nonetheless. I didn't follow the one-two- three, but I let him move me this way and that. He was holding me at arm's length, bringing me back to his chest, and then spinning me until my skirt flared out like a pink umbrella. I liked the feeling of going around the dance floor, where other couples were doing the same. I assured myself that someday I would learn how to dance in tune with the music.

When I returned home that night, I found Mama fuming.

"So, is this how it's going to be from now on? You going out every weekend, and coming home late at night?"

"Maybe, Mama. But I can't predict the future."

"People are gossiping about you. They've seen you with that gringo."

"Not a gringo, Mama. An American man who finds me beautiful." It felt good talking back to my mother that night.

"What's the difference? American or Puerto Rican, men are all the same."

"Mama, how many American men have you known?"

"Don't get smart with me."

"Okay, I won't." With that, I went out to the latrine. On my way back, I walked past her and on to bed. I heard my brother Lorenzo say, "Bring a damned gringo around here, and I'll beat the shit out of him."

"Yeah," José added. "We'll break every bone in his body."

"You'll have to pay the rent around here before you can ever make good on that threat!" I said loudly, to make sure they heard it. Not another word came from my brothers.

I stretched out on my little bed and thought back to the previous hours. Soon I heard Mama's steps. She didn't go to her bed, but sat on the edge of mine.

"If that man reaches for your hand, make a fist. It'll be a step toward destruction if the tips of his fingers touch the palm of your hand. It's the work of the devil. Something creeps up your skin, and you'll let a man have his way. You'll become his property. When a man looks at your tiny waistline, he's thinking *want*, not love. He'll ruin your life, then go out and marry someone else."

"American men are different, Mama. And no one will ever own me if I don't allow it. Men are not all like Papa, and I don't think like you do, Mama. Now go to sleep."

"That mouth of yours," she mumbled while walking to her bed.

Chapter Nine

First Kiss

Frank and I dated for three months, one evening on weekdays, and on Saturday or Sunday evenings. During that time, I took every precaution possible to avoid arguments with my family. However, I worried that my brothers would meet Frank somewhere and beat him up, and there would go my only hope of getting away from them.

Finally, one night I heard the words I had been hoping to hear. It was the perfect night for romance. The moon appeared like a round window in the sky, and the stars winked at us as we walked down the gravel road holding hands. Frank stopped suddenly. "Say, uh . . . I'm in love with you, and I think you love me, too. So I think we should get married. What do you think about that?"

Although I had hoped to hear those words for a very long time, I didn't know what to say. I looked at our shadows, instead of looking at Frank. A soft breeze moved the tree branches, making the shadows dance.

Frank lifted my hand to his chin. "Say, I just proposed marriage to you. You better answer me before I start blushing."

I looked at him, and his eyes seemed darker in the moonlight. "Marriage sounds good . . . but to be honest, I don't know if what I feel for you is love."

"Well, I love you enough for the two of us," he said.

I wondered how it was possible for one person to love enough for two, but Frank's words were so appealing, I wanted time to stand still so we could stay under the moon and the stars all night.

"There's something else that bothers me," I said. "I could never be happy with someone who drinks and smokes like you do."

He laughed. "Oh, Jackie! That's no problem. I'm not hooked on that stuff. I only do those things because in the service there isn't much to do when a man gets off work. I can quit smoking anytime, and I'll drink only at social gatherings. I know I love you and would like to spend the rest of my life with you. I'll do whatever it takes to make you happy."

After hearing all of that, there was no way I could have said no. However, I didn't say yes right away. I walked quietly, our hands clasped and swinging slowly as the grass on each side of the dirt road swayed in the moonlight.

"Yes, I'll marry you," I finally replied.

He pulled me to him and planted a kiss on my lips. That was my very first kiss, but I wasn't sure if I liked it. All the ugly talk I had heard from my mother about men came rushing through my mind like storm water down a steep hill.

"You know," I said, looking down to avoid his eyes. "I have never kissed anyone before . . . so would you do it again, a little slower?"

He didn't answer, but took me in his arms and gave me a longer kiss that made my head spin. I didn't tell him, but I concluded that kissing was awfully good. It made something strange happen to me. I trembled inside my skin. This was probably the feeling some girls had talked about, but I would never tell anyone that it had happened to me. I would kiss Frank again, and never get tired of it, in spite of the smell of stale tobacco smoke.

That night, I lay awake for hours, thinking about living in the United States with my American husband. *Jacqueline Wilson. Mrs. Frank Wilson.*

"I'm going to marry an American," I said, breaking the silence that lingered over the sleepy bodies in our two bedrooms. "The man I have been seeing proposed, Mama."

The silence continued.

"Are you all really asleep, or just ignoring me? I'm going to be married soon – to an American!"

At last, I heard the click of the light switch, then saw Mama seated at the edge of her bed.

"I knew you'd pull that on me," she said. "Bring us here, and then take off with some stranger from God knows where."

"That'll be the day!" said José from the next room. "I'll bash that gringo's head with a hammer if he puts one foot on this property."

"I'll be behind you with a handful of rocks," said Lorenzo.

I made an attempt to get up, but instead leaned on my elbow when my sister, Alicia, jumped down from her bed.

"Oh, Mama," she said. "You'd better tell those two to stop talking like that! It's about time one of us got really lucky. Sabina will be rich if she marries an American. She'll be able to help us even more. I hope that one day another gringo shows up here and takes me away." Alicia stood firmly, wearing a little nighty she had made from a torn white sheet, waving her skinny arms. Her black curls dangled like coils, and her dark eyes traveled from Mama to the doorway leading to the boys' room. The boys didn't appear at the door. Mama and the other girls looked like statues, staring at Alicia.

"You look like the ghost in your school book," Gloria blurted out, laughing, and the conversation became a laughing contest. My older sister, Emilia, was the first to join Gloria, and within seconds, even Mama's face became distorted. My younger brother, Felipito, cracked up on the other side of the wall, and soon the whole house was filled with a contagious laughter that went on for a long time.

That was the first hard laugh we'd had since the day Papa ran scared, and it felt so good. If only we could laugh like that more often, rather than argue, I would not be so eager to find a husband and move far away.

The next morning, Mama handed me a cup of coffee and asked, "So, what do you know about that man? What do you know about *any* man?"

"I know he's an American who loves me, who thinks I'm beautiful, and who wants to marry me. That's all I need to know."

"What did you tell him?"

"I told him yes."

"You said yes? Without bringing him to meet your family? Is that how they do things wherever he comes from?"

"He comes from the state of Minnesota, Mama, and I haven't asked him how they do things there. And I'm not bringing him here to be chased away by my brothers with their rocks and hammers."

"In my days, a *señorita* didn't go out with a man unless she had a chaperone."

"I know. You have said that many times before, Mama. But I believe that kind of protection is why you ended up with a madman for a husband – a slave driver, remember? Now I must go to work – without a chaperon, as I have been doing for more years than I care to remember." I took my wallet and left.

That afternoon, on my way home from work, I stopped to see Doña Inez, and told her about Frank's proposal.

Her face lit up with a wide smile, and she turned from the kitchen counter. "Good for you, Sabina. You deserve all the happiness in the world. Frank is a great guy, and you'll never regret marrying him." She hugged me with such warmth, I couldn't keep from crying.

"I'm glad you think that, because my mother thinks the opposite."

"Pay no attention to your poor mother. She's just afraid of losing you. You go ahead and get married. Go to the United States, where you won't have to work so hard. Life is better and easier there. You'll see."

Chapter Ten

No Ringing Bells

Frank and I were married by a Lutheran minister in the base chapel the first week of September 1954. Doña Inez was the bridesmaid, and Frank's friend was the best man. Frank and the best man wore their khaki uniforms. I wore a light-blue cotton dress I had made, a white hat that had cost fifty cents, white sandals, and my first pair of nylon stockings.

The only one in my family who knew about my wedding day was Alicia, and she had sworn to keep the secret from our brothers, who threatened to throw rocks at Frank.

I walked down the aisle with Doña Inez, who was wearing a pink dress and a smile. The minister began the ceremony. When he said "cherish," I wondered what I was supposed to share. The two words sounded alike to me. Then, when he said, "For better or for worse," I thought, *The reason I'm getting married is to be better off.* "For richer or poorer . . . " *If Doña Inez is right, it will be for richer.* "Until death do us part . . . " *Only death will drive us apart.*

I felt blessed when Frank put the forty-dollar ring on my finger, even though it had cost me ten dollars because he had only thirty. The ceremony took place in the evening, so a few hours later, after coffee and sweet bread at Doña Inez's, we rode downtown in a public car. Frank had paid five dollars for a hotel room across from the Aguadilla Plaza.

We walked down the dim and narrow hallway holding hands, but neither of us said a word. Frank unlocked the squeaky door, reached into the small room, clicked on the light, and then immediately turned it off. He carried me through the door and placed me on the sagging bed. His heavy breathing and the pounding of my heart drowned the noise from the cars and people around the plaza. One question kept ringing in my mind: *What am I supposed to do?*

Enough light from the plaza shone in through the small louvered window, and I could see Frank's trembling hands unbuttoning his shirt. He seemed frantic, and stumbled while taking off his trousers, as if fire was creeping up his legs.

While I searched my mind for the right questions to ask, the clothes from below my waist flew across the room, along with Frank's jockey shorts. He was all over me, mumbling shaky words and kissing my neck, and like a storm, it was over before I knew it. He immediately landed on his back and lit a cigarette.

"Sorry, sweetheart. I was too anxious. I'll do better next time. I promise." He took a long drag and exhaled loudly, then fell asleep with the cigarette between his fingers. He didn't even notice when I took the stinky thing and flushed it down the toilet, which was through a narrow door a few feet from the dingy bed.

I took the longest shower of my life that night, until the hot water ran out. I wasn't a *señorita* anymore. But I didn't feel like a woman – or a wife, either. *Is that what my life is going to be like from now on? Was there something I should have done? Was that what some girls have raved about? What have I missed?* A sick and lonely feeling came over me, but it would be hidden for years to come, for I would never tell anyone about my honeymoon night.

I heard an unfamiliar roar that jolted my heart while I was drying myself with a worn-out towel. Quickly, I put on my dress and opened the door to the room. The sound was coming from Frank's opened mouth. It was a disgusting sound, and Frank didn't look like the man I had married.

While he snored, coughed, and snored some more, I sat on the bed, leaning against the wicker headboard and staring at the streaks of light coming through the louvers. Every now and then, a little breeze blew into the room, wafting the sickening smell of beer and stale cigarette from my husband's mouth.

Didn't he promise me he'd quit drinking and smoking once we were married? And why would an American not have more than five dollars for a room at a nicer hotel? Aren't they all rich?

"I married Frank yesterday, Mama," I said when I went home to get my things. Mama didn't say a word. "We'll stay with Doña Inez for a month, then leave for the United States." She fidgeted around with the sewing machine, her lips tight and eyes squinted.

Alicia and our two younger brothers stood around me while I gathered most of my things. "Aren't you afraid to be going far away?" one of the boys asked.

"No, I'm too happy to be afraid."

"Are you going to be rich? Will you send for us?"

I hugged them. "If I get rich, I'll come for the three of you. But I'll never write, because I don't want Mama and the other boys to give me a hard time. They haven't been nice to me, and I need a new beginning without their interference."

"It will be awful around here without you," Alicia cried.

"I'll miss you three," I said, "but remember that I'll come for you only if I get rich. So don't quit school, because you can still do well even if I don't come back."

We cried in each other's arms, until Mama said, "You're moving away with a man from another world. One day he'll go back to wherever he came from and leave you behind. Just make sure you run to your friend Inez, then. She is a foolish woman. You should have never trusted her."

"I'm married, Mama. Here, I'll show you my marriage certificate."

"That piece of paper? You probably made it up yourself."

I sighed, grabbed my bag and left, blinded by tears. Never again would I try to convince her.

During that month, I quit my job at the laundry and helped Doña Inez around the restaurant to pay her for the room and meals, because she would not take any money from us.

"You have been a wonderful friend, Doña Inez. I don't know what I would have done without your help and support. I feel bad because I might not ever be able to make it up to you. I can't even write to you. If I do, you'll have to tell my family, or lie to them, and I don't want you to have to do either on my account."

"I know what you mean, angel, so don't feel bad about not writing. I know you'll get to the States okay, and Frank will take care of you. He's a good man. Just go with him and be happy, and someday come back for a visit."

Doña Inez had the love and understanding my mother lacked. We talked about many things while working close together, but I never mentioned a word of my ignorance about marriage.

One day, in one of her stories about her marriage, she told me that she had felt incomplete since her husband died. "We married in our early teens," she said. "After years of living together, we became one. We could tell each other everything, no matter how difficult or embarrassing it was. My problems then became his, and his became mine, and together we solved whatever difficulties came our way. You aren't whole anymore when you lose a partner like that."

"That's the kind of relationship I want with Frank," I said. And that night, while his hands explored my body, I asked if there was something I should be doing.

"Nope," he said. "All you need to do is be here for me."

Frank's answer didn't sound right to me, but I had no knowledge of marriage or sex. I felt disappointment, had jumped into marriage too soon, and I feared ending up like my mother. She hadn't known my father before they married, and all I knew about Frank was what Doña Inez had told me. Did she really know the American people? Or was she repeating what someone else had told her?

At breakfast the next morning, Frank shocked me with something he had not mentioned before. "I'm looking forward to civilian life. Three years in the military is enough. Now it's time to go home. We'll be living with my mother, because as her youngest son, she's my responsibility. I've been supporting her since my father died. That's why I don't have much money. Most of my monthly checks go to her. That's why I had to sell my guitar to buy your ring. But I'll buy you a nicer one some day."

I stood up and carried the dishes to the sink, wanting to cry. I had heard that people in the service moved often to different parts of the United States and other countries, and I had hoped to see the world that way. And to top it all off, we would be living with his mother. *What if she doesn't like me? Well, I'll still get to leave the island with an American husband.*

Chapter Eleven

Remember Me

The night before leaving, I went back home to say goodbye to my family. Mama and the older boys weren't there, so I told the girls that I would stop by on my way out early the next day. I hurried out when I saw tears forming in Alicia's eyes.

At dawn, I came back. Frank had gone ahead to pick up his gear at the barracks. I tapped softly on the closed front door, while the gloom of the early morning wrapped itself around me like a cold blanket. I felt hollow inside, and awkward in my first pair of slacks. We were leaving in an Air Force cargo plane, and the women had been told to wear slacks.

Emilia opened the door. Her teary eyes widened. "Now you really do look like an American." Her voice cracked, bringing an immediate lump to my throat − not because it hurt to leave her, but because I sensed a little bit of love.

I walked into the dark house and found Alicia and Gloria in a corner, blowing their noses and patting their red eyes with rags.

"It's hard to believe that you're really leaving us," Gloria said, burying her face in her hands. I went into the other bedroom and found Alejandro and Felipito still in their hammocks, sniffing and wiping their eyes with the sleeves of their sleeping shirts. Mama and the older boys weren't there.

Part of me felt sad and guilty to be leaving them, but the rest of me couldn't wait to leave. I didn't even ask about Mama and the older boys, assuming that Mama was hiding to avoid saying goodbye, and that the boys had left for work early because they didn't care enough to wish me well.

I waved at my little brothers and hurried to the other room to wave at the girls. Then, blinded by tears, I dashed out the door and ran.

As I reached the edge of our yard, I saw Mama staggering toward me.

"What will become of me?" she asked, wrapping her arms around me and sobbing. "Who will take care of me? You were the only one I could count on. If it hadn't been for you, I'd probably be dead by now. Promise me you'll never forget me. Write often and let me know if you're okay."

"I wish you had said those words to me before," I said, tears spilling out like water from a leaky faucet.

"I wish I had, but I just didn't know how." My mother's words came through hard sobs. I felt a huge hand squeezing my heart.

"Let's go inside," I said, guiding her up the steps and into the house. She sat in the wicker chair with her elbows on her knees and her chin in her hands. Her tears hit the floor and splattered like the first raindrops on hard ground after a drought. She looked pitiful in her faded blue, patched-up dress. I stood there, my gaze moving back and forth between my mother and five of my siblings.

"I won't forget you." I squeezed out the words. "I'll never forget any of you. I'll . . ."

My mother finally looked up, tears streaming down the deep creases of her pained face. Her eyes looked like black cups on pink saucers, with red around the rims. I saw a crown of white hair framing her face, and the rest of her hair, still black, hanging loosely over her shoulders. I kissed her forehead and ran out the door, looking straight ahead, with that picture of my mother in my mind.

I made it to the gate without looking back, then rode in a taxi to the airport where Frank was waiting. I imagined crying in his arms. He would kiss me, whirl me around, and promise me that everything would be okay. We would enter a big, beautiful airplane, sit in cushioned seats, and get lifted away. Life would be grand. I would be so happy, I would never think back or miss what I had left behind.

I found Frank in the cafeteria having a breakfast of bacon and eggs with toast and coffee.

He motioned to a chair across from him. "There's no food on the plane, so you should eat something here."

"I'll just have coffee," I said.

I sat staring at my cup in a daze, running the tip of my finger around the hot rim. I heard the clicking of his fork and knife, and thought of Mama's words. *"What will become of me?"* That was followed by the minister's words. *"Until death do us part."* I couldn't shake those thoughts out of my head, nor could I understand why they kept coming back. It was as if I was being tortured for running out on my family.

A scratchy sound rang from the ceiling, and then the voice of a man came through. "Attention all airmen and dependants. Due to turbulent air over Cuba, the flight scheduled for departure at zero seven hundred hours has been postponed until further notice. Do not leave the terminal. We'll be taking off as soon as the weather clears."

I wondered what else would come up to prevent me from leaving. I pictured myself returning to what had become my mother's house, while she reminded me that she had warned me not to count on those Americans.

Frank introduced me to three other couples who would be on our flight. "This is my wife Jackie," he said.

The sound of those words made me feel good, but I didn't feel equal to the other wives. They appeared happy to be going home, but I felt drained and scared.

"Say," Frank said, guiding me to a corner. "I know you're feeling bad. Saying goodbye is never easy. But you had better cheer up before I start feeling guilty for taking you away from your family." He kissed the side of my face. "We had better move on. People are staring." After a few steps, he stopped suddenly. "Say, uh, you don't feel like you made a mistake by marrying me, do you?"

The question shocked me. *Is he having second thoughts?* "Oh, no, please don't think that. Marrying you was no mistake."

Frank took my hand and we walked around, sat for a while, then walked again, had lunch, and walked some more. He talked with some of the people who were also tired of waiting and walking. I thought of Mama, my sisters, and my brothers, and wished I could run back to the house to see if they were still crying.

We sat on some metal chairs under a window, where Frank crossed his arms over his chest and closed his eyes. "Maybe I'll sleep. You should try to sleep, too."

I looked left and right, and then at the opposite wall. The short hand of the clock rested on the number two, the big hand on the number twelve, and the second hand constantly ticked the seconds away.

I heard the change in Frank's breathing, followed by a shallow snore. I worried he'd get loud, and I'd be embarrassed. His head had fallen a little toward me, and I wanted to push it up for him, but he might not have liked that. I closed my eyes, but they sprang open, so I glanced around some more.

Other people walked around, groggy, yawning, and looking at their watches. One soldier stretched himself out on two chairs and rested his head in his wife's lap.

Frank woke himself up with a snore. "Sorry, honey," he said, then yawned. I liked that he had called me "honey."

The afternoon dragged on forever. We stepped outside a few times, only to return inside again. We went to the cafeteria for water, coffee, and Coke. Finally, as the clock struck five, the raspy sound came again from the ceiling. We had been assigned to sleeping quarters, for the weather was still dangerous, and we couldn't leave until the next day. The men were directed to different barracks, and the four women to a guest house, where there would be two women per room.

I ended up with Agnes, a tall blonde who'd been married five years and claimed to be in the puking stage of her first pregnancy. She seemed angry at the whole world. Of the three ladies, she was the only one who never smiled, never said anything more than necessary. Sharing a room with her would be like staying alone. Nothing was working out the way I had imagined.

Frank kissed the side of my face after we had eaten our evening meal, and told me to follow Agnes to the guest house. As we walked across the manicured grass, I looked far into the distance, into the direction where I thought my family would be. Another lump tightened around my throat, confusing me and making me wonder why I felt as I did. My feelings didn't make sense. I had wanted to leave, but now it hurt to be leaving. *Will I ever be free of my family?*

I followed Agnes up a few wooden steps, then entered a musty room that had only one window with a dusty screen. There were two narrow beds, each against a wall, with one sheet covering the mattress and another thin one to be used as a blanket. The bathroom had a toilet, a sink, some soap, and some paper towels. We would have to walk down a long hallway to take a shower.

While looking at the little sink, I realized that my toothbrush was back in the duffel bag Frank had let me use for my things. That bag, and his three, had been checked earlier that morning. No one had said that I'd be spending the night here without a toothbrush or pajamas. This was disappointing. I'd be arriving in America with yellow teeth and wrinkled clothes, for I wasn't about to sleep naked, or in my underwear.

Agnes had her toothbrush and toothpaste in her purse, so she kindly gave me some of her toothpaste, and I cleaned my teeth as best I could. When I returned to the room, I found her in bed, eyes closed, shoes off, clothes still on.

"I'll let you get the light," she said drowsily. "I'm dead on my feet. Hope I don't snore and keep you awake."

"No problem," I said. "Thank you for the toothpaste." She didn't say anything else. Soon I heard her breathing change into a shallow rasping sound. I had hoped she would stay awake so that we could sit and talk like two married women. I would have asked what it felt like to be pregnant, and if she had any fears about giving birth. But with her asleep, all I could do was wonder. Perhaps she was on her way to her hometown, maybe looking forward to seeing her family. The thought of family made my throat tighten again, and the unfamiliar room appeared bigger and unfriendlier once I turned off the light.

Agnes snored while I thought about Frank. He had asked if I felt that my marriage had been a mistake. A few days earlier, he had complained about my lack of interest in sex. *What if he decides to leave me? What if I go to sleep, only to wake up to find out that he's gone, like Mama had said?* Images of my mother unfolded in my mind: her red, teary eyes, the white hair around her forehead and temples, the creases on her face.

The memories of the time I had run away from home came to mind. I saw myself running along the river's edge and falling into the whirling pool, almost drowning, and then getting lost in the jungle and spending the night on a tree branch. I needed Frank in my bed, holding and comforting me. I had not expected to spend the night in a lonely room, with my eyes refusing to stay closed and my brain looking back to years past.

Agnes snored and turned in her bed. I turned onto my side, then went back to the old memories. I saw Marta, the old lady in the wooden cabin on the mountain, who had shared her lunch with me, the first meal I had had in thirty-six hours. I thought of Doña Luisa and Doña Monica, who had found me in their stockroom – a room bigger and darker than this one. I relived the fear of that night, the uncertainty of what was to come: Would they let me stay there for the night, or throw me out? I envisioned every corner of their sewing factory, where I had worked for four years under their guidance.

I heard the two women in the next room talking, laughing, running water, flushing the toilet, and finally quieting down to silence. I stepped out of my bed, tiptoed to the window, looked out at the darkness and the lights faraway, then tiptoed back to my bed, where the thoughts continued.

I thought of the day I had gone back to the old farm to rescue my mother and siblings from my father's drunkenness and cruelty. I taught them how to live free and how to work for pay. They learned fast, but then forgot that I had risked my life to save them. That thought made me angry, but then glad that I would soon be far away from them.

Agnes got up, walked to the bathroom, flushed the toilet, returned to her bed, and resumed her snoring. I tiptoed back to the window again, and stared into the night, thinking of Frank and wondering if he was thinking about me, or if he was sound asleep.

I went to the bathroom, drank water from the faucet, then returned to bed. I leaned back to recite the rosary, determined that if it didn't put me to sleep, I would repeat it over and over until it did.

Chapter Twelve

Up And Away

I slept until a man knocked on the. "It's five o'clock. The weather is clear, and our flight will leave at zero seven hundred."

Agnes suggested that I'd use the bathroom first because she needed more time than I did. And she was right. I listened to her for over ten minutes, as she gagged and coughed, and swear that she'd never get pregnant again, even if it meant getting a divorce.

When she finally came out, we stepped out into the early dawn and cut across the dew-covered grass. A few steps away, we met up with Frank and Richard.

"Good morning, sweetheart," Richard said to his wife, and the smacking of kisses followed his words.

"Yeah, hi, honey." Frank's words were so soft I could hardly hear them, and his kiss was as light as a feather. Perhaps he wasn't the type of man who would ever hug and kiss his wife in the presence of others. I knew I wanted him to show me more affection, but for now I was just glad that he didn't leave without me.

We went to the cafeteria, where dozens of uniformed soldiers were already having their breakfasts. Everyone appeared happy and cheerful. I figured it was because they knew where they were going, and unlike me, they felt no guilt about abandoning a mother and a little sister.

I watched Frank eat scrambled eggs, bacon, and toasted bread, but all I had was a cup of black coffee with sugar. I felt wrapped in a cold gloom, and couldn't even think of eating anything. All I wanted was to get on that plane and leave. The sooner I could begin my new life, the better.

"Everything is good in the United States." I had heard that statement many times, most recently from Doña Inez, who seemed to know a lot about Americans.

After breakfast, we followed the stream of soldiers out to the airplane, then waited until a sergeant called out the names of the married couples first.

"Sergeant and Mrs. Thomas Hawkins. Sergeant and Mrs. Richard Senders. Sergeant and Mrs. Frank Wilson. You all may go aboard at this time."

This is great, I thought. *We're finally leaving.* In the same breath, I felt sadness and fear. I was leaving the only world I had ever known, and hoping for a better life in a land that was hard to imagine. *This is not the time to change my mind. Oh God, let it be okay.*

Frank took my arm. "Right here, Jackie, sit here."

I had often imagined being excited upon entering an airplane for the first time, but entering this plane wasn't an out-of-this-world experience. Maybe something had gone wrong in my brain since my wedding, because even though I knew that my dreams were being fulfilled, I could not feel any joy. It was as if part of me had died.

Frank took my hand as he sat next to me. "Honey, this is a cargo airplane. That's why it's so plain, gray and black. These eight seats were hooked up for us four married couples. Passenger airplanes have colored upholstered seats on each side of a center aisle, and they have stewardesses, beautiful girls, to help people bring up their seats and fasten their seatbelts. Those stewardesses wear uniforms matching the interior of the airplane so people can recognize what airline they work for."

As I listened to Frank, I watched the other soldiers pull down some folding seats from the walls, where they sat with some kind of belts around their middle.

Frank continued to inform me. "That roaring you hear comes from the airplane's engine. And here's another thing you should know. Your ears might begin to feel plugged-up. If they do, open your mouth and twist your jaw like this to unplug them." He demonstrated the jaw movement and went on to warn me that I might feel lightheaded and sick to my stomach, but I'd be okay shortly after landing. I felt loved.

When everyone had settled in their seats, the airplane taxied down the runway, squeaking and bouncing, leaving behind the green grass, the trees, and the base I had enjoyed so much. As it lifted off the ground, I felt as if a strong hand had pushed me so deep into the seat I would never be able to stand up again. My stomach felt so tight I could hardly breathe.

"Now we're over water," Frank said knowledgeably. I thought back to the time I had almost drowned in the river.

"Girls don't need to know how to swim," my mother had said. *"Stay out of the water, and you'll never drown."* She had never dreamed that one day I would fly over the ocean to a faraway place she didn't even know existed.

Frank had his arm over my shoulder, as if to keep me from lifting up and flying out of the airplane. He'd been talking to me in a soft voice that was hard to hear over the roaring of the airplane. I nodded, but didn't tell him that I had not heard his words, or that I really wasn't interested in anything, for I felt an emptiness and uncertainty whirling in my stomach.

My eyes wandered from wall to wall, floor to window, and back. It wasn't so that I could remember my first flight, which was something I had wanted to experience for years, but now it no longer mattered.

Some of the American soldiers I had watched with great desire through the louvered window as they marched down the street were now seated around me, close enough to touch. They were in their khaki uniforms, their long legs stretched out in front of them, ankle over ankle, arms crossed over their big chests. Some eyes were closed, others darting from here to there, but none looked at anything in particular. I saw their shiny black shoes, their blonde and light-brown hair, and their sun-tanned skin glowing. They were the people I had been so anxious to meet. Now I was married to one of them. Why wasn't I happy? Had I lost my desires and curiosity along the way?

Frank squeezed my shoulder. "I'll go get us some coffee." He was off before I could ask where he would get coffee from in a moving airplane. Yet when he returned, I didn't ask him where he had gotten it, nor did I remind him that I liked sugar in my coffee. I just started drinking the bitter dark water.

The airplane was suddenly pulled down, and my arm, along with the coffee, rose toward the ceiling. Frank reached up, took the cup, and pulled my arm down. "It's only turbulence. A common thing. Don't be afraid."

Frank's explanation was clear to me. However, I didn't tell him that I wasn't afraid. I could not imagine anything going wrong with an American airplane flown by highly educated American pilots. I truly believed that anything or anyone American was automatically good – no question about it.

Frank laid his head back, and within seconds, his breathing changed.

A stream of thoughts poured into my mind. *What if Mama goes back to the old farm, thinking she can move the other woman and her three children out? What would Papa do to her and the rest of his family? Maybe I should write and advise her not to do that. Or would it be better for me to keep my word and not let her know where I am? Poor Alicia. I would like to help her, but can she receive a letter without the rest of my family knowing about it?*

I thought about Frank then. *He seems so relaxed and sure of himself. He loves me, and I love him. But will I ever learn to like intercourse? I like the hugging and the kisses, but I don't understand why anything else should be so important. Frank says I need to learn before it becomes a real problem, but he doesn't tell me how I'm supposed to learn. Will I ever be able to talk with him about such matters?*

When the airplane landed in Mobile, Alabama, everyone clapped and cheered – except me, of course. I just waited eagerly to step out into a new world – a world of plenty. A world that was cool, clean, friendly, and full of opportunities.

The four couples were the first to exit the airplane.

"Holy smoke! It's scorching hot," said one of the men.

"Ninety-two degrees," said another.

"Yeah, honey, I forgot to tell you that sometimes it gets hotter here than it does in Puerto Rico," Frank said to me.

"When will it snow?" I asked.

"Here in Mobile, maybe never. But in the northern states, it's probably snowing by now."

A laugh burst out from ahead of us. Richard slowed his steps and looked over his shoulder. "I hope you told her just how much snow she'll see where you're taking her. Minnesota! Of all places." He turned his head and hurried to catch up with the others, who all chuckled at his remark.

"Oh, I told her," Frank said. But his voice was so soft, I didn't think anyone had heard it. I felt bad for him. I would never want to hear anyone talk to my husband in a way that made him feel stupid.

Chapter Thirteen

Mobile

We were taken by a bus to the barracks and guest houses. It was afternoon, and the sky was clear, but the bright sun was blisteringly hot. While the men and women chattered and chuckled, I looked out the window, hoping to see a tree or bush that might resemble the ones back home. I saw none, not even wildflowers alongside the road. My stomach suddenly felt washed-out, and a bitter taste settled in my mouth.

When the bus pulled in front of several rows of two-story buildings, everyone stepped out onto the hot concrete of the parking lot. Duffle bags and bundles were pulled out from under the bus, and the uniformed men, faces shiny with sweat, hurried to find their baggage. Soon everyone, weighted down with duffle bags, headed down the sidewalk toward their designated rooms.

With one small bag in each hand, I followed Frank. He carried the two big ones up a wooden stairway to the second floor of the building. I felt as if my eyes were sunk deep into their sockets, my cheekbones higher than usual, and my head empty.

Inside the building, we walked down a long hallway, passing closed doors left and right, to find our room.. When Frank opened our door, a warm, musty breeze escaped past us and into the hallway.

The room had one window, and two single beds without sheets. Each bed was against a wall with a small chest of drawers next to it. Above each chest of drawers was a shelf with a wooden rod and some clothes hangers.

"I'll pull those beds together," Frank said, sweat running down his face. "These rooms were set up for two single people, not for honeymooners."

"What are honeymooners?"

"Two people who just got married," he said.

"*¿Luna de miel?* But we married almost five weeks ago."

"I know, honey, but our honeymoon won't be over until we return to Puerto Rico for our first visit."

A sound of romance shone through those words from my husband, and the hope of us returning to the island someday as Americans on vacation excited me. *What will my family say about me then?*

"I'll go get the sheets so we can make the bed," he said. "Afterwards, we'll go take our showers, and go to the mess hall for dinner. Then we can go see a movie, if you'd like."

"I'd like that. But where are the showers?"

"Oh, yeah. The showers and toilets are at the end of the hall, women on the right and men on the left." He gave me a quick kiss and left. I stood at the window and watched him walk down the sidewalk and disappear behind another building.

Turning from the window, I looked at the bare white walls, the wide-boarded ceiling, the blue-striped mattresses and pillows on the narrow beds, and the wide-boarded floor with the varnish worn off in the center. *Why do I feel so empty and blue? Am I not in the United States, married to an American, something I have so badly wanted? Why am I not bubbly and jumping for joy?*

Frank came back with two sheets, two pillowcases, and two sets of towels. I helped him move the bed, lifting it so the metal legs wouldn't make any more scratches on the floor. We put the two beds as close together as possible, then covered the mattresses with one sheet, which became dotted with drops of Frank's perspiration. He said they would dry fast in this heat.

Finally, we left for the shower rooms with our towels, Frank turning left as I turned right. The steamy room was large, with a line of toilets on one side and shower stalls on the other. Short walls separated one toilet from the other. Higher walls separated the showers, but feet and heads could be seen from shower to shower.

Outside the stalls were two women wearing only bras and panties, one wrapped in white towels, and two completely naked. They reached for their towels casually, as if they didn't care who saw them. I held in my gasp and tried to appear calm and open-minded. I had never seen naked women before. My mother would call them indecent. She would ask me if I was planning to become bold and shameless like these American women.

I didn't want the women to see that I was embarrassed, but I didn't feel ready to undress in front of anyone. Even my husband had not seen me completely naked. Ever since our marriage, I had been wearing a robe from the bathroom to the bed, then hurrying to get under the sheets with my undergarments still on.

My face turned red as I hesitated before entering the next available stall. I tried to think of something to say that might ease my nerves, but my brain was locked somewhere else. The women were chatting away, some even chuckling, as they dried their crotches and armpits.

The more I hesitated, the worse I felt, so I took off my slacks and blouse only, hung them on a hook, hurried into the stall, and quickly pulled the short door closed. The water felt good on my warm skin, but I hurried to finish before someone might pull my door open.

Wrapping the towel around myself, I threw my slacks and blouse over my shoulder and quickly returned to the room. Luckily, Frank hadn't come back yet, and by the time he did, I had put on a dry bra, panties, and a green dress. Except for a little lipstick, I didn't wear make-up, so all I had left to do was comb my hair, which I pinned to the side with a white barrette.

"What a beautiful blonde," Frank said as he walked in. "I didn't expect you to be back so soon. I thought women took longer in the shower than men do."

"Sometimes I take longer, but there were women waiting." I looked into my hand mirror to avoid Frank – he was wearing only a towel around his waist. If he dropped it, I didn't want to see anything embarrassing. I knew that my modesty wasn't normal, but I couldn't talk with Frank about such things. I just didn't know how, and the thought of mentioning things like that made me break into a sweat. I hated those feelings.

Frank wasn't shy about his problems. He came up to me with his crooked little smile, kissed my shoulder, and then my neck and ear. "I didn't get to hold you last night."

I saw the hard thing through his moist towel, and backed away quickly. "You said we were going to dinner."

"We are. Afterwards." He laughed, chasing me around the bed, red-faced, his blue eyes beaming.

Somehow, I managed to convince him that it was too hot.

"Hot is good," he said, then turned his back to me.

I felt guilty as he wiggled his stiff thing into his uniform. "I'll make it up to you."

"I know you will," he answered, smiling. "Ready to go?"

"Ready." We walked out holding hands.

The mess hall was huge, with many white-topped tables on black iron legs. The chairs were also metal, gray with legs to match the tables. We each took a tray and joined a line which led to a long counter, where huge steaming pots of fried chicken, mashed potatoes, roast beef and gravy, baked beans, and green vegetables were set.

Young men wearing white shirts and caps stood behind the counter ready to scoop the food onto people's plates. I had never seen so much food displayed before, so the look of it took my appetite away.

"Oh, honey, let me tell you how this works," Frank said, with a tone that told me this was important. "They'll put on your plate whatever you want, but you must eat it all."

"But I'm not even hungry." I shoved my tray under Frank's and stepped out of the line, embarrassed.

I thought that Frank might get mad at me for acting stupid, but instead he said, "Go choose a table. I'll bring you something."

Minutes later, he joined me with a tray of food.

"I got you a little Jell-O and canned peaches. You have to force some food down, because I won't have any money for doctors if you get sick."

"I feel better now," I said after eating the Jell-O and peaches. But it was just a lie to make him happy. I didn't want to tell him that I felt like half of me was there, and the other half was somewhere between Mobile, Alabama, and Puerto Rico.

"You're not feeling homesick already, are you, honey?" Frank's eyes peered into mine from across the table.

I straightened my back. "No, I'm not. But everything is strange to me."

"I know it must be. Don't worry. I'll take care of you," he said, with a wink that made me feel good.

We didn't go to the movies after dinner, but instead met Richard and Agnes, who invited us to take a walk with them.

"That's a good idea," Frank said. "Starting tomorrow, you girls should keep each other company when we report for duty every day."

"Yeah, honey," Richard said. "You can even give Jackie some points on married life." He chuckled.

"What makes you think she needs points?" Frank asked, and I felt glad that he had defended me.

"I'm just joking," Richard said.

We walked on, and came to a place where grown men sent huge balls rolling down wooden lanes to knock down a group of white, bottle-shaped wooden pins. It was a big place, cool and bright with lights. It had many lines of seats where other men, women, and children sat, cheering and clapping every time one of the men knocked down all the pins at the same time.

"That's called bowling," Frank whispered to me. "It's a fun sport. I'll teach you someday so you can play, too."

"Those balls look heavy."

"Oh, they have lighter ones for women," he said. I felt proud of him. He was smart and talented, played musical instruments, danced beautifully, and knew about sports. The only thing I had learned in my lifetime was how to work hard.

Back in the room that night, Frank and I argued about the wife's obligation to her husband, and the husband's marital rights.

"You need to learn that this is an important part of a marriage, before it becomes a problem," he said. "It's something men and women have been doing for ages, and they aren't going to stop anytime soon."

"But does it have to be, even when it's so hot that both people get bathed in sweat?"

"It can be anytime. Whenever the man gets the urge, whether it's hot or cold." Frank turned to face the wall, frustrated, but he fell asleep within minutes. I lay there listening to his breathing and wondered if there was something wrong with me.

Suddenly, I heard some loud squeaks on the other side of our wall. The sound grew louder, as if someone was trying to push a headboard through our wall. I shook Frank and told him that someone was breaking into our room.

He sat up. "That's Richard and Agnes. They have the room next door, and they're making love. See what I mean? Everybody does it. Just listen and learn." He let himself fall back on the bed.

The squeaks grew louder and louder, followed by a long cry, like that of an animal in pain, and then all was quiet.

Frank sprang up again. "See what I mean? Everybody does it." He kissed my forehead and lay back down again.

I stayed sitting up, feeling glad that he could not see my red face in the dark.

Chapter Fourteen

A Change of Thought

The next five days were filled with loneliness and wonder. Every morning, I watched Frank and Richard walk down the long sidewalk and disappear around the buildings. I met Agnes and walked with her to the cafeteria, while she growled constantly about her morning sickness.

We had coffee and toast, then went back to the guest house. She stayed in the seating area downstairs, looking through the bookshelves for things to read. I went to my room and started a letter to my family.

Dear Mama, sisters, and brothers,

I had not intended to write to any of you, but I'll burst if I can't tell you about everything I have seen so far. We arrived here at the Air Force base in Mobile, Alabama, yesterday. There was a storm over Cuba, and our flight could not leave as scheduled. We had to stay on the base for the night, and sleep in guest houses, women in one building and men in another. We'll be here for four more days, until Frank receives his discharge papers. Then we'll head to Minnesota. I can't wait to see you again and tell you about this beautiful part of the world.

Frank is good to me. He loves me very much. I'm so glad to be married. I wish you were all here with me.

I tore that letter up and threw it into the wastebasket, promising myself to send the next one I wrote. I felt bad, because I really wanted to write to Alicia, but how would she keep a letter from the others? I believed that she could be trusted, but I couldn't take a chance and have my two oldest brothers find me someday. I couldn't write to Alicia without having some money or something to send her. Then there was our mother. Even though she had never been fair to me, I still felt sorry for her and wished to help her somehow.

If I did write to my mother, I wouldn't tell her that I felt lonely and homesick already, that I was having a difficult time being a wife, and that she should have told me what a wife was supposed to do for her husband.

My mother would never understand that her weird teachings about men had handicapped me, so why would I mention something about that? I made up my mind right then that no matter how difficult the years ahead would be, I would never let her know. She and my father had kept us children from learning, so that we'd have no choice but to stay close to home and be their slaves. I would not give them the satisfaction of knowing that I felt like a bird whose wings had been clipped, and then was sent out into the world to fend for itself.

I promised myself that I would improve my English, read many books, and learn as much about the world as possible. If my family ever saw me again, I wanted them to be surprised at my knowledge and accomplishments. They might never admit it, but they would be proud of me. I would never tell them about whatever hardships I had faced due to my lack of education.

For the next four days, I stayed downstairs after breakfast and joined Agnes at the bookshelves. I sat across from her and looked through the pages of magazines, struggling to understand the words, afraid that if I stayed on a page too long she would realize that I could not read English.

At noon, Agnes put down her book and hurried to the bathroom, and then we walked back to the cafeteria. We sat together, and sometimes another lady or two joined us. Agnes still had little to say, but the other women asked me questions: How long had Frank and I been married? Why was I so light when all the Puerto Ricans they had seen were dark? And was I going to like the cold winters of Minnesota?

I answered everything honestly, until the women turned to talk with each other. Then I listened, smiled when they did, and laughed when they laughed. I heard that Agnes was on her way to her hometown in the state of Virginia, and that she could hardly wait to see her mom and three sisters.

"I have three sisters, too," I put in, excited that we had something in common. The three women looked at me.

"That's nice," said one of them, but then they continued to talk to each other.

After lunch, we all scattered out, each to her building. Agnes went up to her room, book in hand, so she could fall asleep reading. I went to my room, stared out the window for a while, then stretched myself on the bed. I wondered what awaited me in Minnesota. *What if Frank's relatives don't like me? What if Frank changes his mind about our marriage and sends me back to Puerto Rico? I'd become the gossip subject of the barrio.*

Every evening after Frank returned, we went to the mess hall, then for a little walk around the buildings, sometimes alone, and other times with Richard and Agnes. A few times we sat outside the barracks, or in the seating area where the men talked, told jokes, and laughed, while the women had their own conversations. I mostly listened.

Chapter Fifteen

The Long Bus Ride

When Frank received his discharge papers, he walked into the room with a wide smile and bright eyes. "I've decided that we will go the rest of the way home by bus so my honey can see the country." He wrapped his arms around my shoulders. "It will take us a few days and nights to get home, but I think you'll enjoy that. What do you think?"

"I think it's very nice, but I've never done anything like that before."

"Oh you are going to be doing a lot of things you've never done before."

Normally, I would have shown great excitement over something like that, but the truth was, that deep inside I wanted nothing more than to go back home. It was a hard feeling to understand, so I didn't say anything about it to Frank.

We left at six in the morning. The weather had turned from blistering hot to a sharp chill. The sky looked gray, and there was no sign of the sun. I shivered as we stood waiting to board the bus, for I was wearing a summer skirt and blouse, a flat pair of black shoes with thin soles, and no socks or stockings.

"I'll buy you a coat somewhere along the way," Frank said, pulling me close to him. It was then that I noticed a group black people a few feet away from us and the other white people. Then, when the bus pulled close to the sidewalk, two doors opened. The whites entered through the door near the driver, but the blacks entered through the other door and took their seats at the back of the bus. I found that odd. But I didn't want to appear stupid or nosy by asking.

Frank let me sit by the window so I could see more. As I sat, I pushed my hand through the bend of his arm and snuggled close to him. And for the first time, I felt a little romantic, as if this was finally a real *luna de miel* (honeymoon.)

The bus rode on for some time, then stopped for two more groups of people. The whites entered through the front, and the blacks through the rear door and stayed back there.

Frank whispered in my ear, "In this part of the country, black people must ride only at the back of the bus."

"Why?"

"It's the law."

"What kind of a law is that? Aren't they people, too?"

"Yes, they are, and some activists are working to change that law." He patted my hand. "I'll explain things to you more clearly when we get home."

I leaned on Frank, feeling something heavy in my heart. I had thought that in the United States people weren't treated one way or another because of the color of their skin. I, myself, had been treated differently by my family because of the color of my skin and eyes. Perhaps my mother was right when she claimed that people were the same everywhere. The perfect picture of America that I had created in my mind was becoming rather gloomy.

In the outskirts of another small town, we rode past a park where white children played on one side, and black children on the other. Each side had swing sets, but the white side looked newer. Each side had its own little post with a shallow sink and water faucet. A cyclone fence separated the two sides of the park, and high up on the fence were two signs. The one on the side for white children read in big letters, *Whites*. The one on the other side read *Negroes*.

"Frank," I whispered. "I thought everybody was treated equal in the United States. Was I wrong?"

"No. But I'll explain all that when we get home. A bus filled with strangers is not an ideal place for that discussion."

"What's freedom of speech? Am I wrong about that, too?"

"No, but there's a time and a place for everything."

I didn't ask any more questions, but looked this way and that, wondering if what lay ahead would be totally different from what I had expected. What would I do if I found that American people weren't very different from the people I had run away from?

The countryside had many trees, but they were fruitless. The bushes were flowerless, and the grass was turning brown. We went through towns and villages, over some bridges, and under others. At bus stops, some passengers got out, while others came in. I heard people talking, chuckling, and snoring. Even Frank threw his head back often and snored.

In one little town, the bus pulled up into a terminal where we had a small lunch and then transferred to another bus. Soon the bus was turning left and right, and the sun shone on someone's face one minute, and on another's the next. The routine of stops and passengers leaving and coming in became tiring. I looked out the window, leaned on Frank, straightened up, and took deep breaths. No matter what I did, the seat remained hard and uncomfortable. I needed to stretch out on a bed or floor. I thought that my spine would break if I had to continue sitting for another long day and night.

At sunset we pulled into a bigger and more crowded station, where we had our evening meal and waited some time to board another bus. In this place, I saw the lines of black people on one side and the whites on the other. Bathrooms were also divided, yet everyone went about apparently unbothered by such arrangements. This was not at all like the America I had expected to find.

In the white women's bathroom were shiny boxes on the doors. No one could enter the stalls before putting in a nickel. I didn't have a nickel, so I crawled under the door like another girl had.

The night lights had come on everywhere by the time we boarded the next bus. For a long time, the scenery was more interesting than during the day. I could see the clothing and fabrics inside the stores, and the pretty lamps and nice furniture inside the homes. Even the gas stations looked bright, with all the lights and colorful flags swinging in the wind.

Gradually, the lights fell behind as we moved further into the countryside, where fields of darkness reached away from the road and met with the far horizon. In some areas, I saw distant lights shining on dwellings.

"This is farm country around here," said Frank. "In the summertime, you'll see miles and miles of corn, wheat, potatoes, soybeans, and patches of grass with nothing but cattle."

"Cattle are cows?"

"Yeah, and some farmers raise only cattle."

I could not imagine a farm with nothing but cows. But then again, imagining anything at all had become difficult since I had left home. Sometimes I wondered if it could be possible to be two persons in one, keeping each other confused. One minute, I felt glad to be so far away from the world of fruit trees and flowers I had known, but the next minute I longed to see an orange tree and a blooming bush. I felt glad to be away from the family who had made me miserable for years, yet I wished I could tell them about everything I saw.

Stepping out of the bus into the midnight air of a strange city in the state of Tennessee was like walking into one of my weirdest dreams. Buildings, trees, shrubs, and even the air appeared dormant. People walked around with sleepy eyes and lazy feet. They gazed one way and then another, stumbling, then stopping as if wondering which way to turn. We walked into another terminal where a raspy voice was announcing departures to different cities, and people were scrambling to different gates.

We boarded another bus, and from then on, I stared straight into the darkness, not thinking or remembering, but feeling groggy with the steady humming sound of the engine.

Chapter Sixteen

Moving Stairways

The beginning of a new day appeared through a gray sheet of gloom, and the air's chill stung my skin as we staggered out of the warm, stuffy bus. We entered another terminal, had a quick coffee and pastry, then hurried into another bus. The routine became boring, and everything appeared drab and unappealing, especially the yellow and brown trees along the highways. All I wanted now was to get to where we were going so I could begin a new life in my new country.

We stopped several times to transfer to different buses before reaching Chicago. In one town, the wait was more than an hour, so Frank said we had time to buy a coat for me. We walked down a crowded sidewalk to a department store that had several floors. The women's coats were upstairs, and the steps to get there came one after another from under the floor, making a clop-clop sound as they constantly moved upward.

"This is an escalator," Frank said, and off he went. The farther up he went, the more nervous I became. This was to me like jumping on a speeding horse. Finally, worried that Frank would disappear and I'd be alone in this strange town, I jumped on. I landed on all fours, moving upward, unable to stand up, my head throbbing and my face burning hot. I heard some people gasp, yet I could not turn to see who was watching or if Frank was still there.

I wanted to die in his arms when he caught me at the end of the ride.

"I'm so sorry, honey. I didn't explain how the escalator works. Are you hurt?"

"No, but I feel stupid."

"Why? You didn't have escalators in Puerto Rico. We should hurry, or the bus will leave without us."

I followed Frank around the department, and he chose a bulky gray coat with wide sleeves.

"This is a temporary one. I'll buy you a nicer coat once I start working."

Frank took me by the hand on our way down the escalator. I didn't look around to see if people were staring at me, but I knew they were.

We made it to the bus just in time. It was full, and started out as soon as we got on. From then on, the further north we went, the more near-dead trees I saw. The few leaves they had left were either brown or yellow, and they were falling to the ground. To me, the falling of the leaves meant that the trees were dying, and I might never see anything green again. I couldn't share my feelings and fears to Frank. He might see me as a complainer, who would not adjust to living in his home state.

Night came again before we reached Chicago. By then, Frank had been dozing in and out of sleep, and his cheeks and chin were covered with short whiskers, making him look tired and unfriendly.

"We're taking the train from here," he growled. "Can't get any sleep in a damned bus."

"What's a train look like?"

Frank perked up. "Oh, that's right! You've never seen a train. No such thing in Puerto Rico."

"At one time, there was one, but it was discontinued before I was even ten. But I got to see the remaining tracks, which made me wonder what a train would look like."

"A train is a line of railroad cars connected to each other and pulled by a locomotive. Sometimes those cars are packed with passengers, but most of the time there are a lot of empty seats. Maybe this will be our lucky day, and we can get some sleep."

"The train will have beds?" I asked.

"Some do, but we can't afford that. The seats will have to do. If it isn't too crowded, we might get lucky and get a whole row of seats to ourselves. I'll get some sleep. I hope you can, too."

"I could never close my eyes in public, where someone might stare at me."

"If you get sleepy enough, you will." Frank spoke matter-of-factly, so I said no more. I didn't want him to get tired of me. Still, I felt as if a wicker basket had been placed over my head. Everything and everyone I saw appeared distorted, and my feet felt so heavy I could hardly lift them.

I have no recollection of how we got from the bus stop to the train station. But the building was the biggest building I had ever seen. It went on forever, and had dark walls and a ceiling as high as the sky. It had the steady hum of a deep tunnel, and the sounds of voices and moving objects roared like thunder. Frank told me to sit on a bench and keep my eyes on the bags while he went to buy our train tickets.

He returned shortly and said that we had a two-hour wait for the eleven o'clock train to Saint Paul. We couldn't walk around with our heavy bags, so from then on, one of us stayed with the bags at all times. He stayed while I went to the women's room, where I brushed my teeth and freshened up. It was a big washroom, and there wasn't a line of women waiting, so I changed my clothes, combed my hair, and put on some lipstick.

I had been wondering if I would have the opportunity to bathe before reaching Saint Paul. The thought of meeting my new in-laws without bathing or changing my clothes for three or four days made me feel embarrassed and nervous, but that was another thing I hadn't mentioned to Frank.

When I returned, he went to the men's room, and later came out clean-shaven and smiling, as if glad to be going home.

He found a newspaper someone had left on a bench, and sat down to read it. Suddenly, he said, "Well, I'll be damned!"

"What happened?" I asked.

"It says here that the meat packing company I worked for before going into the service is shutting down. That means I'm out of a job!"

I didn't understand Frank's concern. This was America. You lose one job, but find another.

"Damn! I was counting on getting a job there again. What in the world am I going to do if they're closing the damn place!"

"Go back into the Air Force," I said.

"Oh, no! I'm not going back into the Air Force. I have no intention of spending my whole life in the service. I have to make a go of it on the outside!"

I knew not to mention the Air Force again, just by hearing the tone of Frank's voice. But deep inside, I believed that our lives would be a lot better if he stayed in the service. He had said that the men who were discharged would receive a thousand dollars if they re-enlisted within ninety days. A thousand dollars would make us rich.

Frank had told me that if I married him, I would never have to work to support myself. He would work, and I would take care of him, the house, and the babies we might have. Now he seemed threatened by the fact that his old place of employment was closing, but he didn't see the Air Force as a solution. I figured that he would come up with another idea in order to keep his promise to me. I didn't think that unemployment existed in the United States.

Chapter Seventeen

Gray and Black

"That's our train," Frank said as a man's voice broke through the echoing noises. He took the two big bags, and I followed him with the two smaller ones. Entering the train was like walking into a large tube with dim lights and seats on each side of a narrow aisle. We squeezed past the strangers who were shoving bulky bags up into some compartments.

We went to the far end of the car, where Frank said, "This is the place." The seats on each side of the passageway were empty. "You can sleep there, and I'll sleep here," he said, placing the bigger duffle bags in front of the seats and the smaller ones up in the compartments. He kicked off his shoes and stretched out on the seats. "Try to sleep, honey. You'll have a big day tomorrow."

"Do they have bathrooms here?"

"Oh, yeah, it's over there." He pointed back toward the opposite end of the car, then immediately closed his eyes.

I took the long walk back, feeling as if the passengers were staring at me because I didn't belong here. I saw two doors side by side, but there were no signs indicating bathrooms. I grabbed one of the handles, turned it, and a panel popped open. I stood facing a wall covered from top to bottom with a net of red, blue, and yellow wires, all twisted like long spaghetti, and a million tiny bulbs blinking red, green, and orange.

My heart thumped and pounded so hard I felt myself spinning with my face on fire. I waited to hear the passengers laughing at me while I stared at those wires. When I didn't hear laughter, I turned, but saw no faces staring. Finally I took a deep breath, shut the door, and hurried back to my seat, where I sat all night with a full bladder and ringing ears.

The train moved slowly at first, screeching and blowing white smoke to the sides, gradually pulling away from the station. Then it increased its speed and rode into the black night. I looked back and saw an old woman on the seat behind me with her eyes closed and her arms wrapped around a black purse.

A young couple huddled together on the seats across from the old lady. Some passengers had their heads thrown back and their mouths open, while others rested their heads on a companion's shoulder. Everyone appeared at ease and unafraid. I seemed to be the only person in the whole train who felt alone, awkward, and out of place. I knew that in my gray coat with the wide sleeves, I didn't look like the women and girls I had seen boarding the train, or any throughout the entire trip. Anyone who looked at me from that moment on would know where I came from. I felt sure about that, and my need to hide became greater than my desire to go on.

Frank slept soundly. He knew where he was going, and that his family was waiting for him. Things were different for me. I was going to a strange place to meet people who might not like me. If only I could make myself look nicer and prettier, but I didn't have face creams or make-up. My shoulder-length hair was pinned to the side with a white barrette.

I could not understand how Frank could sleep in a moving train. Didn't he care that I felt alone? Did he really think I would sleep in a train filled with strangers? I wouldn't even lean back and close my eyes, for fear that I'd find a face looking down at me whenever I opened them again.

The night was so black that whenever I tried to look out, all I could see in the window pane was the reflection of my hands crossed on my lap. The black and white squares of my checkered skirt appeared distorted, and my knuckles were extra large, with deep creases. I quickly unlocked my fingers and crossed my arms over my chest, aiming my gaze in another direction.

The train shook constantly, squeaking and popping as if the cabinets and doors were going to snap off. A few feet away from our seats, our car connected to another, but one went up while the other went down. I worried that the two cars would pull apart and that I'd fly out into the dark of night.

After what seemed like hours, the door between the two cars swung open, and a man in a black uniform and a rounded black hat walked through. "Tickets," he announced. Everyone, including Frank, woke up long enough to hand over their tickets. The man clicked something on the ticket, handed it back to its owner, and moved on to the next passenger. Then Frank and everyone else returned to their sleep. I went back to staring. The only difference was that I stopped worrying about the two cars pulling apart. If there had been a problem, the ticket man would have noticed it.

Every now and then, I could see dim lights shining from poles onto narrow and lonely roads that seemed forgotten. I could not imagine anyone traveling on such roads, only to disappear into the blackness of the night.

That chilled feeling of darkness and loneliness reminded me of how dark the woods back home became once the sun went down. The memories of my childhood unfolded in my mind, one after another. I thought of the songs the hill people sang while working in the coffee fields. They made up songs about anything, like *pana* soup with *panas* on the side.

Panas, or breadfruit, grew in abundance in our hills. During the 1940's, when a war on the other side of the world caused a shortage of rice and sugar on the island, the hill people lived on *panas*. They removed the green pimply skin of the *pana*, carved out the spongy stuffing, then cut the slices into small cubes to make *pana* soup. They boiled some of the slices in salty water to eat with the soup. The next day, the men working in the fields sang about being tired of eating *pana* soup with *panas* on the side.

My next thought was of the night my father's cousin, out of breath from running through the dark woods, knocked on our front door. "Come see for yourselves! It's the end of the world. Come see the beams of blue light moving across the sky from horizon to horizon. I know it's Jesus. He is searching for us! Come see for yourselves, please! I am terrified."

My parents jumped out of their beds and opened the front door. There was Mateo at the foot of the steps, panting and walking in circles.

"See what I mean? There they come. Have you ever seen anything like it?"

My sister and I heard the voice and pressed our faces to the wall cracks. We saw our parents looking up to the sky, and then at Mateo. Soon Papa leaped to the next room and returned with a gallon jug of rum. We watched the three of them on the front steps, where they spent most of that night talking about the end of the world and taking one drink after another, and looking for Jesus in the beams of light.

The hill people didn't go very far from their homes in those days. A trip to a little town from the hills was an all-day event, and not everybody could afford to go more than once a year. Radios and newspapers weren't available out in the country, so the news was old by the time it reached us by word of mouth. That was how we learned that the beams of light had been to announce the grand opening of the new Air Force base on the island. The rich Americans who would live on that base would provide jobs for many of the island's people. The men would work as gardeners, and the women would clean the homes and iron khaki uniforms.

I thought about the first time I had gone to the base, years after the grand opening. I fell in love with the idea of working among Americans, with the hope of one day marrying one. I never imagined that I'd end up riding through a dark world in a train, alone, with a sleeping husband across the aisle.

A voice announcing the name of a station brought me back to the present. The train gradually stopped, and clouds of white steam rolled past my window. I saw a man cut through the steam, pulling the collar of his dark coat up to his ears, and run to a small dwelling with poor lighting which stood on a platform next to the tracks. He disappeared through the narrow door. I wondered if there were other people in the dwelling. It looked lonely, empty, cold, and dead. Why would he get off the train in such a deserted place?

Fear shot through me then. *What if Frank is taking me to a place like this?* I wanted Frank to wake up without my asking him to, sit with me, and keep me warm with his big arms. I felt so cold and alone. My legs and feet were freezing. I had no stockings on, and the soles of my black loafers were thin.

When a loud horn sounded, the train shrieked and slowly continued on its tracks, leaving the little dwelling on the flat field of darkness. I felt sad for the little building, and for the man who had gone inside it. It stayed in my mind, like a picture in a book.

I pulled my feet, shoes still on, up onto the seat, and covered myself with my coat. I stared straight ahead, where the two cars came together and moved, one up and the other down.

I thought back to the day I had said goodbye to my family while I tuned my ears to the steady humming and screeching. I saw my mother's sad face, the white hair surrounding it, her raw eyes and tears. I saw Alicia's bright eyes and encouraging smile.

I felt hot tears rolling down my cheeks. I watched the drops splatter on my coat and soak into the gray fabric. Frank should have bought me a red coat, since everything I had seen so far on this trip had been gray, black, and brown. There had been a gray airplane, gray buses, gray streets, gray buildings, and a gray train – everything gray and black, gloomy and dead.

If Frank had sat next to me, I could have told him everything that had gone through my mind in the past two weeks. I hadn't told him much about myself – not that I was ashamed to or anything like that, but simply because he never asked. In fact, he never asked me why I was so light, while most Puerto Ricans were dark. I knew that Doña Inez had told him some things about my background, but he should have asked me.

As I looked across the aisle, the man I had married seemed like a total stranger. A heavy stone settled in the pit of my stomach, and I just wanted to go back to my island, where I could rest on the green grass under the sun.

Chapter Eighteen

Faces Under Gloom

At last a man's voice announced something about the St. Paul station. Everyone in the car stirred, yawning and murmuring. Frank sat up and looked at me, but I quickly crossed my arms over my chest and turned to stare out the window so he would realize that I didn't like being left alone all night.

The sky was gray, the dawn dark and gloomy. The train reduced its speed. Now I saw more brown shrubs and dead grass along the tracks. I decided that the fumes from the train had killed everything that grew near the tracks, because no cold or snow could do that. Inland from the tracks stood trees all stripped of their leaves. The country I had imagined as bright and rich appeared dark and dead.

I tilted my head to look at the sky, but could not see where the sun would be coming from. Frank had said that we'd arrive in Saint Paul at about eight, but it was too dark outside to be eight o'clock.

Up a little ways from the tracks, I saw cows, many of them, in groups, brown ones and white ones. They were moving lazily, swinging their tails. But these cows were different from the ones back home – these cows appeared to be smoking. As the train moved on, I kept my eyes on the smoking cows until my chin touched my right shoulder and I couldn't see them anymore. This was something I had to write to Alicia about. She would never believe it. Amazing! Smoking cows?

After the cows, I saw homes with smoke rising from the roofs. Did people in the United states cook with wood, too? I would be very disappointed if they did, for I had never liked having to blow on a little flame in order to ignite the wood between the rocks on the bench we called a *fogón* back home.

"Did you get some sleep, honey?" Frank had moved to the seat next to me, but I had been concentrating on the smoke and had not heard him.

"No," I said, without taking my eyes off the brown and gray scenery.

"Well, some people can't sleep in a moving train. I can sleep anywhere when I'm tired. Oh well, we're almost home. You can sleep there all you want."

"Sounds nice when you say we're almost home, but I feel far away from mine." I heard my crying voice, but I still didn't look at him. He shouldn't have left me alone all night.

"Oh, honey, but it's your home, too. You're going to your new home." He put his arm on my shoulder and pulled me to his chest. "It's your new home, that's for sure."

I nodded and wiped my tears with the back of my hand.

"See that tall building over there?" Frank stretched his arm past my chin. "Way over there, see it? That's downtown Saint Paul."

I could tell that he was beaming with joy, but I opened my eyes wide, and what I saw didn't cheer me up: dark buildings and more dead trees.

Soon, our view to the gloomy outdoors was replaced by another train next to ours, on my side, so close that I could see the freckles on a boy's face who stared from his window into mine. I turned and noticed a dark brick wall outside the other window.

"We've arrived at the train station," Frank said.

All of the other passengers stood up, yawning and reaching for their bags, then hurried to exit the train. We took our bags and stepped out onto a narrow passage that led to two sets of double doors. This was another huge building with dark walls and high ceilings. Men, women, and some children passed us left and right with their bags and suitcases as we made our way toward a line of telephones from which Frank would call his mother.

While he made the call, I followed a line of women to the restroom. At last I would get rid of the pressure in my bladder. But oddly enough, I sat on that cold toilet for the longest time, and not a drop of urine spilled out. Women did their thing, flushed their toilets, and hurried out. I waited.

When nothing happened, I went to a sink to freshen up before meeting my mother-in-law. By then, my eyelids felt dry and itchy, and I knew that Frank's mother wasn't going to like me. *What will I do if she doesn't like me? Will Frank still keep me if his mother tells him I'm not pretty enough to be in her family?*

I washed my face in the sink, hoping to remove the stress and tears.

Then I looked in the mirror and noticed that my face was whiter than it had ever been before. I put on lipstick and wiped it off again. My lips were too dry, so I put the lipstick back on. I combed my hair one way and then another. More women came in, and reached around me to wash their hands. I stayed there, still trying to make myself look pretty. I tucked in my blouse, smoothed my skirt, and looked at my legs, which seemed as white as plucked chickens. I buttoned my coat, fluffed my hair over my shoulders, and looked into the mirror once more.

When I finally came out to where Frank waited, his mother and her friend were there.

"Honey, I was getting worried, wondering if something had happened to you in there."

"Sorry, I couldn't help it."

"Here, this is my mother and her friend Leo."

"Welcome to the family," the lady said, taking my hand. She looked beautiful, with silver-white hair, a brilliant smile, and sparkling blue eyes. "My name is Vera, but you can call me Ma. And this is my friend Leo."

Leo, a husky man with dark skin, brown eyes, and gray hair, took my hand and kissed it. "I came to this country from Czechoslovakia when I was about your age, so I know how strange you must feel. But don't worry, you'll be fine. You married into a good family." He turned to Frank. "Beautiful girl, congratulations." He went on to say that I had nothing to worry about in this country of freedom. "It takes time to adjust to a new culture and weather changes, but you'll be just fine," he assured me, as if he was afraid I might want to go back home.

Frank picked up the two big bags, while Leo took the two smaller ones, and we headed toward the exit. Loud voices were coming from speakers above us, announcing arrivals and departures, and more people hurried past us with their bags and suitcases. I walked behind the other three, dragging my feet, trying to understand if what I felt was joy or fear. I had accomplished my dream, but I felt so overwhelmed. So many strangers passed me on the left and right, all with pale faces, and bundled up in dark brown, gray, purple, and black coats.

We walked through two sets of double doors, then out into freezing cold air and down some old concrete steps. While my lower teeth clicked against the upper ones, I noticed white smoke coming through square holes between the street and the sidewalk. Was there fire under the road? Would people laugh at me if I asked? I decided not to take the risk.

When we reached Leo's black car in the parking lot, Frank opened a door to the back seat and, acting like someone I had never met, said, "Get in, kiddo. I'm riding in front with Ma, because I have a lot to talk to her about." He practically shoved me in, shut the car door quickly, and hurried to sit next to his mother. Their conversation began instantly, but all I could hear was a deep humming.

I had pictured my journey to the United States as an exciting and happy experience. I had expected to have my husband at my side always. I would never be alone, especially in strange places. Before we married, he said he wanted to be with me all the time. He hated the weekdays, because our jobs separated us. But somehow I ended up alone in the dark, cold back seat of a strange car.

I blinked my tears away and stared out the window at the gloom that lingered over the tall buildings and dead trees. I wanted to ask why there was white smoke rising through the square holes between the gray sidewalks and the black streets. But I was there all alone, even though there were three people in the front seat.

I wanted to feel glad that I had left my familiar world to move here, but the feeling of not belonging made happiness impossible. I saw men and women walking on the sidewalks and children playing in front of their homes, which lined both sides of the street. I felt disgust and sadness. They were dressed in dark, bulky clothes, and like the cows near the train track, they all had smoke rising from their mouths.

Will living here mean that I'll be blowing smoke even if I have no fire? If I ever change my mind about writing to Doña Inez, I must tell her about the strange things I have seen. She had planted in my mind a beautiful picture of the United States, but what I had seen so far seemed like a cold, dark pit to me.

"Here we are," Leo said, pulling up onto a cracked driveway next to a gray, two-story house. He swung open his door and hurried to open mine. "Our house is going to smell like turkey, because we have one in the oven," he said happily.

I couldn't believe my luck. I had never eaten turkey before, but if it smelled anything like chicken . . . well, I hoped they didn't expect me to eat some.

"Our home is yours," Leo said, unlocking a door to the kitchen. He made a sweeping motion. "Walk right in and make yourself at home."

I walked into the steamy kitchen, and saw the naked, pale turkey through the glass oven door. Then I realized that Frank and his mother had stayed outside. I wondered what they were talking about. Frank had said that we would be living with his mother, yet Leo spoke as if this was his house.

"Mother and son have much to talk about," Leo said. "Of course, he's Vera's baby boy who has been gone for a long time."

"Baby boy?"

"Well, I mean he's the youngest son."

I followed Leo across the yellow linoleum floor and into the living room, where I saw four light blue chairs, several dark, shiny tables, and a television set in a corner.

"Sit down, sweetie," Leo said. "I'll put a record on, a polka by Frankie Yankovic. Oh, I suppose you don't know Frankie Yankovic. His father and I came to this country on the same ship. We met there, and have stayed friends all these years." Leo lifted the needle onto the record, and fast, loud music blared throughout the house.

I excused myself and left to find a bathroom, where I sat on a cold white toilet and shivered. I wondered what a bladder looked like. For how long could it collect urine? Was it possible for urine to travel through one's body, perhaps through the veins, and in time cause a person to die? I felt so stupid then, suffering from a problem which I would never talk to anyone about.

I looked at the green leaves and purple clusters that hung like grapes on pink paper someone had pasted on the walls. I checked out the white bathtub, which had legs with dog paws. I saw five shelves in a corner loaded with tiny black and white cows, pink poodles, and brown and orange wax turkeys with open wings.

The thumping of Leo's music vibrated through the house. I sat there, wondering if I would soon die with a night's urine running through my veins. Frank would bury me in the ice cold ground. This was very sad, for I had come to America for a better life, not to die and end up underground in a strange part of the world, where no one in my family would ever find my bones.

There was a knock on the door. "Honey, are you okay?"

"Yes." That was a lie.

"Are you sure you're all right, honey?"

"Yes," I said, then flushed the toilet, which had only the water it had when I first sat on it.

On my way back, I stopped to look at the pictures in the hallway, black and white photographs of Leo when he was young. An oval frame held a picture of an older couple sitting on a bench. Next to that was a larger photograph of an old house, surrounded by tall grass and yellow flowers.

I heard Frank calling me, so I went to the kitchen. He was sitting at the table with a cigarette between two fingers, sipping coffee out of a black cup. His mother was hovering over the sink, peeling potatoes under running water.

"Oh, there you are," she said, with a friendly smile. "Have some coffee, and tell me how you like the States so far. Frank, pour her a cup, and give her some doughnuts or cookies, or both. Don't be shy."

"You want sugar and milk in it?" Frank tapped the cigarette with his middle finger, and the ashes fell into a silver ashtray I thought was too nice for such a purpose.

"No, thanks," I said. "I really don't need any coffee." To his mother, I said, "So far I like everything, except for the cold air."

"Oh dear," she said, turning from the potatoes. "It isn't even cold yet. But you'll be just fine. You sure are pretty. I expected you to have dark skin and black hair, being Puerto Rican."

"Actually, Ma," Frank cut in, "I heard that true Spaniards are white with green or blue eyes."

Vera turned to me with a smile, seeming pleased, as if "Spaniard" sounded better to her than "Puerto Rican."

I stayed in the smelly kitchen, feeling bloated, and compared Frank's mother to mine. This lady was pretty, with short, curly hair, rosy cheeks, clean skin, a fine nose, and bright blue eyes. She wore fine stockings and a dress of soft fabric with a belt around her waist. She had raised eight children, yet she looked young, healthy, and rested.

My poor mother had looked old, tired, and wrinkled for years.

Chapter Nineteen

The Dream House

"We'll take you kids home," Vera said, "so you can rest a little before coming back for dinner."

"I don't understand," I said. "I thought we would be living here."

"Frank will explain things to you later," she answered.

"Yeah, honey, you're going to like Ma's decision," Frank said, and reached for my hand.

This time he even sat in the back seat with me. I figured that mother and son had talked about whatever decision she had made when they had stayed outside earlier. All the murmuring and secrets made me feel uncomfortable, but I didn't want to seem suspicious, so I nodded and asked no questions.

The drive to our new home was probably ten minutes. I saw more dark streets, dead trees, sidewalks, long lines of homes, and children in heavy jackets playing outside. The day had lightened a little, but there was still no sign of the sun.

"There are too many dead trees," I said. It was my first complaint.

Frank laughed. "Did you hear that, Ma? She said we have dead trees."

"Oh, no, you must explain that to her."

"They aren't dead, honey. They just lose their leaves for winter, but they get new ones in the spring."

I could not imagine those trees ever looking green. They appeared about as dead as any dead tree could be.

Leo turned onto a straight street with a long, solid line of homes on each side. Every home had its own driveway, some made of concrete, and others of blacktop, and every now and then I saw one that had two narrow strips of gravel with dead grass in between. There were cars parked in some of those driveways, and children playing here and there.

"There's our place . . . see it?" Frank pointed to a beige house up on a slope. It had a door and two windows facing the street, two strips of concrete as a driveway, and a big, leafless tree on a grassy patch of land between the sidewalk and the street.

Leo held a glass door open so Vera could unlock another, and we walked into a square entryway. We then walked up two steps into the kitchen, which had a shiny maroon floor that matched the counter top.

This was my dream home, equipped with more luxury than I had ever hoped to have. The kitchen walls were light yellow, the curtains over the three windows white, as were the cupboards, the sink, and refrigerator. I felt overwhelmed. Back home, only the rich had refrigerators. Now I had one, too. I even had a big metal stove – a green one with a flowery design. It stood on the floor, connected to its own gas line. And the most exciting discovery was the black telephone at the end of the kitchen counter. I had never dared to hope that I might have a telephone someday. That was another thing I had to write to Alicia about. She would be so happy for me.

Frank appeared a little overwhelmed himself. He put his arm around me and said, "Ma left all these for us. Isn't that nice?"

I nodded. "It's very nice. Thank you, Ma."

"Until you kids can buy your own stuff," she said.

She had left a wooden table with six chairs in a space of the kitchen across from the stove and refrigerator, dishes up in the cupboards, cookware on the lower shelves, utensils in the drawers, dishtowels, and potholders. All we had to do was enjoy our new home.

I looked out one window and saw the back yard, a large spread of green and brown grass lined by low, leafless trees. All the homes on both sides of ours had similar back yards that connected to the backs of another line of homes facing the next street.

The floor through the rest of the house was made of wood, narrow boards tightly fitted together, and so shiny it looked as if it had just been polished. We walked through a short hallway and into what would be our bedroom. There was a yellow chenille spread on the bed and matching curtains on the windows. It even had a yellow rug on the floor by the bed, paintings on the walls, and a black and white picture of Frank's father, a handsome man dressed in a dark suit and tie.

Across from our room was another bedroom for our babies. Those walls were light blue, and the curtains were white with crispy ruffles. A round rug was in the center of the floor, and an old treadle sewing machine that had belonged to Frank's grandmother sat in a corner.

"It still works fine," Vera said, when I ran the tip of my finger over its wheel. "You may use it, if you can sew. It's something neither I nor my daughters ever learned."

"Yes, I can sew, and I will use it. Thank you."

Frank's eyes beamed. "Oh yeah, Ma, Jackie will use it. She can sew just about anything."

His mom grinned. "Good, I'm glad to hear that. You might be able to use some pieces of fabric Leo brought me from his trash collection. Make yourself a quilt or something."

"I'd like to have the fabric, but what's a quilt?"

Frank hurried to explain. Then he went on to tell me about Leo's trash collection. Leo had a part-time job hauling broken furniture and old clothes to the dump. They had no trash pickup those days. People had to burn their trash in a metal barrel in their back yards, but clothes and furniture made too much smoke and drifted into people's homes.

"Oh, I can bring you a lot of used clothing, too," Leo said, seeming thrilled that I could use what others had thrown out. "And some of those clothes are in pretty good condition, I might add."

"That's very nice," I said, thinking that one would have to be rich to throw away clothing. In Puerto Rico, most people had to wear their garments until they could no longer hold another patch.

"And here is the bathroom," Vera said, pushing open a door. "It's not very big, but it's nice, I think."

It was gorgeous to me. My own bathroom, with a yellow curtain on the window and a small yellow rug on the black linoleum floor. It had everything that was necessary: a white toilet, a sink, and a bathtub.

The living room had one window facing the street and one facing the driveway, both with green, flowery drapes that opened and closed with a string. It had a green velvety sofa and chair, one small table at each end of the sofa, and a coffee table over a round blue and green rug. A large mirror hung above the sofa, with a picture of Frank's mother on one side, and one of his father on the other. An old television set, which had to be hit on its top to make it work, stood in the corner.

I couldn't picture myself looking into a black and white twelve-inch screen – not after seeing movies in color at a real theater on the base.

Frank kept thanking his mom for all she had left for us. Leo repeated over and over that this was the perfect little house for two young people starting out.

I didn't know how much Frank had told his mom about the way I had lived in Puerto Rico, so I didn't say that this was a dream come true for me. But I did tell them that the house was very nice, and that I would always keep it clean and pretty.

"We know you will," Vera said. "Now we must go tend the turkey. Leo will call before he comes for you. We'll eat around two o'clock."

We watched them drive away. Frank wrapped his arms around me and said, "For years I've wished to one day have a house like this, and a beautiful little wife like you. And here we are. But the best thing is that Ma is going to marry Leo. She's already moved her things into his house, and we can live here by ourselves. What do you think about that?"

"I think it's great. Now I want to take a bath and a nap."

"Okay. I'll try out the television set."

I filled the bathtub with warm water and sat there thinking: *This is so good, a new beginning, an escape from the hardship, the cruelty, the gossip, and the fear.*

I closed my eyes and saw my mother's face, and Alicia's, and everyone else's. They were so far away – and that was what I had wanted for a long time, yet now I longed for them. If I could only show them the roads I had traveled to get here and show them my new house, which had more furniture and household items than they had ever seen. I would show them everything, and they'd go back home leaving me satisfied that they had seen how well I had done.

After my bath, I was able to get rid of the urine my bladder had held for so long. Then I stretched out on the old bed where many others had slept. Now it was mine – my room, my house, and everything in it mine, until we could buy everything new.

The phone call awakened me. I felt clean and refreshed, and put on clean clothes. I looked at myself in my long mirror, then went with my husband to my in-laws' house for a turkey dinner.

Chapter Twenty

Turkey Plus

The turkey had turned a succulent golden brown, and was on the stove top as we entered the kitchen. The unpleasant smell had become an appetizing aroma, and the warm kitchen appeared cozy and inviting.

Frank's mom had made a creamy sauce she called gravy, and a salad of lettuce, pale tomatoes, cucumbers, onions, and mayonnaise. She had even mashed the potatoes into a fluffy, creamy heap.

She carried the turkey on a platter to the dining room table, and told Leo to carve it. Leo handed the knife to Frank.

"Now that you're a married man, it's time you learned how to carve a turkey."

"Well, if you say so," Frank said. Then he cut into the turkey breast, and steam rose from the juicy slices that fell onto the platter.

"Great job," his mother said, walking in with the gravy in a deep yellow dish. She placed it on the table, then went back in for the mashed potatoes. Next she brought in hot dinner rolls and cold cranberry sauce. Finally, she came out with a dish of cut-up apples, canned peaches, sliced ripe bananas, chunks of oranges, and marshmallows all mixed together with whipped cream.

"I can help you bring the food to the table," I had said, but she insisted that I was a guest and should sit and enjoy the meal. I watched carefully to learn the American way of eating, but the mixed fruit confused me. Back home, we would never eat two different fruits at the same time. The mixture would create toxic acids that could make a person explode.

Vera had set the dining table earlier with plates that had gold around the rims, and silver forks, knives, and spoons, on a white lace tablecloth. When they turned on the chandelier above, the tableware glittered, and I knew that these people were rich.

Leo sat across from Vera, and Frank across from me. They heaped

mashed potatoes on their plates, slices of turkey meat next to the potatoes, and covered both with the brown gravy. They passed the heavy
platter and potatoes around, reached for the hot rolls, cut them open
with knives, and smeared butter on both halves.

When each dish reached me, I took little bits of everything, including turkey, which I would not eat because it smelled too much like
chicken, and I passed on the fruit salad.

"You're going to eat more than that, aren't you, sweetie?" Leo
asked.

"She's suffering from culture shock," Frank said.

"Oh yeah," his mother agreed. "This is a different world for her.
But she'll get sick if she doesn't eat."

"You should force yourself, honey," my husband said with a mouthful of food. "I don't have money for any doctor bills."

"This is all I feel like eating right now. But don't worry, I will not
get sick. I've never eaten mashed potatoes and turkey meat before, or
mixed fruits that might cause an explosion." I was being sincere, but
they thought it was funny. The first to laugh was Frank. He talked about
the Puerto Rican customs and beliefs.

Leo responded by telling us about the foods his mother prepared in
his old country when he was a boy, and about the customs of his people.

Vera merged into the conversation, and mentioned the Norwegian
dishes her mother used to serve. Every now and then, she or Leo asked
me something about the crops we grew in Puerto Rico, and if I didn't
answer right away, Frank answered for me. I didn't like that he spoke
for me, but I didn't let him know it. In my untrained mind, I expected
him to guess what I liked, didn't like, and felt. This behavior wasn't
something I had decided to learn. It had just grown on me since we
married, but it felt right to be that way.

"We should take her for a little drive," Vera said, once we finished
eating. "How about the zoo, Frank?"

"Sounds good to me, Ma. She's probably never seen a monkey
before. They don't have a zoo in Puerto Rico."

Frank was right. I'd never seen a monkey, or a lot of other things.
But I didn't like him saying it as if I wasn't there. "But we have something you don't have here," I said, squinting at Frank. "We have sun-

shine, and you don't!"

"Oh, we have sunshine," Vera answered. "But we often have cloudy days at this time of year. Don't you have some cloudy days in the tropics?"

I realized then that this was an American custom. I talked to Frank, and his mother answered. She talked to me, and Frank jumped to answer her. "Not often," he said. "But when they do, it's usually warm."

I gave him a cross look.

Frank sat in the back seat again in the car, but I moved close to my window, leaving a huge space between us. Vera and Leo must have realized that I was unhappy. They suddenly seemed eager to point out things they thought would be interesting to me.

"There to the right is Como Park," Vera said. "It's a big park, and I'm sure you'll enjoy coming here in the summer − it has a lot of flowers. But I bet you see flowers all year round where you come from."

"Yes, we have flowers everywhere," I said, and silently wished to go back home. *Will it really get colder than this?* I could not imagine how anyone could survive a colder day. I could feel warm air blowing from underneath the steering wheel, but it was a dry air that smelled bad and burned my nose.

Leo maneuvered the car around a curve and said, "Ah, but we have flowers here that would not grow in the tropics, like peonies and lilacs. Those bloom in the springtime. You're going to love it. Just wait and see." He looked in the rearview mirror for my reaction.

I nodded. "Yes, I will wait."

Leo laughed. But Frank reached for my hand and whispered, "I love you."

I moved close to him then.

Leo pulled up to a parking space, and we entered the zoo, a park with buildings, dead trees, and animals locked in cages. Frank stayed close to me. He pointed out an animal here, and another one there. I was supposed to cheer up, and make a big fuss about the cute, innocent animals in prisons.

Other people wrapped in heavy coats walked around, pointing at the monkeys and chuckling. Some couples had children who jumped around and stood on their toes, stretching their necks, yelling and imitating the monkeys. All I wanted was for the clouds to lift away and the sun to warm up the freezing air.

Leo could see that I felt miserable. "I think we should come back here in the summer. It's been a long day for this young lady."

"Yeah, maybe we should take you kids home now," Vera said.

"That's a good idea," Frank added. "Before she freezes." He didn't realize that I had been freezing ever since we got off the train. I was still wearing the same shoes with thin soles. The long coat he had bought me was too wide and didn't keep the cold air from creeping up my legs and back.

We left the zoo, but before taking us home, Leo stopped the car in front of a white house. Everyone stepped out and started up a sidewalk to the door. Vera told Frank that I should go, too. He held the car door open for me, but didn't tell me why we were there. Of course I didn't ask.

A man answered the door, and Leo and I followed Frank and his mom inside. The man who let us in pointed to a small royal blue sofa and chair in an enclosed patio. Frank and his mom talked to the man in their low voices, so I assumed that since she didn't have a sofa in her home, she was buying this set for herself.

It was getting dark by the time we left there, and the sun had never shown its face. I was glad that this day had come to an end. Hopefully tomorrow would be a brighter one.

Vera and Leo had dishes to wash, so they dropped us off and left. Frank and I walked into our new home alone for the first time. I expected him to get romantic since the last intercourse had been on our last night in Mobile. Surprisingly, he stayed up watching TV. I didn't hear him come to bed.

Chapter Twenty-One

Buttons And Lace

A whisper in my ear awakened me. "It's Monday morning." I opened my eyes and saw Frank's face.

"I gotta go check on a job," he said, "but on my way home, I'll stop at a car lot and hopefully find us a set of wheels so I can take my sweetheart for a drive." He kissed my forehead and left.

When I heard the kitchen door bang shut, I jumped out of bed, hurried to the living room window, and watched as he ran up the sidewalk and disappeared. I immediately felt the house grow bigger and emptier. A popping and snapping sound began under the floor, and stale air came through the square holes where the walls met with the floor. I stared at the gloom outside the window. I was in a strange town, with no one I could turn to.

The house continued to crackle and pop, and the air smelled bad, but felt a little warm. Either a fire had started under the house, or ghosts were hiding there. My heart jolted and pounded so hard I could hardly breathe. I thought of running out of the house, but where would I go in my pajamas? I went as far as the front door, but turned around and ran to the bedroom, bumping my elbow on the doorknob, and dove into bed, pulling the blankets over my head.

Even through the covers, I could hear the snapping and popping. Whatever was under the house would reach the room soon, jump into my bed, and crush me to death. A long time passed before the sounds stopped, but when they did, it was only for a short while, and then they began again. I noticed a different pitch to the sounds now.

But whatever it was never reached my room. I stayed there anyway, thinking. Maybe I had been imagining things. My mother would say that this experience served me right for always reaching beyond my means and biting off more than I could chew. A lot of her sayings poured into my head: "You made your bed, now sleep in it. Children who go far away from their parents get lost forever. Whatever they try to accomplish eventually turns against them."

I pushed the blankets off the bed, exposing myself to the warm air in the room. The windows, curtains, pictures, and mirrors peered down at me. They were like my mother pointing her finger and saying, "I told you he would leave you."

"I'm not afraid," I said, jumping at the sound of my own voice. The walls seemed to move toward me, as if to squeeze me in. I had to dress quickly and leave the room. As I pulled clothes out of my bag, I repeated loudly, "I am not afraid. Not afraid. Not afraid." I put on a pink skirt and a white cotton blouse and stepped into the hallway. The boards squeaked, and I jumped, yelling, "I'm not afraid! I'm not afraid!"

Saying that I wasn't afraid was one thing, but convincing myself was another. I reached the kitchen with my heart pounding so hard it hurt. Things didn't look as they had the previous night. The yellow walls appeared cold and dead, and some of the chairs were pulled away from the table, as if waiting for someone to sit on them. The phone on the countertop looked like a black puppy dog rolled up sleeping. The popping sounds were still loud, and warm air blew through the square holes at the foot of the walls, slightly moving the sheer curtains.

I saw another white door closed, opposite the kitchen door, which I couldn't remember seeing the previous night. This added to my fear, because closed doors had always spooked me. They could swing open suddenly, and a fearsome creature could barge through, startling me to death. Still, I could not go back to the living room or the bedroom without knowing what might be on the other side of that mysterious door. I had to conquer my fears if this was going to be my home.

I pulled open one of the drawers, looking for something I could use to defend myself. There, with some cooking utensils, I found a roll of hard wood with a handle at each end. This gave me a little courage, so I wrapped my sweaty hand around one of the smooth handles and tiptoed to the mysterious door.

I squeezed the wooden roll, grabbed the doorknob with my left hand, and turned it slowly, pulling the door open an inch at a time. A piercing shriek came from the hinges and jolted my poor heart. I pushed the door shut quickly, leaned on it, and panted like a racing dog, wondering how I would ever recover from such trauma. How had I gotten myself into such a predicament? The entrance from the outside into the kitchen wasn't very big, probably thirty-six inches square, so if I leaned on the spooky door, I could easily reach the knob of the back door and run out if necessary.

While panting and trying to decide what to do, I spotted a light switch up high near the doorjamb. It had to be a light, so I pushed on it slowly with one finger, expecting to be startled again. The only sound then was that of the switch. I saw a streak of light coming from under the mysterious door. Now I would be able to see into a lighted closet, or whatever was behind that door.

I pulled the door open slowly, in case something scary was going to jump out at me. Cold, musty air came through the doorway, and I saw a small lightbulb shining down on a stairway that led to a dark room under the house. My heart thumped again, but I squatted down, my left hand around the knob and the roll of wood in my other hand. Right there, in the center of that dreary room, I saw a grotesque metal apparatus that appeared more spooky than anything I had ever seen before, and I already had experienced a lot of spooks. This monstrous thing had long, silvery arms that were bent like tree branches and reached up through the beams above, making popping and snapping sounds.

I fixed my eyes on the ghostly thing, and I was sure it took a few steps toward me. I backed away, slammed the door shut, and hopped up into the kitchen, gasping, where I stayed while my heart thumped like a pony trying to escape his corral. Then, as if that wasn't enough to make me crazy, the phone rang as loud as a fire alarm. I sprang from the floor, screaming and hopping around like someone dancing over burning charcoal.

When I came closer to the phone, I leaned against the wall, picked up the receiver, and cried, "Hello!"

It was Frank. "Yeah, honey? Is that you, honey? Are you okay? I forgot to explain to you about the basement and the heating system."

"Too late!" I yelled. "I have been shaking ever since you left, and I never want to be here alone again!"

"Honey, calm down. I'm sorry I forgot to tell you. Try to relax and let me explain. The furnace will make strange noises when it goes on, but don't be afraid. Nothing will happen, and I'll be home soon. Do you understand? Honey? Answer me, please!"

"I understand," I said, then hung up. I sat down on the floor and leaned against the kitchen counter, shaking and crying and wishing that Mama and all my siblings, including the rotten ones, were there with me. At that moment, I felt regret for having jumped into a marriage just to get away from misery. I felt more miserable than ever before, and there was no place for me to go.

When monsters didn't come up from the spooky room, I went to the living room and looked out the window, since Frank had said that he would be home soon. I saw some cars turn into our street, but they kept going.

I went to the hallway and opened a door which Vera had said was a linen closet. It was like going into a store. She had left sheets, pillows, blankets, towels, hair rollers, face cream, Christmas cards, a box of photographs, a box of buttons, and a box filled with thread, lace, and sequins. I forgot the basement and the fear, and took down the box of photographs. I sat on the throw-rug in the hallway and began to pull out old pictures of children and grown-ups who looked like Frank and his mother.

I returned the box to its shelf and brought out the box of buttons. I carried that one to the living room and dumped the pounds of buttons on the rug. There were red, green, yellow, and purple buttons, every color one could imagine. Some of the buttons had glittering diamonds in the center or around the rims. I felt like a small child with a lot of new toys. There were many different sizes, and more buttons than I had ever seen in my whole life. I spread them out with my hand, stretching my arms over the pile of colorful, beautiful buttons. I gathered them into a pyramid, collected some into my hands, then let them spill out, clicking against each other. I thought of the times my mother had searched the cubbyholes and corners of our house looking for just one lousy button. She would absolutely die if she could get her hands on this many buttons.

I formed one line of red buttons and one of each color. I went back to the closet, brought out the sewing box, and threaded a needle. I busied myself stringing the buttons according to color. I put the strung ones on the rug, red next to green, pink next to blue, and so on. I was stringing the yellow ones when Frank drove up in a black car.

"I bought us a car, honey," he said, walking through the kitchen. "It's a Ford, 1940, but runs like a charm. Paid one hundred dollars for it. Get your coat, I'm taking you for a ride in the countryside."

I scooped the buttons back into the box, put on my coat, and followed my husband to our new car.

"Brace yourself," he said, opening the door for me. "The heater doesn't work, but I know how to fix it. It smells like hell, but I'll clean it tomorrow. I've got to fix that damn hole, too." He pointed to a round hole on the wing window on the passenger side, from which cold air began to blow on my right ear the minute we started moving.

I hated to complain and spoil his mood, but my ear started hurting, and was getting worse the faster he drove. I moved closer to him to escape the cold.

"I can't drive with you under my arm!"

His tone was unfriendly, so I slid back to my corner, where my ear would freeze, and wondered how he could be so nice one minute, and so crabby the next. "You should have told me about the furnace. It scared me so bad, my heart still hurts from pounding so hard."

"Honey, I said I was sorry. There are a lot of things you have to be prepared to learn. You're a married woman now, not a little girl anymore."

I looked at his profile. He was blowing smoke through his nose, which looked like a fat bubble glued on the center of his face.

"I feel more like a little girl than a woman right now – a little girl choking on cigarette smoke. You promised to quit. It's making your nose bigger, too."

"Honey, don't say things like that. Look around. We're coming up to the prettiest lake around here. Wait till summer. You're going to love it." He parked the car facing the lake and, putting his arm around me, pulled me closer to him. "Sorry I didn't tell you about the furnace. Forgive me?"

"I forgive you," I said, then looked around for the beauty he wanted me to see. A lake so small that I could see the other side wasn't very impressive to me, especially with dead trees around it. A lake didn't compare to the creeks, rivers, or ocean back home. But I was in Frank's arms, and life would be okay for me in the United States.

"I practically grew up here," Frank went on, staring straight through the windshield, the tip of his fingers making little circles on my upper arm. "I did a lot of swimming and fishing in the summertime, and ice skating and car racing in the winter with my friends."

It took me a while to realize what he had said. "Car what?"

"Racing," he said. "We raced cars across the lake."

I knew he loved to tell jokes, and I thought maybe he was trying to cheer me up, so I laughed.

He cuddled me. "What's so funny? Don't you believe me?"

"I believe the fishing and swimming," I said, "but racing cars in the water?"

He tried to convince me. "The lake freezes," he said.

But that made me laugh even more. I couldn't see how all that water would ever freeze. He had to be kidding.

"Stop laughing at me," he said, spreading kisses all over my face and neck, and for that moment I felt in love. "We need to go home," he said. "Everybody's coming over tonight. All of my brothers and sisters and their spouses and kids are coming to meet you."

"They are? Am I supposed to dress up? Dust the furniture? Cook some food?"

"No, they'll probably bring prepared food, and gifts. All you need to do is be your sweet self." Frank turned the key and backed out onto the street.

"Why would they bring gifts?"

"Because people give gifts to newly married couples."

This was great news. Back home, no one gave gifts to anybody, for weddings or anything. I didn't tell Frank, but I could hardly wait to get home. I would actually be receiving gifts, just for getting married? Maybe Doña Inez was right. Everything was better in the United States.

Chapter Twenty-Two

Like Cats From a Barrel

We barely had enough time to eat some noodle soup with peanut butter crackers before the first car pulled into the driveway. Another car followed, and one after another, until there were seven cars in front of our house, one of them belonging to Vera and Leo.

As the couples got out of their cars, I noticed that none were carrying gifts. But ten children poured out like cats from a barrel, and ran into the house ahead of their parents. Ten pairs of shoes shook the floor as they stomped through the kitchen and into our bedroom. Jackets, coats, and mittens piled up like a mountain on the bed, and then the tribe ran back through the kitchen and down the stairs to the basement.

Two of Frank's brothers had three children each, and the two sisters had two each. Among the ten children were two with brown hair and dark eyes. The rest were blonde with blue eyes.

"This is Jackie, my beautiful bride," Frank said to the grown-ups, who stood around me in the kitchen. I looked from face to face, repeating all the American names. There was Nathan, a brother, and his wife Darlene. There was Matthew, another brother, and his wife Loretta. Arthur was another brother, and his wife was Nadine. His sister was Roberta, and her husband was Philip. Donna was the youngest sister, and her husband was Gerald. One of his brothers, Bill, and one of his sisters, Rebecca, weren't there. I would meet them sometime later.

The four brothers looked alike, except that Nathan and Matthew had brown hair, while Frank and Arthur had blonde. They were all of the same height, and they spoke with low voices that hummed.

The two sisters were short and slender with blue eyes, Roberta with brown hair, and Donna with blonde. The oldest sister-in-law, Darlene, was large all over, with black hair, dark eyes, and an ear-piercing voice.

Matthew's wife Loretta was a petite Italian girl with black hair and brown eyes. She smiled a lot, and according to Darlene, had less brains than a fish. Nadine, who was also a little heavy, was a light blonde with blue eyes and a constant smile. She was the quietest of the bunch.

Each of the four brothers and one brother-in-law played a musical instrument, and each of them had brought his along. Once I had learned all the names, the men went to the front room and tuned the instruments, but not before each one lit a cigarette. Minutes later, the airtight house was filled with tobacco smoke and the sound of music.

Five of the women sat at the kitchen table with me, while Roberta got two coffee pots going. She said this was my welcome-to-the-family party, so I should just sit and visit. She, Donna, and Darlene were chain smokers, so they each had a cigarette between their fingers. The cloud of smoke met with the cloud from the living room, then trailed into the bedrooms and bathroom.

I had never been in a smoky environment before, so my nose closed up and my eyes burned and filled with tears. In Puerto Rico, we had closed the doors and windows only to sleep at night or to keep out the rain, so no matter how much smoke there was from smoking and cooking, it never accumulated.

I unlocked the window next to the kitchen table and pushed it up, only to find another panel of glass fixed in place. I looked here and there for some kind of hook, but found out that the panel, called a storm window, was screwed on from the outside.

"Oh, my God," I said. "We'll suffocate."

"Why? Cigarette smoke bothers you?" Donna asked, while two streams of smoke flowed from her nose, which looked just like Frank's.

"Oh, well, start smoking, and it won't bother you anymore," Darlene put in. "Since almost everyone else in the family smokes, you don't have much choice but to start."

I realized that Darlene was too blind from her own cloud of smoke to see that I had better choices than to start smoking. So I ignored what she said and answered all the questions coming at me through the stinky haze. Soon the discomfort became unbearable, so I excused myself and left the kitchen.

I went to the bedroom and pressed my face to the window, feeling the coolness that was trying to come in from outside. I unlocked that window and lifted it up, desperate for a breath of clean air, but found another panel of glass that could not be opened, even as hard as I tried. A layer of fog covered the panel, and it felt cold and wet when I wiped it with my hand. Since it was so dark outside, all I could see was my reflection in the wet glass, and the dim lights in the houses on the other side of our back yard.

Suffocating, I pulled down the main window and headed back to the kitchen. Through the cloud of smoke in the hallway, I saw the brothers playing a fast tune and tapping the floor with their shoes. The brothers-in-law stared and clapped their hands. None of them saw me staggering and gasping.

I made it through the kitchen and headed down to the basement, which I would see from one end to the other for the first time. It was another amazing experience. *How do people make basements? Do they build a house, carve a hole under it, then make walls out of concrete squares? Or do they make the basement, then build the house on top of it? Someday I'll ask those questions, but will I sound stupid?*

The air down there was cool and stuffy, but there was no smoke. I made my way to a corner, staying close to the wall as I passed by the noisy children who were playing cowboys and Indians and tearing up cardboard boxes. Only two of them glanced at me, but then they turned back to their game. I went past the round metal structure, which sent heat to the upstairs, and wondered who had come up with such an idea. A metal structure with fire inside of it, but yet the house would not catch fire from it. My mind flashed back to my sunny island, where we hadn't needed heaters to heat the homes. I felt so far away, and so cold.

In a corner beyond the furnace, I saw an old blue chair, its fabric torn and stuffing exposed. I sat on it anyway. From there, I saw a washing machine under the stairway, against two concrete sinks. Vera must have left it there for me. It would be my first washing machine. This was incredible. I had become rich so fast. A washing machine was something I would never have had in Puerto Rico. What a shame that I could not write to Alicia about this. She would be so happy for me.

While watching the wild children, I decided that mine would never behave like that. Those rough, wild, noisy Wilson children were trying to destroy everything in the basement. Hadn't they been told that this was no longer their grandmother's home, and that in my house they should not act like that? And should they be tearing those cardboard boxes? What if I wanted those boxes for something? Why weren't the mothers coming down to check on their rowdy children?

I couldn't watch any longer, so I went back upstairs. My nose closed up again, and stayed closed for hours after the smokers left.

"I thought you said they would bring us gifts," I said to Frank.

"Oh . . . well, I was wrong. Are you coming down with a cold? Your nose sounds plugged up."

"It's from all the smoke."

Frank turned on the TV set and stretched out on the floor. "Go on to bed, honey. I'll be in soon."

Early the next morning, Frank left again to look for work. As soon as he left, the loneliness of the day before returned. But this day would be a little bit different. Sometime in the middle of the morning, Leo and Matthew knocked on our front door. At first, I wondered if they were coming to visit Frank. But then I saw an old pickup truck in front of the house with the blue sofa and chair we had seen on our way back from the zoo.

"We're here to pick up the sofa and chair," Leo said as I opened the door.

"Why? I did something wrong?" I was puzzled, and disappointed, for I had liked that green sofa and chair, and had thought it was mine for keeps.

"Oh, no. You haven't done anything wrong," Leo said. "Vera had not intended to leave that sofa and chair for you. She explained that to Frank. Didn't he tell you?"

I shook my head and stepped aside so they could walk in.

"That's why Frank bought you that set," Matthew said, pointing to the truck.

I didn't say another word, but stood at the window, feeling a little sick, and watched them carry the blue sofa and chair in, and carry out the pretty green set.

"This is a nice set," Leo said. Matthew agreed, but both men seemed a little concerned. They were probably wondering if they had done something wrong. And they had. But they smiled, said they would see me soon, and left. I watched them drive away, then turned toward the new sofa and chair. It was an okay blue, but I had liked the green better and had thought it was mine to keep.

When Frank came home that night, I said, "You told me that your mother left all these things for us. But Leo and your brother took away the green sofa and chair. They left those blue ones, but I liked the green better."

"Oh, yeah, I didn't explain that to you. Well, Ma wants most of the things back whenever we buy our own furnishings. And she also wants me to buy the house, but I don't think I can make the seventy-three-dollar-a-month payments."

"Does she want the washing machine back, too?"

"No, not the washing machine. Leo bought her a new one, so she left that one for you."

"Good. I can't wait to try it." I felt thrilled.

"Well, don't get too excited. The rollers don't work, and I might not know how to fix them. You'll have to wring the clothes by hand."

"It's still better then no machine at all," I said.

"Yeah, that's right," Frank said, then went to sleep.

I lay awake for a long time, thinking about the green sofa, and the gifts I never got. Then I thought of my mother's warnings: *"People are the same all over the world. No one will give you anything for free. You're marrying a man from another world. You'll be crawling back with nothing."*

Frank left to look for work early the next day, and all the days that followed, coming home every night, only to leave again the next day. Each time, he walked in tired, disappointed, and worried, for there were no jobs to be found.

Every night I felt sorry for him, but never told him how sick with loneliness I had been all day. Yet I feared getting up the next morning to spend another day looking out the windows, waiting, wiping away the tears, and wondering if I should break down and write a letter home.

Chapter Twenty-Three

Treats or Tricks

One night, I didn't turn on the lights at dusk, so that I would be able to look out the window without my own reflection in the glass startling me. But instead of my reflection, I saw a group of two-legged creatures walking up to my door. I quickly lowered myself to the floor, then heard the doorbell ring, and squeaky voices calling out unfamiliar words. I stayed down, petrified that the creatures outside would hear my heartbeat. I waited there, hoping they would go away, but they kept knocking and yelling. I thought it might be the neighbor's children trying to scare me, but would American children do things like that?

The voices finally trailed away, and at the same time, the phone rang. I crawled on my hands and knees to the kitchen, hoping it would be Frank. It was, but he started talking before I could tell him what had happened.

"Listen carefully, honey. I'm waiting for an interview, and won't be home for another couple of hours. I forgot to tell you that today is Halloween. The neighborhood kids will start coming to the door dressed in funny costumes and masks asking for candy. If you don't give them any, they'll wax the windows. So I sent you a bag of candy with Roger. You remember me mentioning my friend Roger, don't you? Anyway, he'll be over with the candy soon and you'll have some to give to the kids. Don't be scared. Just give them the candy, and I'll be home soon."

Frank hung up the phone before I could say a word, so I sat on the floor shaking, and thinking, *He sounded so far away. He won't be home for another two hours. The masked creatures will break down the doors and come in.*

I crawled to the kitchen door to make sure it was locked, then crawled back to check the front door. As I backed away, I heard more voices and the bell ringing. I crawled to the bathroom and turned on the light, thinking no one would see it from the street. I locked the door, filled up the bathtub, and got in. I don't know why that seemed like a safe thing to do, but I was too afraid to make any sense. I would not come out of that bathroom for anything.

The doorbell rang again and again, voices shouted, and fists pounded the door. Then the sounds moved to the kitchen door. The bell kept ringing, the voices calling, and the fists pounding. Suddenly, the pounding grew stronger and I heard a man's voice. *Oh! I forgot about the friend called Roger and the candy.*

I stepped out of the bathtub and put on my bathrobe, which barely reached my knees because it was meant to be worn in warm weather. I turned off the light and hurried to the kitchen in the dark, leaving a trail of water in the hallway.

Freezing cold air rushed around me as I opened the door. There stood a tall man with a bag in his hand.

"Hi! I'm Roger. I've been knocking for a long time. Where were you? Frank sent you this candy. Did you know it's Halloween? Do they have that in Puerto Rico?"

"No, we don't have Halloween. I was in the bathtub, and now I'm freezing."

The man handed me the bag, but stayed there blabbering. I was naked under the skimpy robe and thought he might be trying to see me, even in the dark. I shivered from the cold and the embarrassment, but I didn't think it would be right for me to shut the door in his face.

"So, what do you think of America so far?"

"America's good. Thank you for the candy, and goodbye." I slammed the door shut, then ran back to get dressed. However, I slipped on the wet spot and landed on the floor with the loudest bang I had ever made.

Feeling embarrassed and scared, I got to my feet and went to get completely dressed. When the bell rang again, I turned on the outside light and opened the door. There stood a monkey face holding a bag open. "Trick or treat," he said in a raspy voice.

I opened my bag of candy and saw a lot of yellow boxes of Chiclets, and a smaller bag with about twenty of the same, but neither Roger nor Frank had told me how many to give each child. I reached in, pulled out the little bag, and dropped it in the monkey's sack.

"Wow! Thank you!" he yelled, then did a crazy dance. "Thank you, lady. Thank you very much!" He hopped down to the grass and ran, raving, and yelling to others, "Make sure you stop at this house. This lady is really nice. She gives a lot of candy!"

The next six or seven masked children cleaned out my bag. They each got all the boxes I could grab with my hand. I then closed the door and locked it, sat on the sofa in the dark, and listened to the doorbell ringing, the voices yelling, and the pounding.

Finally, I saw the car lights coming up the driveway, and I ran to meet Frank.

"What the hell happened?" That was his greeting to me as he walked in and turned on all the lights from the kitchen to the living room. "Didn't Roger bring you the candy? The damn windows are waxed!"

"He did, but I ran out." I backed into the living room and sat on the sofa.

Frank followed me. "Ran out?" A strand of blonde hair dangled over his startled eyes. He grabbed the strand angrily and slammed it back up on his head. "A hundred and twenty-five pieces of candy? Did we have that many kids at our door before ten?" He stepped toward me, hesitated, then turned away to look out the window, the seat of his pants hanging empty as if he had lost his behind.

"I don't know how many came. I didn't count them."

"Well, how many pieces did you give each?"

"Only a handful."

"Only a handful?"

The way Frank stood and yelled reminded me of my father, and I suddenly felt as if I had returned to the things I had worked so hard to escape from.

"You were supposed to give them only one piece each. Damn! What am I going to do now!"

I buried my face in my hands, and he came to sit beside me.

"I'm sorry, honey. I know you didn't have Halloween in Puerto Rico. I should have told you about it earlier."

I wanted to cry in his arms, but as I faced him, the strong smell of booze made me back away quickly.

"Oh yeah, I stopped to have a few drinks with a friend. Not being able to find a job is driving me crazy."

I felt so guilty, so embarrassed for being stupid, and so sorry for Frank. "Don't worry, you'll find a job soon," I said. "And don't worry about cleaning the windows, I can do that tomorrow. And I promise you that I'll give only one piece of candy per child next time."

Chapter Twenty-Four

Darlene's Frozen Can

Not every home in America had indoor plumbing with real sinks, bathtubs, and toilets. I was surprised to discover that fact on my first visit to the homes of Frank's brothers.

Nathan, the oldest brother, and his wife Darlene lived twenty miles outside the city limits, off a dirt road in the middle of an abandoned farm. Their old house, which they were renting, was made of wood. The walls were warped and had been painted many times over wallpaper. The floor sloped, and the windows were so twisted that they would not open.

Whenever Darlene needed water, she or her husband stepped outside, grabbed hold of a long rusty iron bar, and pumped it frantically. The water took a while to come up, but then it gushed out icy cold through a rusty pipe. They filled only two buckets and hurried back inside.

When Nathan was at work, Darlene pumped ten to twenty buckets of water to wash clothes. She carried two at a time into a dark room behind her kitchen. There, she had an old washing machine with rollers that would wring the water out of the clothes.

In that same room, there was a bench with a hole in the middle. Directly under that hole, I saw a tall, round can.

"That's our toilet," said Darlene. "You don't know how fortunate you are to have moved into that cute little house in town, with all the modern conveniences. We've been married five years, and still can't afford anything better than this old place. This ain't too bad yet. You should see what happens in the middle of winter. Everything in this room freezes solid, including the shit in the can."

I could tell that Darlene wasn't happy, and I felt guilty for being the one with the nice house in town. "You think someday you'll move to town?"

"Hah! Someday, but only God knows when. Come, let's get the heck out of here before you freeze."

I followed her back into the kitchen, wondering which would be better, a frozen can in a dark room, or a hillside in the blistering sun. I would never tell Darlene everything about the way we lived at the old farm back home.

The second brother, Arthur, his wife Nadine, and their three children lived in another farmhouse with an outdoor latrine, no running water anywhere, and no telephone. But Arthur and Nadine appeared as if they had everything. They both had a constant smile, and Nadine spoke softly, never complained, and never talked bad about anyone.

The third brother, Matthew, and his wife Loretta, and their three children lived in the city, in her parents' old house. They had running water, real sinks, a toilet, and a bathtub. But according to Darlene, they seldom stayed home because Loretta kept a messy house, and they loved to eat like hogs but hated to cook.

I soon learned that weekends and holidays were for visiting relatives because no one had the money to visit faraway places, go to the movies, or go out to dinner. And since most of them didn't have a telephone, they dropped in on each other, especially at meal time. Sometimes these families met on the road on their way to each other's home. They would stop, talk things over, and one car would turn around and follow the other. None of these families would spend a weekend or holiday in their own homes alone.

The most popular place to visit was Roberta's home. Her husband Philip had a high-paying job with a car dealer, so their home, which stood by a lake, had all the modern conveniences, including wall-to-wall carpeting, which the rest of the siblings couldn't afford. Visiting Roberta meant ice-skating in the winter and her homemade beef soup by the fireplace afterward. In the summer there was swimming and backyard picnics, with lots of beer, ham, potato salad, chips, roasted marshmallows, and watermelon. But Roberta limited her hospitality, claiming to be too busy with her husband's working associates. So everyone headed to Nathan's place. There, they would eat well, thanks to Darlene, who claimed to be the best cook in the bunch.

The routine of visiting the families, eating what they cooked, and trying to escape the tobacco smoke became tiring, so I turned down some invitations. Frank accused me of disliking his relatives just because they smoked, and Darlene reminded me to start smoking before I lost my husband. My situation became impossible. To please my husband, I had to accept the smoky environment, and to keep him, according to Darlene, I had to start smoking. One choice was as bad as the other.

There was no clear way out of my new problem. Darlene decided that I should not enjoy my nice home alone, so a couple of days a week, she rode into town with her husband when he left for work. My doorbell rang early in the morning, and there she stood, big as a barrel in her dark brown coat, black hat, and black mittens.

"No sense in you being all alone in this dollhouse while I freeze my rear-end way out in the sticks," she'd say.

I felt delighted the first time, because I didn't like being alone either. But I soon realized that Darlene was the kind of gossiper I had run away from. Back home, people who belittled others by saying bad things about them behind their backs gave me stomach cramps and made me want to move far away, where no one knew my name.

Darlene's high-pitched voice hit the walls and bounced back to pierce my ears with each word. She lit one cigarette after another and began her conversation with friendly compliments. "You have beautiful hair, and a gorgeous figure, too. I can see you're a hard worker. This place has never looked so clean. Frank's mother never did much cleaning. She's a lousy mother-in-law, too. Wait till you get to know her better. Don't expect anything from her. She won't even cook you a decent meal. I've cooked hundreds of meals for her and all her kids in the past five years. They all go home raving about my pot roasts, cinnamon rolls, and apple pies, but they never do the same for me, oh no, they don't.

"And the youngest of the bunch, Donna . . . well, she's about as rotten as they come, let me tell you."

Darlene's eyes glittered like two small black marbles in the sun. She pressed her teeth together. They were small and straight, but brown with nicotine, and her red lips spat out the words like seeds from a watermelon. The kitchen chair screeched and its wooden legs wobbled as she rearranged her large bottom on it, her thighs hanging off each side. She screwed the cigarette into the ashtray until her fingers touched the ashes, then lit another and blew out more smoke.

"Oh, that girl's so rotten that she even got herself knocked up before her wedding. It almost killed her poor father, who thought the world of her. And just think of it, that Gerald is Catholic. Ever heard of a Catholic doing anything like that?"

I managed to cut in with a question. "Other Americans, not Catholic ones, don't do things like that?"

"Hah," she laughed. "I love your cute accent, but honey, let me tell you. Americans are just like the people in the rest of the world. They all do stupid things, but Catholics should know better."

I looked at her through the curtain of smoke. *How can this happen to me? This is not the kind of American I want to become. How could I have been so wrong, and my mother so right? She said that people were the same all over the world.* I wanted to puke. Still, I held onto my good manners.

"I am so sorry," I said. "I thought that, perhaps . . ."

Darlene interrupted. "Oh heck, don't apologize. It's all right. You'll learn. But anyway, as I was saying, that damn Gerald made an honest woman out of Donna. He married her, and they live with their two kids in a garage behind his parents' home, which they made into a three-room apartment. Wait till you see it. It has indoor plumbing, cold water, and a toilet, but no bathtub or shower. I treat them nice, you know, but I've never liked them. They're hypocrites, if you ask me.

"Oh, and wait till you get to know Matthew, that's Frank's third brother, the one married to Loretta. Let me tell you, that couple will make your hair stand straight. He drinks most of his weekly pay, and Loretta keeps the dirtiest house and dirtiest kids you'll ever see. Just wait, they'll invite you over soon, and you'll see what I mean. Oh, and you won't want to eat anything Loretta cooks. She's terrible, never washes her hands, and burns even the mashed potatoes. But she's a good woman, you know. She never says bad things about anyone, is always smiling and happy. And boy, does she love to eat at my house.

"Of course, I'll never turn her away. I have a big heart, you know. I work all day to prepare huge meals with all the trimmings for my in-laws, if need be. They love my mashed potatoes and gravy, my meat loaf, and my fried chicken and dumplings. Oh yes, they're a lucky bunch to have me as a member of their family, but with darn good reason."

The next time Darlene invited Frank and me over to her place for dinner, the first people I saw at her table were those she talked so badly about. I wondered if Loretta and Donna would eat if they knew what Darlene had told me. I felt really sick, but would never tell on her. I prayed that she would not find bad things to say about me.

Chapter Twenty-Five

Whirling Flakes

Each day, when Frank went out to look for work, our house became the same ghostly monster it had been the day before. It seemed to grow to twice its normal size, appeared darker and colder, and the crackling and popping sounded louder.

The huge furnace in the basement belched different noises constantly. As soon as I got used to one sound, out popped a new one. When the pipes were cold, they clicked and popped. When they began to heat up, they screeched, whistled, and snapped, as if something inside was fighting to burst out. The crazy sounds kept me jumping all day. Occasionally things would quiet down for a little bit, but then they would start again just as I began to relax. I jumped every time, and the more I jumped, the jumpier I became, until I felt like screaming so loud that I would have alarmed the entire neighborhood.

That would probably have been the only way I'd get to see what everyone looked like, anyway. So far, I had only seen the woman across the street getting in and out of her car. Several times I had caught the neighbor watching me through the kitchen window. I'd walk to the sink and see her curtain raised about an inch, and then it would quickly drop down again. One day, two ladies came to the kitchen door bundled in heavy coats, with sunglasses hiding their eyes and scarves covering their hair.

"Yes?" I inquired, opening the door.

"We just came by to say hello," one of them announced, while the other nodded.

"Well, please come in," I said, feeling glad to have company. But they just stared at me, then turned and walked away. I would find out later that summer who they were and why they had come by. They had heard that a Puerto Rican girl had moved into their neighborhood, and they came to see what such people looked like.

The loneliness and the mysteries became overwhelming, so I decided to try the old televison set. I pounded on it until the picture came on. As I leaned back on the sofa to watch a show, I noticed what looked like small white feathers whirling down past the window. At first I thought birds were fighting somewhere and the wind was stirring up the little feathers. But the feathers kept coming down, so I sprang from the sofa, turned off the set, and stood at the window. It was snow, floating and whirling down onto the grass, the sidewalk, the street, and everything for as far as I could see. It was so beautiful and exciting.

I ran to the kitchen and looked out those windows to see more flakes coming down. Next I ran to the bedroom, making sure the white fluffy flakes were on that side of the house as well. It was as if the sky had opened, and all those fluffy white flakes were floating out in huge numbers.

I had to run out and catch some of the flakes to show Frank when he came home. I had to hurry before the snow would stop coming down, but putting on my coat became a struggle. I could not line up the buttons with the buttonholes, and the scarf I tried to wrap around my head kept sliding off.

I was sweating and shaking by the time I finished getting all bundled up. Finally I ran out the kitchen door with a cup in my hand. I felt a gust of cold air shooting up my legs, while stepping onto the thin layer of flakes that covered the walkway. Still, I held out the cup and caught some of the flakes, then hurried back into the kitchen, where I tasted the snow.

How disappointing it was when the snow instantly turned into cold water. I wouldn't be able to save some for Frank, and it was too cold for me to run back out to get some more. I went back to the window and watched the snow accumulate on the grass, the sidewalk, the street, and the roof of every home as far as I could see.

I ran to meet Frank at the door when he came home at about eight o'clock that night. He walked in complaining. "The damn windshield wiper broke off. The damn snow came too soon, before I could buy a new one." He didn't ask what I thought about the snow, and he looked too crabby, so I went back to the window. "I ate at Ma's," he said on his way to the shower.

When he came out, I took my shower and went to bed. He stayed up watching *The Honeymooners* on TV. I was awake when he came to bed, but I pretended to be asleep. When he started snoring, I tiptoed out of the room and stared out the living room window most of the night.

From that day on, it snowed almost every day, for weeks and months, until I forgot the color of the earth and grass. Every morning, Frank shoveled the driveway, scraped the windshield, pushed the frozen old car to start it, and disappeared.

Darlene had stopped coming over, and weeks later we heard that they had been snowed in, way out there in the sticks.

Through the window, I watched children bundled in heavy jackets, mittens, caps, and boots throwing snowballs at each other. Grown-ups drove through the dancing flakes, got stuck at the edge of the snow-covered road, pushed themselves out, and went on as if nothing was impossible. I must have been the only person on my street who spent the days looking out the windows, wishing for the snow to stop coming down. I had found it beautiful at first, but I did not need to see it forever.

I finally decided to go outside and try to play like the children across the street. I looked through a bag of old clothes Frank had brought me from Leo's trash collection, put on an old red sweater over my dress, and a black sweater over the red one, and my big coat over all that. Next, I put four socks on each foot, all of different colors, then shoved my bulky feet into a pair of black snow boots some big woman had thrown away. I found red, blue, and green scarves, and wrapped all three around my head and neck. By then I was sweating, but I searched in the bag until I found a bunch of mittens, all of different colors, and put three on each hand.

Even though I was weighted down with all the clothes, I made it across the kitchen to the back door, then struggled to turn the knob with all those mittens on. When I finally managed it, a gust of cold wind pushed me back inside, and slammed the storm door against the outside wall. I fought to conquer my fears and build endurance against the Minnesota winds and snow.

Staggering like a drunk with the wind in my face, I made it to the back yard. I looked up to see the snow coming from the sky, but the cold flakes fell into my eyes. One of the scarves came untied and the wind took it away. I wiped my eyes with my mitten-covered hand, then retrieved the scarf. I held a corner of it, and it became a red flag flapping in the air.

Facing the fact that I hadn't been conditioned for harsh winters, I started back to the house. Once again, I struggled with the storm door. Not only did the wind push the door against the wall, but it pressed me against it. Meanwhile, my coat and scarves were all trying to fly away, while I desperately tried to hang onto everything.

By the time I walked inside the house, my nose and ears were in terrible pain, and my eyes were burning. The cold wind had even penetrated my mittens, boots, and socks. One solid pain rushed through my body from head to toe. After being outside, the air in the house seemed too warm, and it stung my burning eyes, made the pain in my frozen ears unbearable, and turned my nose into a warm water faucet.

I felt exhausted, and I promised myself that I would never go outside again, until the wind stopped blowing and the snow quit falling.

Chapter Twenty-Six

A White Goose

My days became long and boring while I waited for my husband to return home every night with the same bad news that there were no jobs anywhere. The next military check he would receive would be the last one, and the house payment, and the gas, electric, and phone bills were due. Our cupboards were empty, and I needed winter clothing.

The snow stopped coming down sometimes, but only for two or three days. I didn't look out the window that often anymore, for when I did, sadness overwhelmed me.

I finally reached out to the only thing available to me: the old TV set. I turned it on and hit it until a picture appeared. I saw something familiar while I was turning the knob. A white goose was running inside a house, while an old woman chased it with a broom. It reminded me of when I had to chase the chickens off the corn my parents had spread around the house to dry in the sun. I kept the set on that channel, waiting to see more geese.

By the end of the show, I was wishing to be like the young girl who played *My Little Margie*. She had no fear of her father. She talked, and argued with him, and even sat on his knee at the end of the show.

From that day on, I looked forward to the next day, and turned the television on when Frank left in the morning. I discovered enough fifteen and thirty-minute shows to keep myself entertained all day. The soap operas became my favorites, for they would continue the next day and the characters became familiar. *Love of Life* was the first show. It had a couple, Paul and Veneza, who had friends and neighbors, and something new happened every day. I paid close attention to the women – how they dressed, how they wore their hair, and how the men treated them.

The next show was *The Guiding Light*, with Bert and Papa Bauer, who often had a second cup of coffee in the morning and talked about

Bert's husband's problem with alcohol. The shows were interrupted often while someone else talked about laundry soaps that would make clothes cleaner and brighter, and hand lotions that kept hands looking soft and young.

I learned new words every day from those shows, and I wrote the way the words sounded to me on any scrap of paper I could find. Learning to write the words would help me read English. Reading English would improve my vocabulary, and if Frank found a job, I could buy magazines and books to read. In time, I would learn enough to write poems and short stories. These were some of my dreams and hopes. As my godfather had said many years earlier, I would someday become "a writer."

"Tune in tomorrow," a man's voice requested at the end of each show. That became a personal invitation to me, so I faithfully tuned in the next day.

One afternoon I discovered another show, *The Edge of Night*. That became my favorite out of all the other shows. I fell in love with the man, Mike Kerr, a handsome lawyer who wore a suit and tie, carried a briefcase, and brought flowers and chocolates to his wife Sarah.

Soon I wanted to be like Sarah and dress like her, in flared skirts and high- heeled shoes. I wanted Frank to wear a suit and carry a brief-case instead of his black metal lunch box.

When the shows were over for the day, I kept Mike Kerr in my mind. I talked to him, and he talked to me. When I went down to the basement to do the wash, he would emerge from the walls and bring me flowers and candy.

Sometimes after Frank left, especially in the gloomy winter morn-ings, I stayed in bed and fantasized about Mike Kerr. He would cuddle with me under the covers, where I would tell him all the things I could not tell my husband. Mike always kissed and comforted me the way Frank never had.

The feelings of those fantasies stayed with me all day, and before long they turned into nighttime dreams. One time, I woke up in the middle of the night on my back with my lips puckered up toward the ceiling. Feeling terribly embarrassed that someone might be looking down at me, I opened my eyes in the dark, only to realize that the man in my bed was Frank. Frank's snoring had brought me back from the soft pink cloud in which Mike had been kissing me like no one else ever had. It was the kind of kiss that made me melt and float at the same time. Being interrupted at such a time was painful, and that night Frank came pretty close to getting hit on the head for snoring.

Frank had been the one doing our grocery shopping, and was always buying the same things: a dozen eggs, a loaf of bread with red and blue dots on its wrapper, a package of day-old cinnamon rolls, and ground coffee that came in a tin can. The coffee tasted nothing like the rich Puerto Rican coffee I had grown up drinking.

One day I felt a desperate craving for the kind of soup we made back home. We would brown a few ounces of ham with onions and garlic and make a pot of soup with chunks of potatoes and fine noodles that pleased the palate and warmed up the stomach. So when Frank came home, I convinced him to drive me to the store.

In Puerto Rico, we had bought our groceries by the ounce and half-pounds in small stores called *cantinas*. Walking into an American supermarket was an overwhelming experience, to say the least. I had never seen such high shelves loaded with so many different groceries. I saw can after can of fruits, with pictures of mouth-watering sliced yellow peaches on their wrappers. There were cans of sliced pears, pineapple rings, tomatoes, beans, corned beef, and even chicken. I saw jars of olives, pickles, strawberry jam, and grape jellies, all with pictures vivid enough to taste. On other shelves, I saw boxes of Cheerios, corn flakes, and shredded wheat, cans of shortening, bags of flour and sugar, cake mixes, cans of coffee, potato chips, crackers, nuts, and so much of everything that I suddenly wanted my whole family to come see the abundance of groceries in the United States.

As we reached a huge pile of potatoes, I took one in my hand and looked it over carefully. "Are these real potatoes?" It didn't look like the small, shriveled ones we bought back home at the *cantinas*.

Frank chuckled, with one eyebrow up and the other down. "Yeah, well, uh, these potatoes haven't been transported from far away, like the ones you'd find in Puerto Rico."

"I didn't know that potatoes came in such large sizes."

Frank tilted his head like a pigeon. "Well, now you know they do."

After returning the potato to the pile, I moved on, feeling unsure about the way Frank explained things to me. It was as though he was trying to appear intelligent by making me feel small and stupid.

I reached the shelf of straight spaghetti in boxes, Minute Rice and macaroni, but I could not find the twisted fine noodles we used for our soup back home.

"These are better," Frank said. "They're thicker. More to chew."

I grabbed one of the smaller boxes and moved on to a glass counter filled with freshly cut meats. A man wearing a white jacket came forward. "May I help you?"

"I'll take a half pound of ham," I said.

The man, seeming puzzled, peered at me. "I beg your pardon?"

Sure that the problem was my accent, I pointed through the glass. "A half pound of that ham, please."

Then I saw Frank hurrying toward me with a hand cupped around his burning cigarette. "Oh, honey, wait! They don't sell it like that here. We'd have to buy the whole ham."

"Oh," I said. "Okay, we want that ham, please."

The man flashed a bright smile. But Frank quickly grabbed my arm. "Honey, I don't have three dollars for a whole ham. You'll have to make your soup with something else, like a beef bone, or strips of bacon."

"I don't know how to make beef or bacon soup," I whispered, my face hot. I would be disgraced if the man behind the counter heard that certain foods were unknown to me.

"Well find something else," Frank said. "It's a big store!"

"It's big, but it's stupid if I can't buy a piece of ham."

"You need to make your soups from other things, because it'll be a long time before I can buy you a whole ham."

I looked at Frank's cold face and felt a knot forming in my stomach. I walked out of the store without another word, my eyes to the floor, wondering what else I would have to learn to do without.

Chapter Twenty-Seven

Thanksgiving Day

During my early years in the hills of Puerto Rico, the fourth Thursday of November had been the day when families recited extra prayers in thanksgiving for good health and whatever good fortunes they had had throughout the year.

For Frank and his family, Thanksgiving Day was for the men to watch ball games on television and drink beer. Two or three couples would get together in one home, and two or three in another. Each man brought a six pack, or they pitched in and bought a whole keg.

Weeks before that day, the women made out the menu and assigned the preparing of the turkey and gravy to one, the green salad to another. One of them would make the fruit salad, and another the pies. The meal would be served around two o'clock in the afternoon.

Frank and I had been invited to Matthew and Loretta's home. We didn't have to bring any cooked food because I was new to the family. Frank would not have to bring beer, because he had been gone from home a few years and didn't have a job or money.

It started to snow just before we left, and I thought it was pretty the way the flakes whirled down to land on the windshield faster than the wipers could sweep them away. If it hadn't been so cold, and if Frank had been livelier, I would have found this quite romantic. But riding through the gloom with a boring husband to the house of Loretta, who, according to Darlene, burned even the mashed potatoes and had dirty, undisciplined children, for a turkey dinner which I wouldn't even eat, wasn't anything like I had pictured in my dreams. This was more like a nightmare. And to make the day gloomier, my shows had been replaced by boring ball games, and I would have to wait until the following Monday to see what happened to my TV friends.

I looked at Frank's profile as he gripped the steering wheel with both hands, which were thick and muscular. He held a cigarette between his teeth, and smoke drifted out of his bubble-like nose. He had covered the hole on the wing window and fixed the stinky heater, but he still did not speak while driving. Did driving demand all his attention? Didn't he think I might feel lonely?

While I knew that something important was missing in our marriage, I feared Frank's reaction if I told him. A snappy answer from him might make me want to disappear, and I had no place to go.

I stared out the side window, noticing two or three cars in people's driveways and children in thick jackets playing in the deep snow. I wished for the power to lift the thick gloom and bring in the sun, melt the snow, and invite the smell of the ocean. The cars on those driveways would belong to people I knew. The homeowners would be my sisters and brothers. With my magical powers, I'd change them into caring siblings, and I would make our mother into the most loving mother in the world. With that kind of family, I would never feel so alone, and Frank's silence would not matter as much.

While getting out of the car at Matthew's place, I smelled cinnamon, apple pie, and turkey, but I didn't like it. I noticed that in that neighborhood, too, there was more than one car in each driveway, and a lonely feeling settled in my stomach that made me want to cry.

Luckily, Matthew met us at the door with a brilliant smile. "I'm so glad to have you here, brother, and delighted that you married this lovely young lady." He kissed my hand. "Let's go into the kitchen. Loretta is fixing a great feast."

I expected to see dust on the tables and clutter on the floor while walking through the living room, but the opposite was true. The place had been cleaned. And if it had been because we were coming, then it meant that much more to me.

Loretta was mixing flour with water in a deep dish. She looked up with a bright smile. "Good to see you. Make yourself at home. I'm making the gravy."

"May I watch?"

"Sure, I'll even let you stir it."

She let me stir the gravy, which turned thick and brown. Frank and Matthew watched over our shoulders. "Ooh, that looks delicious," said Frank.

"Oh yeah," said Matthew. "Make lots of it,"

Loretta chuckled. "Don't worry, we will."

This was a good, cozy feeling, the four of us over that white metal stove with a steamy aroma rising from the deep pot of gravy. For the first time, I felt a sense of belonging. I wanted to tell Loretta and Matthew that, but then they might think I didn't like the other relatives. So I said, "I feel so happy to have my first Thanksgiving Day dinner in America with you."

"It's nice of you to say that. It makes the event more special," Loretta said, her dark eyes gleaming.

Frank put his hand on my shoulder. "Isn't my wife the nicest?"

His brother winked at him. "You bet she is."

Loretta had set the table ahead of time, and it looked very nice and clean. Contrary to what Darlene had said, the children, two boys and one girl, were well behaved at the table. During the time we were there, I didn't once see them jumping on the furniture.

Frank and Matthew had wine throughout the meal, while Loretta and I had water and the children had milk. The dinner was simple: turkey meat and mashed potatoes with gravy, green peas, yams with only butter on them, dinner rolls, and pumpkin pie with coffee for dessert.

It was good that I didn't have to taste too many different foods. If I ever did invite any of those relatives over to our house for dinner, I would not want to load the table with ten or twelve different dishes.

I didn't eat much of anything that night because I had that terrible washed-out feeling in my stomach, but I felt quite comfortable in Matthew and Loretta's home. I helped her with the dishes after dinner, while Frank and Matthew drank more wine and watched television in the living room.

I found that Loretta was down-to-earth and simple, wasn't stupid or dirty, and didn't say anything bad about Darlene or anyone else. I felt disappointed in Darlene, and wondered how to tell her that she should look for the good things in people, rather than criticize them.

Frank came into the kitchen with a red face from too much wine. "We best be going, sweetheart. It's still snowing, and driving is gonna be rough."

We said goodbye and left. The snow was coming down so fast that the wipers couldn't keep it off the windshield, which fogged up on the inside. Frank had to wipe it clean with his hand. Other cars passed us left and right, while our old Ford roared tiredly through the deep snow. Shivering, I watched the snowflakes dance in front of the headlights.

"I could like that stuff if it wasn't so cold," I said.

"Oh, honey," Frank said with a chuckle. "That stuff can only come down when it's cold."

"I hope it goes away soon, or else my bones will break from shaking."

"Yeah, well, don't hold your breath. Snow will be coming down for many more months. But you'll be okay. It only snows outdoors, never inside the house."

He could have said something romantic, like "Don't worry, honey, I'll keep you warm." But I couldn't tell him that. I was just glad that he had spoken, although I knew it was the wine.

Chapter Twenty-Eight

Sky and Snow

The snow continued to fall through the rest of November and the next five endless months. It would stop for a few days, then start again, and again. People scraped the tops of their cars, and the wind blew some snow off the roofs, but the snow kept coming. Noisy snow plows moved up and down the street several times a day, pushing the stuff off the road so men could drive to and from work.

Early in the mornings, the neighborhood men scraped the ice off their windshields and drove off, all bundled up in thick, dark jackets and heavy mittens. Their cold cars roared through the salted, mushy snow, leaving a thick, whitish smoke lingering in the air.

Frank had been out every day looking for a job, but still had not found one by the middle of December. I had kept myself busy doing the same things every day: cleaning, washing, mending, ironing, counting buttons, watching the "soaps" on TV, and fantasizing about Mike Kerr. Still, the washed-out feeling in my stomach grew worse. My nose seemed longer, my cheekbones higher, and my eyes sunk deeper into the sockets. Two months in America, and I had become a skeleton.

"You're losing too much weight," Frank said one night. "You're starving yourself. I'm taking you to a doctor. I have no money for a funeral."

I had been to a doctor only once in my nineteen years of life, and it had been to a female doctor. My reason for that visit had been for a physical check-up to work on the base.

Frank found a doctor and made the appointment. The next day, I got ready without asking Frank anything about the doctor or what I should be expecting.

I didn't even feel nervous, since I believed that anything in America would be nothing less than good. The doctor would ask me a few questions, then write a prescription for some pills, and that would be it. Whatever problems I had developed due to the culture shock would soon be gone.

Frank hadn't mentioned the doctor or anything about what might be wrong with me, either. The few words he spoke while driving there were about whatever came up on the snowy road. Although I knew he never said much while driving, I trusted that he would at least show concern if he thought that something serious could be happening to me.

That day, I had the biggest, and most degrading shock of my life. We walked up to the second floor, where we saw *Dr. Watson, M.D.* printed on the door. Frank opened the door, and we entered a room where two ladies waited, each with a big belly and a darling baby on their laps.

"May I help you?" asked a stocky woman with reddish hair and thick glasses.

"I made an appointment with Dr. Watson for my wife Jacqueline."

The women opened a booklet and handed Frank a clipboard and a pencil. Frank sat with me in a corner away from the other women. He asked me one question after another, but the most personal was about my menstrual period. When had I had the last one? My face felt hot. *How dare he ask such a question in a place where other people might hear?*

"It's an important question," he whispered. "This information is for the doctor only. It's confidential."

I then realized that I was almost a month late. But that would also be part of the culture shock, wouldn't it?

We waited a while before a nurse called us in. She wrapped a tight band on my arm and squeezed a round black balloon that made my arm hurt. She wrote something on a clipboard, said the doctor would be in shortly, and left, closing the door.

Shortly after that, a man in a dark suit walked in. "I'm Dr. Watson."

Frank stood up and shook hands with the doctor. I sat in my chair, wondering, *Why didn't I ask Frank if he knew the doctor?* I felt the moisture on my palms, yet I stayed there waiting, not knowing what to expect.

"What's the problem?" the doctor asked, reading the paper Frank had filled out.

Frank told him that I wasn't eating and was losing too much weight, that we had been married for three months, and that I was from Puerto Rico.

"From 'Portoricah?' That's a traumatic change for you, isn't it? And aren't you too white to be 'Portorican?'"

I was too shocked to speak, so I nodded, and shook my head.

"Sit up here," the doctor said, tapping a bench-like table covered with white paper. Then, while asking Frank questions about the Air Force, he poked a cold, pointy light into my ears, then up my nose, and down my throat. Next he placed a cold round disk on my back and asked me to inhale and exhale. Finally, he had me lie on my back so he could feel my stomach. "Tiny one, aren't you?" So far everything had been fine. Then he said, "The nurse will be in shortly to prepare you for a pelvic exam." He was gone before I could ask what he meant.

I sat up quickly and asked Frank if he knew what the doctor was talking about, but the nurse walked in before he could answer. "You can wait in the waiting room," she told Frank. This all happened so fast, I think even Frank was confused. Still, he said that the nurse would explain things to me and left the room.

The nurse didn't explain anything; she just gave orders. She was about two inches taller than I, and maybe ten years older.

"You'll need to remove your panties," she said.

"I need to what?"

"For your pelvic exam, you need to take off your panties."

At the expense of sounding very stupid, I explained to her that I had never been to a male doctor before, and that I was scared.

Her attitude softened immediately. "Well," she said tenderly, "don't be scared. It really isn't that bad. Besides, a pelvic examination is necessary, and every woman has them often." She seemed sincere and sympathetic, so I decided to trust her. This was no place to create a scene. If that was the way Americans did things, well, I had come here to become one.

Coming to such a conclusion was one thing, but going through the embarrassing humiliation was another. Before I could think straight, my feet went up on some kind of brackets, and a paper sheet came over my lap like a tent.

The doctor walked in, put on plastic gloves, then began to look for something inside my body. The nurse stood at my side holding my hand, and I felt my heartbeat in my ears and the heat on my face. I swore silently never to let this happen again. I would eat like a pig from then on, and put on some weight so Frank wouldn't think I was sick and take me to a doctor.

"Looks like you're pregnant." The doctor's voice came through the paper sheet.

"What?"

"You're going to have a baby," the nurse said.

"No, this cannot be. It's impossible."

"Why? Don't you want children?" the doctor asked.

I could not answer, and something tightened my throat. Obviously, I had been wrong about the special permission to get pregnant.

"Get dressed, and the nurse will bring you to my office," he said, then left. The nurse helped me sit up, waited until I put on my panties, and walked me out by the hand. I sensed that she was puzzled by my reaction, but I couldn't explain. My words were lost in my head.

Frank was already in the doctor's office in a chair across from the doctor's desk, staring at the floor, elbows on his knees, fingers interlocked under his chin. The doctor glanced at him and told me to sit down. The nurse patted my shoulder and left. I knew the doctor had given Frank some terrible news about my health. Surely news about having a baby would not make Frank look so worried and scared. No, the news about the baby would make him jump for joy and kiss me in front of everybody, like Mike Kerr did when Sarah told him that she was pregnant.

The doctor gave me a small bottle of white pills, some brochures for both of us to read, and said he wanted to see me in a month. He shook Frank's hand. "Don't worry. Things will turn around soon, and everything will be fine." He headed out, then stopped with one hand on the doorknob. "And you take care of yourself, young lady." He smiled and walked out.

When we left the doctor's office, I felt more concerned about Frank than about myself. He walked down the steps ahead of me, and I saw him as a man carrying a heavy load on his back, totally aware only of himself. I felt more alone than ever before, lost in a strange country, and pregnant.

"I don't know how I'm going to pay for a baby," he finally said as we reached the car. "Can't find a damn job." He usually held the door open for me, but this time he walked to the driver's side and got into the car. I had to open my own door.

"So, you're not mad about the baby? Just worried because you can't find a job?" I felt relieved and excited.

"Oh, honey, I'm so sorry. Mad about the baby? Of course not. It's just that I'm tired of looking for work and not finding any. The only part-time job I've found so far is playing Santa Claus at a department store. Can you imagine that? Me as Santa? For God's sake! How much worse can things get?"

The pensive look in Frank's eyes made me feel guilty, but I knew he didn't like to talk while driving, so I remained quiet and thought all the way home. *How can I be pregnant? I haven't asked for a baby.* Someone had played a trick on me. I had agreed to be loyal and love my husband, but no one had said anything about having a baby so soon. Hadn't I thought that in order to get pregnant I would have to do something other than intercourse?

Ah, but a baby would keep me from feeling lonely. A baby would be something nice to write to my family and Doña Inez about — but that would also be the beginning of more problems. I had no choice but to keep all these changes bundled up in my chest. If I could just write to Alicia or Doña Inez to share with them my new discoveries — but that would put them in the position of keeping secrets. How would they receive a letter without anyone else seeing it?

This fear of writing to them was becoming too painful. Still, I could not take a chance. If one of my brothers showed up on my doorstep someday, my life would turn from bad to worse. No, writing home must wait.

Chapter Twenty-Nine

Babies Happen

"So I'm going to be a daddy," Frank said when we arrived home. He pulled me to his chest. "I'll find a job somewhere."

"I'm sorry, Frank. I didn't think I'd have a baby without asking for one."

His brow furrowed. "Honey, babies happen even when you don't ask for any."

"They happen with regular intercourse? You don't have to do anything different?"

Frank chuckled. "Just intercourse, nothing else."

"But I thought that a woman would have to give the man special permission to get pregnant."

"You gave your permission the day we got married. Now fix us a sandwich. I've got to go find a job."

Frank ate his bologna sandwich in a hurry, washed it down with a cup of cold coffee, kissed me on the cheek, and left.

I stood at the window and through teary eyes watched him drive away. I had hoped that he would have stayed home the rest of the day, talking about who the baby would look like, and choosing a name.

I finally dried my tears, moved from the window, and turned on the television. I had missed *Love of Life* and *The Guiding Light*, but *The Edge of Night* came on faithfully. I stretched out on the sofa and told Mike Kerr the news about our baby. I imagined his arms around me, his love and understanding, and his promises that everything was going be all right.

Frank returned around six o'clock that afternoon. "I found a job," he said with a smile. "Things will be better for us soon. I'll get paid in two weeks, and the last military check will come. I'll pay the rent and the other bills, and will have some money left for groceries.

That night, when he turned on the television, I stayed up with him, thinking that he would want to talk about the baby. But for Frank, watching television was like driving a car. It took all his concentration. Any question or remark I had would have to wait until later. Usually, by the time he did listen, the subject was long forgotten. He didn't even notice when I went to bed.

After two weeks on the job, Frank came home with a long face and a frown, and smelled like a barrel of beer. "That son-of-a-bitch fired me. I worked too slow, he said. After I worked my tail off for two damn weeks. Too slow, my ass!"

I felt so bad for him that I didn't even mind the smell of beer and tobacco smoke. "You know, Frank, I've been thinking that maybe you should go back into the service."

"I've been thinking the same thing," he said, perking up. "We won't have to pay for the child – well, five dollars if it's a boy, and we'll get a thousand dollars up front. Yeah, that's the best thing to do. And, honey, let's keep the news about the baby a secret for a while. What do you say?"

"Oh, that would be nice. I'd love to keep it a secret." That turned into a wonderful night. Frank hadn't had too much to drink, but enough to be loving.

"You are the most beautiful woman I've ever seen. I touch your soft skin and feel glad I'm alive. I love you so much it hurts. You've made me very happy, and you're going to have my child, maybe a son. That's enough happiness to last a lifetime." He kissed my forehead, my eyes, my mouth, my breast, and my navel.

I touched his belly, his chest, and his shoulders, and kissed his temple, his neck, and his chin. I felt good doing all of that. Then, for the first time, I even liked the intercourse. It made me feel warm inside, and tingly all over. It made me reach a point I had never reached before. I didn't tell Frank, for it might not be a normal thing for a woman, but I knew that something had felt awfully good, and I would look forward to that kind of feeling again.

The next day, Frank called his mother and told her his decision about re-enlisting. She told him that she hated to see him go, but jobs were hard to find, and if he could have a better future in the service, he'd have her blessing.

The phone call didn't end there. The minute they hung up the phone, she called one of her daughters and passed on the sad news. That afternoon, our phone rang, and continued ringing into the night. One brother after another, and the three sisters, gave Frank their strong opinions, and none were in favor of Frank's decision.

The phone calls, the advice, and evening visits went on through the end of the month, which meant Christmas, a time of more sadness and disappointments. Everyone in the neighborhood adorned their homes with colorful bright lights, but we didn't even have a Christmas tree. We wouldn't need one, the relatives said. We had enough homes to visit, and we could stay overnight if we wanted to. In their homes, we saw packages under the trees, and felt bad because none were from us.

For New Year's Eve, everyone gathered at Arthur's home with their musical instruments. Everyone except us brought some prepared foods, such as ham, baked beans, potato chips, bread, cakes, cookies, and pies. There was food everywhere, along with soft drinks, beer, tobacco smoke, and a lot of noisy children.

Frank tapped a glass with a fork for everyone's attention, and with a wide grin, announced that we were expecting a baby. Everyone clapped and cheered. The women gathered around me, expressing their joy.

"I knew it!" Loretta exclaimed.

"So that's why you haven't been eating," someone else said.

The men across the room had their own questions and comments among each other, and then they played a fast tune, as if to celebrate Frank's accomplishment.

Later, in the kitchen, Donna said, "So I guess Frank will give up the foolishness of going back into the service now that you're pregnant." She sucked on her cigarette and blew the smoke toward the ceiling.

"The baby is the reason he's going back," I said.

"You mean, he's going back because you're pregnant?"

"Well, yes. We need money to have a baby, and he hasn't found a job."

"That's bullshit," Darlene cut in. "Everyone else in the family has kids, and they aren't going into the service."

"Yes, but your husbands have jobs. Frank hasn't found one. He'd have more opportunities in the Air Force."

"Oh, hell, our husbands have jobs, but we're all struggling to make ends meet. Why should you and Frank have it better than the rest of us?"

I felt a knot in my stomach, and I said nothing else. If I told Darlene that she sounded jealous, she might start talking bad about me. I couldn't help remembering my mother: "People are the same everywhere." The knot in my stomach grew worse.

At midnight, everyone stood up and began hugging and kissing each other. It was the craziest thing I'd ever seen. Suddenly I was turning my head one way, then another, trying to escape the puckered lips coming at me from the men. Finally, Frank explained that this was the custom to bring in a new year.

"Fine, but I don't like it," I said, and the men went back to their music.

On our way home, I told Frank what Donna and Darlene had said about his returning to the Air Force.

"Darlene said that?"

"Yes, she did. I was shocked and embarrassed."

Frank hit the steering wheel, "That does it! First thing Monday morning, I'm going to Minneapolis and I'm signing in. That'll teach them not to be jealous."

While Frank steered in and out of snow banks, I thought about my mother. *"People are all alike."*

Frank drove to Minneapolis early Monday morning. He had a bright smile when he left, but came home with a long face. The offer of a thousand dollars had expired two days earlier. Yes, he could still go back into the service, but minus the thousand dollars.

"But at least you'll have a job," I told him.

"That's true," he said. "If I don't land a job in another month or so, I'll sign up. No need to hurry now. I already lost the thousand dollars."

Chapter Thirty

A Blade of Grass

Dear Mama,

I'm sure that Alicia and Doña Inez have told you that I would not write to any of you for many years, as I needed to concentrate only on myself. However, I have changed my mind, for there isn't much for me to do here and I have a lot of free time. I hope that all is going well for you and the others, and I am sorry that I don't have a few dollars to send you.

Frank finally found a job a few days ago, cleaning engines at a railroad company. It doesn't pay much, and he comes home covered in grease, but there are few jobs in this part of the country. He says that the first few checks will go toward paying old bills. Then we need to stock up on groceries, because our cupboards are empty. After paying everything, we won't have any money left, so we will be unable to send you a few dollars, for which I'm very sorry.

You'll be glad to know that I'm going to have a baby. I hope that makes you happy. I'm really happy myself. I can't wait to hold my own baby in my arms, although I won't have money to buy the baby things for a long time. I had hoped to buy a crib like some I had seen on the base before Frank and I married, one that will allow me to raise the mattress while the baby is small and lower it as he grows. But the baby will probably be walking by the time we can buy the crib.

The days are long and boring right now. If I could just buy some flannel, I could sew diapers to pass the time. I spend my time looking out the window, hoping to see Frank drive up the driveway, and wondering where all the snow that is now piled around the house really comes from. You can't imagine what it's like to look out the window week after week and see dead trees, smoke rising from chimneys, and miles of white, glaring snow.

Writing that letter had been a bad idea. I tore it up and threw it in the wastebasket.

I stood at the window every day while watching Frank drive off to work. Then I ran to the bedroom to look at my belly in the mirror, disappointed at first because it wasn't bulging out. Next, I went into the second bedroom and pictured the crib with a cuddly, blonde, blue-eyed baby kicking and gurgling. I imagined a red wagon filled with toys in one corner, and a little dresser with tiny outfits and folded diapers near the crib. Then I felt bad because I couldn't make those dreams a reality right away.

Every day, I did the cleaning and the washing, then watched television the rest of the day. During some of the shows, I mended Frank's trousers and shirts, then ironed them. But during my favorite show, *The Edge of Night*, I did nothing but sit back and watch. I imitated Sarah, trying to walk and speak like her. I practiced some of the words Mike Kerr used during the trial scenes, like *"Did you, or did you not?"* It felt good to sound powerful, and before long I was talking that way to Frank.

"Where the hell did you learn to talk that way?" he would ask.

"On TV," I would answer.

"Well, maybe you'd better stop watching the damn thing."

"What else is there for me to do?" Frank didn't have an answer for that question.

On clear days, the sun made the mountains of snow around the house glitter so much it blinded me whenever I tried to look out. Only in the late afternoon, when the house created shade on the driveway, could I look out the window.

One day I noticed that a strong breeze was blowing the snow off the bank next to our driveway, and dumping it where Frank would park the car. The breeze stopped momentarily, then suddenly came in gusts, whirling the snow down. All my shows were over by then, so I went to the kitchen, brought back a chair, and put it next to the window, where I sat staring out.

The pile of snow on the bank kept getting lower and the one on the driveway, where Frank would be parking the car, kept getting higher. Then I saw something that appeared dark green through the snow that was left on the bank. Each time the wind blew off some more snow, the patch became clearer. This was exciting, so I prayed for the wind to grow stronger and uncover all the hidden grass. I felt that seeing anything green would make me feel better. It would be the first sign of the end of a long, disgusting winter.

The next-door neighbor had trimmed the bank every time he mowed the lawn, but when the weather turned cold, he left it long. During the first snowfall, the long grass stood straight up, refusing to be knocked down. Eventually, the inches of snow accumulated, and our driveway and the bank became one. Frank had shoveled enough snow out of the way every day to drive the car up as close to the kitchen door as possible, but he had always left the wall of snow against the bank.

Another gust of wind came up, and another, until one blade of green grass sprang up as if it had a coil underneath. It stood straight as an arrow, and when the breeze blew again, it swayed back and forth, as if dancing to show me that there was hope of spring and summer. I cheered for the blade of grass to stay up, and wished for the wind to grow stronger and uncover all the suffocating grass.

The wind didn't blow all the snow off the bank, but it cleared a patch of green grass about the size of a dinner plate. It was the prettiest green I had ever seen. I held my eyes to it, afraid of losing it if I looked elsewhere. I pictured myself walking on green grass, its sweet smell rising to my face.

I wanted Frank to get home early so I could tell him about the blade of grass. However, he didn't show up until almost nine, and he smelled like a beer barrel and an old chimney. He went straight to the living room, turned on the TV, hit it, and stretched out on the floor to watch *The Honeymooners*. I went to bed feeling disappointed, but I fell asleep and dreamt that I was walking on miles of green grass with Mike Kerr.

Another foot of snow fell during the night and made the green patch of grass disappear. All day, I felt as if someone had died. If it hadn't been for the shows on TV, I probably would have lost my mind. As time moved on, I came across other shows: *The Tennessee Ernie Ford Show* and *The Gary Moore Show*. Those television shows became my companions, teachers, and inspiration. I repeated the words I heard and wrote them on scraps of paper the way they sounded to me.

Each time Frank bought groceries, he received green stamps he could paste on the pages of a blank book. When the book filled up, he could trade it in for any household item he wanted, or any toy for our future babies. We could even get a crib if we bought enough groceries to fill up a lot of books. He received gold stamps whenever he bought gasoline, and those stamps were to be pasted in a different book.

One day he brought home a catalog for the green stamps, and one for the gold ones. Those catalogs became my first reading material in the United States. I would sit for hours comparing the pictures of so many lovely things on the books to the words below. I repeated the words aloud, then wrote them on my scraps of paper.

The freezing cold continued, and Darlene came back to visit again. Early in the morning, the doorbell rang, and there she stood. "I hope you don't mind, but I can't stay in that old house and freeze."

"It's fine," I said. "I'm tired of being alone, too." But as soon she lit the first cigarette, my nose closed up and I wanted to tell her to stop smoking or stay away. But if I did, she might start talking bad about me.

Darlene began her gossip right away. "That damn Donna is so spoiled. She ruined my wedding day by wearing pink instead of blue. I'll never forgive her for that, so help me." Darlene screwed her cigarette into the ashtray and lit another.

I felt I would suffocate if I didn't make her change, but I needed to do it without making her hate me. "Darlene, do you know how to sew?"

"No, I don't, but I wish I knew. I only have three dresses to my name. It's hard to find dresses that fit me. Not many stores carry my size. But I heard that you can sew pretty good. Think you'd be willing to make me a dress someday?"

"Yes, I know how to sew. And I'd be glad to make you a dress. I'll even teach you how to sew, if you want to learn."

"Well, thanks, but I don't think sewing is my thing. I'll ask Nathan for money next payday, and I'll buy some fabric. How many yards should I plan on getting?"

"Well, depending on the style you choose, you would need more fabric for some than for others. And I'll make you a deal. Teach me how to cook American food, and I'll sew you some dresses."

Her face lit up. "Oh, boy! Cooking is one of my favorite things to do. You got a deal!"

"But can you cut down on the smoking? It plugs my nose up and brings tears to my eyes, and I would not be able to see well enough to make your dresses."

"Oh, hell, I'll cut down," she said. "I don't smoke that much when I'm busy, anyway."

The cooking lessons began that afternoon. We made beef stew and an apple pie. The next time she came, we prepared a pot roast. Then she brought me one of her cookbooks and showed me how to read recipes.

In three weeks, I made her three dresses and a nightgown that took about five yards of fabric. She liked her nightgowns to reach her toes, and to be very wide so she could lie on her side and bring her knees close to her thick middle. She praised me daily for my ability to make her a perfect fit with just her measurements.

Darlene cut down on her smoking, but not enough to make a difference. I ended up in the hospital with a rapid heartbeat and a blinding headache.

"When did you take up smoking?" the doctor asked when he looked down my throat.

"Never. I hate tobacco smoke."

"Your throat says otherwise," he said.

"But she doesn't smoke," Frank cut in.

"Then make sure she stays away from smokers. And don't you smoke around her, either. Too much tobacco smoke will suffocate her, and the baby, too."

The doctor kept me in the hospital for three days for observation. The day he discharged me, he warned Frank not to smoke in the car or in the house.

The news kept Darlene and the other smoking relatives away from our house. But now Frank had a better reason to stop at the bars every day after work, where he could be free to smoke all he wanted. So I found myself alone again, looking out the windows and waiting.

Chapter Thirty-One

A Crimeless Country

I usually left the TV on after my shows were over and watched whatever else came on. I never paid much attention to the news, because everything reported took place in faraway places. However, one night, I recognized the name of a street in our neighborhood. The reporter said that three teenage boys had broken into a lady's house, tied her to a chair, stuffed a dishrag into her mouth, and ransacked her kitchen. They took everything out of the refrigerator and scattered it all over the floor and threw a dozen eggs, one by one, up to the ceiling so the contents came down over her like slippery rain.

I sprang from the sofa and turned off the televison and the indoor lights. Then I turned the outside lights on, made sure the doors were still locked, grabbed the rolling pin from the kitchen drawer, and ran to the bedroom. I crawled under the bed and stayed there, shaking and wondering how such a thing could happen in the United States. I had been so sure that crime did not exist in a country where people were educated.

This reminded me of a silk blouse I had bought a few years earlier. It had been the only garment I had ever purchased, and I only bought it because it was soft and creamy-white like the petals of a gardenia. One day someone smeared ink on my beautiful blouse and tarnished it forever. No matter what I did to remove the ugly stain, the blouse remained ruined. Now, as I shivered under my bed, I saw the United States tarnished by crime. This was painfully disappointing.

"You silly little girl," my husband said when he came home close to midnight and saw me crawling out from under the bed with the rolling pin in my hand. When I told him the story I had heard on the news, he said, "Well, sweetheart, we don't have that many eggs, but keep the doors locked anyway."

He went to bed and was snoring within seconds. The stench of smoke and booze filled the room, and I ended up on the sofa for the rest of the night. His reaction to my feelings added to my fear. I knew I could not count on him to help me understand anything.

That night, as I turned one way and then another on that royal-blue sofa, I thought of something Darlene had tried to tell me. In a put-down way, she had said that drinking alcohol was a problem that ran in Frank's family. At that time, people didn't think of alcoholism as a disease. In Darlene's words, Frank and most of his family were drunks.

As a child of drunken parents, I had learned the term *borrachones*, which meant drunks, or drinkers. But since I had made up my mind to make my marriage work, I had refused to admit that my husband was a drunk. The times he had come home three or four hours late from work, I had figured that it was a normal thing for men to do. I felt disappointed that an American husband would drink so much, and so often, but I reasoned that at least he didn't beat me, as my father had beaten my mother.

Darlene had said that Frank's oldest sister had a beer upon rising every morning. "When most of us have coffee, she drinks beer. What kind of a lady is that? Her brother Bill is in and out of the hospital all the time. They dry him out, and as soon as he hits the streets, he's back in the bars again. A few days later, back into the hospital he goes. And Matthew? Well, he spends half of his weekly checks in the bars, too. That's why his family hardly ever has food in the cupboards."

As I had been listening to Darlene, I told myself that it would not be the same with Frank, because he loved me too much to let that happen. However, I had to admit to myself that Frank loved booze more than he loved me. But what could I do? There was no place for me to go.

By the middle of March, I was lonely, nervous, and worried about how to deal with Frank's drinking. Still, I kept myself busy making diapers, quilts, and little outfits.

Making the diapers out of flannel was painful, because I had pictured myself folding the long, ready-made diapers like the ones the women on the base in Puerto Rico used. Instead, I had to buy the 27-inch-wide flannel Darlene had suggested, because Frank said that he had no money for ready-made diapers. The flannel cost only ten or fifteen cents a yard.

I made the quilts and little outfits out of the pieces of fabric and old clothes Frank's mom had brought to me from Leo's trash collections. First I cut off the worn-out parts of the trousers, men's shirts, and women's dresses. I washed the good pieces, and ironed everything before cutting the little outfits or the squares for the quilts. I had always enjoyed working with fabrics, so I did have some fun doing all of that. Frank's mother always complimented me on my ability to make lovely things out of old clothes other people had thrown out. She would also say that Frank was a lucky man because his wife made his money go a long way.

On days when Frank didn't stop at the bars, we would have dinner together and he would tell me about things at work, about applications he had sent to different companies trying to find a higher paying job, one that would be more pleasant than cleaning oily engines and floors.

"Why not go back into the service?" I asked.

"If I don't find a better job soon, I'll do just that. But I'm not sure if that's what I want to do."

I would show him the things I made for our baby, and he would kiss me and say that I was the best little wife any man could hope to have. I'd take those opportunities to bring up the subject of drinking.

"I worry about you stopping at the bars so often," I'd say, softly and carefully, always afraid that he would get mad and run to the bars. "And I miss you. I get awfully lonely when you're not here."

"Well, I'm a big boy. I don't need you to worry about me. I'm sorry you're lonely, but a man's gotta do what a man's gotta do."

That answer always made my stomach twist, so I would turn away from him, wishing I could throw his things out and make him leave.

In the last week of April, the weather started to warm up. Sometimes it didn't snow for days, and the sun melted some of the snow off the roofs. I still couldn't look outside without squinting, but I enjoyed seeing the melting snow dripping down to the ground like rain-drops.

As the days passed, more and more snow melted. Soon I began to see a patch of grass here and there, and muddy water rushing steadily between the sidewalk and the street. The branches of the trees began to look a little puffy in the joints, and people in the news talked about spring. I looked out the window every morning upon rising, just to see the progress on the trees. I could see that the green leaves were beginning to break through. Summer couldn't come soon enough for me.

Gradually, the snow disappeared. The soaked ground began to dry, the precious grass sprouted, and soon the neighborhood men were outside mowing the lawn. The smell of cut grass filled the air. Like magic, the leaves on the trees popped out everywhere, and in a week's time, it was hard to believe that everything had been under several feet of snow for many months.

Tulips emerged from the ground around the neighbors' houses, and green plants came up overnight in front of our windows and at the edge of our back yard. Soon the taller plants, lilacs, bloomed in lavender. Peonies, the lower plants by the windows, had large green leaves and put out white blooms as big as dinner plates.

The warmer weather brought out the neighbors, but I was the youngest wife in the neighborhood. I could see the women hanging clothes on the lines and then sitting on their steps while their children played and fought. The few times I had walked over to introduce myself, I felt as though I was intruding. I always went back inside feeling bad. Perhaps they thought I was too young. Or maybe they thought that as a Puerto Rican, I wasn't suited for their neighborhood.

One day, Frank said we were going to something called a picnic with Matthew, Loretta, and the children. The picnic would be by a lake, where he and Matthew could smoke all they wanted and the smoke would not bother me. Loretta and I could sit in the shade and talk, and her children could run around and climb as many trees as they wished.

We arrived at a lake which had been frozen and used as a skating area all winter. It was now filled with clear water, which captured the greenery of the surrounding trees and was lovely and pleasing to the eye.

Matthew and his family arrived shortly after we did. They smiled as if they were thrilled to meet with us on this spring Sunday afternoon. Matthew opened the trunk of his car and pulled out a brown bag, which contained a heavy, fully-cooked and ready-to-eat ham. Another bag contained a gallon of homemade wine which Loretta's father had made.

"Old Mainer made wine and gave me some," he said, seeming

pleased with the precious gift, which would later send him and his brother home blind drunk.

Loretta dragged a blanket out of their car and spread it on the grass. She hurried to the car and returned with a bag of potato chips, hard-crusted rolls, pickles, and paper plates.

The three children ran around, then plunged themselves into the shallow water. Matthew and his brother stretched out on the grass, each resting on an elbow, murmuring and taking turns with the gallon jar. They passed it back and forth, taking big mouthfuls, and never set it down until half of the wine had gone down their throats. By then, both had red faces, were trading dirty jokes, and laughing so hard they doubled up and coughed.

Loretta unwrapped the ham, and the two brothers ate one slice after another, washing every bite down with wine, passing the gallon jug back and forth.

Chapter Thirty-Two

Rodney

The month of July arrived hot and humid. We had no air conditioning, no fans, and no ocean to send us a cooling breeze. I headed for the basement every day by noon. The air down there smelled musty and old, but it was cooler than the air upstairs. However, sitting alone in the basement made me feel confined in solitude, as if I had done something terribly wrong and this was my punishment.

To keep my sanity, I began the one thing I could do alone: daydream. I would sit back in an old brown chair that once belonged to Frank's grandmother and let my imagination take me to faraway places. I'd see myself at the ocean, walking on the wet sand with a man who would never stay out drinking after work. That man would not leave me alone any more than necessary, and he would not say things like, "A man's gotta do what a man's gotta do." He would not tell me that he had no money to pay for the things I needed. And when I complained of loneliness, that man would never tell me I was being silly.

My fantasies were so realistic that when the phone rang upstairs, or some noise brought me back to reality, I always felt as if I had been to a fun and refreshing place.

My ability to mentally escape from an unpleasant situation did not help me with the unexplained pains of childbirth. On the last day of July, I awakened with a pain in my lower back that felt as though someone was trying to split my spine in two. The pain didn't last long, but it came back, went away, then came back again, spreading to the front of my stomach and across my abdomen. I didn't suspect labor pains, because no one had explained to me what childbirth and labor pains were like. In my fantasies, I had pictured myself awakening to find a cute and clean little baby lying next to me. Sure, I had heard women talk about labor pains, but how was I supposed to imagine what labor pains felt like? Pain was easy to imagine, and labor meant work, so what did work have to do with having a cute, cuddly baby?

By the time Frank got home, I was twisting on the floor, trying to roll onto my stomach to make the pain go away. I was sweating and moaning like a cow tangled in a mass of rope. I wanted to go down to the basement, but the steps were too difficult. Besides, there were no toilets down there.

I heard Frank's car coming up the driveway, the back door opening, and finally his steps across the kitchen floor. "What the hell!" he exclaimed when he reached the living room. He stood there, startled. "Is it time?"

I looked up and saw the dirt and grime on his pants and shirt, which I had ironed the day before. Another pain struck across my back and belly, and I let out a yell and tried to bring my knees up to my chest, a total impossibility. Frank turned and grabbed the phone. I heard him say "Yes" and "Okay," and then, without much explaining, he reached for my arm and helped me to my feet.

"We need to go to the hospital at once."

I fought Frank as he struggled with me across the kitchen floor and out to the car. He insisted that we must hurry, and I yelled that I couldn't walk. Somehow we made it, and he drove faster than ever before.

"Why the hell didn't you call Ma?"

"Don't yell, Frank!"

"What if I hadn't come home? Were you planning on having the kid on the living room floor?"

"You'd better shut up, Frank!" I was afraid to move, for fear that my entire bottom would explode. Sweat and tears rolled down my face and landed on my huge belly. Frank's eyes were aimed at the road as he maneuvered the old Ford through the heavy traffic. His face had never been yellower.

"I should have stayed home this morning. Why didn't you tell me you were in labor?"

"I didn't know anything about labor, Frank!"

"Okay, okay, honey. Everything's going to be all right. Just don't get upset."

Mound Hospital was a wooden building near the Mississippi River. It had no air conditioning, and it looked to me like the most unfamiliar and unfriendly place on earth. If the nurses and doctors there ever smiled, they looked the other way, because I never saw anything more than stern, greasy faces.

Without saying much at all, a nurse ordered my husband to the waiting room, which was somewhere down the hall and to the left. Then I was told by the same crabby face to climb up on the narrow bed, where she proceeded to shave my pubic hair. This was a very unusual and scary procedure, yet I had no one else to reach for, and the horrible pains were intensifying by the minute. At some point, the pain was so strong that I didn't care if she cut me with her damn razor. I just wanted her to finish and leave the room. But she wasn't done with me yet.

She walked into a bathroom in the same room and returned shortly with a long tube, which was attached to a red bag filled with warm water.

"Please turn to the side," she ordered. "Have you ever had an enema before?"

Before I could answer, she shoved the little tube into my bottom. I felt the pressure growing all the way to my ears, and thought I would die.

After about twenty trips to the bathroom, I was able to stay in bed. I was very worn-out from the treatment I had received, but my husband was brought back into the room. He tried to tell me jokes, which were supposed to take my mind off the pain.

The nurse came back about every five minutes to torture me. Each time, she sent Frank out of the room. He finally decided to go home and shower off the dust and grime of his day's work. There was still no baby when he returned, and no baby by midnight or morning. Meanwhile, the pains had continued, and the mean nurse with her long finger had not missed a visit.

The pains made me twist, cry, wish I could die, hate my mother for not telling me that such things could happen to a girl, and hate Frank for doing whatever he did to make this happen. There was still no baby when daylight broke through the windows and the sunlight shone through.

Another nurse had come in during the night, while the mean one left. The new one was a little friendlier, but not friendly enough to ease the agony I felt from the pain and from the behavior of the people around me.

Another nurse walked in with a tray of food. "Oops, I forgot that you can't eat," she said. Then, turning away, she asked my husband if he would like to eat my breakfast. He was delighted, and I hated him for pigging out while I moaned and wept. I had not been given even a drop of water, yet sweat poured out of me. My hair and my skimpy hospital gown were soaked.

I was beginning to lose faith in God and his people when the doctor finally walked in. "How are you doing, Mrs. Wilson?"

"She's very tired," I heard the nurse say. "But she is actually doing very well."

I didn't have the strength to say what I thought or how I felt, and my ability to dream pains away had disappeared. The only thought in my mind then was death. If death came, my problems, nervousness, and insecurities would be solved.

"They are going to take you in. Good luck." Frank's voice sounded as if it came through a long tube, and when he kissed my forehead, it felt like there was a cloth stuck between my skin and his lips. I opened one eye, barely, and then his face blurred. A dark haze came over me, and Frank faded away. The next thing I knew, someone was pushing my bed out of the room.

"We're going to the delivery room," a raspy voice said, but I was not able to open my eyes or turn my head to see the person. My next memory was a half dozen hands lifting me onto another bed, a narrower and harder bed. I thought of kicking to get away, but my body felt heavy and frozen. The thought of my father butchering pigs during my childhood came to mind as my legs went up on some kind of bracket. Quickly, my arms were stretched at my side and my hands were wrapped around a metal handle, tied at the wrist. In my worn and confused mind, I had become a pig about to be butchered.

The pains came one after another, and the nurses poked their fingers into me hundreds of times. I could feel my bottom exposed for viewing, yet I couldn't protest. Then someone splashed something cold down there and began scrubbing as one would a sink.

"How is she doing?" I heard Dr. Watson ask.

"She's doing fine," a female answered.

I felt several hands on me, some pressing my rounded belly, and others searching for something between my thighs. I didn't feel embarrassed anymore. I only wanted them to do whatever was necessary and then get out of there. These were terrible people who seemed to enjoy torturing me, without explaining what they were doing or what they would do next. I vowed to never let myself go through such a horrible ordeal again.

The hardest pain was yet to come. It took my breath away. In the meantime, someone pressed on my lower ribs with a fat arm, and I felt my insides spilling out. There was no doubt in my mind now that I had become one of the pigs my father had strapped to a bench and butchered.

I heard a train speeding toward me. The roar got louder and louder as it came closer. I tried desperately to run from it, but I couldn't, and it finally whisked me into darkness.

Someone slapped my face. "I think she fainted," I heard a woman say. "It's a hundred and ten degrees in this damn room. Hot enough to make anyone faint."

"No, I think she's just asleep," I heard another woman say.

I tried to open my eyes, but they seemed glued shut. I tried moving my fingers to signal that, yes, I had fainted, but my fingers felt numb. This brought a huge lump to my throat, and I felt hot tears rolling down my face.

"See that! She did faint, and now she's coming back. Jesus, it's been more than ten minutes. Go see if the doctor is still here. This girl is in trouble. Hurry!"

Through the rest of that day and night, I felt people injecting me, pressing on my tender abdomen, tickling the bottom of my feet, and shining bright lights into my eyes. When they finally left me alone, I drifted away. I saw my baby for the first time after twenty-four hours had passed.

Awakening was bad news, because "after-birth labor pains" hit me with full force. At times, those pains were as bad, or even worse, than the initial labor pains. The doctor ordered the nurse to give me aspirin, but the aspirin didn't even dull the horrible pains. While I twisted and moaned, a young and smiling nurse bathed me in bed.

Afterward, another nurse brought me my beautiful baby. I had never seen such a gorgeous little boy. He had big blue eyes, curly, light blonde hair, and was exactly the baby I had dreamed about. In spite of the pains, I cuddled the sweet bundle, my gorgeous baby son, kissed his tiny hands, the tip of his nose, and the top of his head.

He was worth all my pain and fear. I would give him all the things my parents had denied me. I would raise him with a lot of love and never deprive him of an education. He was going to grow up happy, with the best life I could give him.

Chapter Thirty-Three

The Homecoming

I had pictured myself coming home with my new baby and Frank carrying both of us into the house, where candles had been lit and flowers and chocolates had been set on the table.

The opposite took place. Frank ran out of gas halfway home. He had to empty his pockets to find enough coins to buy two gallons of gas. He kept a quarter to buy a can of formula for the baby.

When we finally reached our house, I walked in carrying the baby. Frank had to stay out to change the flat tire on the old Ford. I had been gone for five days. The house smelled smoky, and six empty beer bottles rested on the kitchen counter. I counted five coffee cups and five plates in the sink. Our cupboards were empty, except for a few potatoes, which Frank cooked when he finally came in; but he forgot to add salt, and nothing tastes worse than boiled potatoes without salt.

I went straight to the baby's room, hoping that Frank had managed to surprise me with a new crib. In my fantasy, I would run back to thank him for the pleasant surprise. However, all I found there was the old buggy his mother had used for her eight babies. The poor thing didn't even have color anymore. After so many years of steady use, what was supposed to be blue had turned a grayish brown. The old buggy had also traveled from one home to another every time a new grandchild was born.

I went to my room and laid my baby on my bed. He was much too pretty and special to have to lie where so many others had drooled and peed.

The next day was payday, so Frank stopped at The Salvation Army store and bought an old playpen for fifty cents. The baby had kept us awake the night before, and he made up his mind that our child would never sleep in our bed again. He sanded and cleaned the playpen, and I folded an old blanket in four, then covered it with a white sheet. My baby slept there for seven months before we could charge a crib on the

Sears easy-payment plan. By then, Rodney was standing and crawling, so I could not have the mattress on the highest brackets, as I had hoped.

By that time, I had learned a lot of things the hard way, but the most embarrassing lesson took place when Rodney was two months old. One day, the phone rang at about eight o'clock in the morning. A female voice congratulated me on my new baby boy.

"Thank you," I said. "Who told you I had a baby?"

"I read it in the newspaper," she said. "Mrs. Wilson, I would like to send a photographer to take pictures of your baby."

"Take pictures of my baby?" Those were the most exciting words I had ever heard. *My baby must be someone important to have his name in the newspapers. And somebody wants his picture?*

"Okay. You can take the pictures."

"Thank you, Mrs. Wilson. I'll send someone out this morning."

As soon as she hung up, I ran to the bedroom and kissed my baby. "You are very important, because somebody wants your picture."

I shook with excitement while bathing and dressing the baby in his best outfit. Then I held him with a diaper on hand to catch his spit before it soiled his outfit.

About an hour later, a fat, bald-headed, limping man arrived at my front door with a big black camera mounted on black rods he called a tripod. He didn't smile, not even at my precious baby. He got down to business.

"Where do you want the pictures? In the kitchen? The living room? On a sofa? On a chair? Or on the floor?"

I felt confused. "You want the picture, so you say where."

"It's your baby, lady."

"Okay, maybe in that chair. You think it's good?"

"Anyplace you want, lady. It's your baby."

I didn't like the crabby man, but I still sat the baby carefully on the blue chair. The man snapped his fingers and made silly noises to get the baby's attention. A bright light flashed several times and made the baby blink.

"Let's take some on the sofa," he said, grabbing my darling baby with fat, sweaty hands. He sat Rodney on the corner of the sofa and flashed the lights again. I stood, ready to snatch my baby away if the man reached for him again.

"You're going to give me some of the pictures, right?"

"Sure," he said, with a look of surprise. "You can have as many pictures as you like." He thanked me and left.

That afternoon, I met Frank at the door. "Guess what nice thing happened today! A man came and took pictures of Rodney, and he's going to give some to us. Our baby is someone special – he was in the newspaper. Isn't that great?"

"Wait! Stop a minute!" Frank didn't look too happy about this. "Just how much money are those pictures going to cost?"

"Oh, no money. It's free!"

"Free, my ass!" Frank's eyes nearly popped out.

"No, Frank, the pictures are free. Nobody said we must pay."

"Who the hell is that man? Did he leave his name and phone number? I want to call that dirty crook right now!"

"I don't know his name. He didn't say we had to pay."

Frank and I had our first real fight that day. He yelled that I shouldn't answer the phone until I learned how to handle calls like that. "I don't want you agreeing to pay for things I can't afford."

I yelled back, "I love my baby, and I want pictures of him. The man said I can have some, but he didn't say I had to pay." I covered my face and cried.

"Okay," Frank said. "This is what you'll do. When the man comes with the pictures, you tell him that we have no money. The joke will be on him then. So dry your tears and go fix supper."

A few days later, the man returned with a lot of beautiful black-and-white pictures. I could get three pictures in a paper frame for ten dollars. Or I could get one big and two small, or one five-by-seven with a bunch of wallet-sized ones which I could give to relatives.

"I have no money. You never said I had to pay, but you said I could have as many pictures as I wanted."

The man gave me an ugly look. "You didn't think I'd go around taking pictures of babies for free, did you?"

"You didn't say I had to pay."

"Well, I don't know where you come from, lady, but in this country, nothing is free."

"My husband said you're a crook. He's right. You are a crook."

"Listen, little lady. You want the pictures or not?"

"What are you going to do if I can't buy them?"

"I'll throw them away. They mean nothing to me."

"Throw those pretty pictures away?" I imagined my baby's pictures burning in a trash can. "If you're going to throw them away, why not give them to me?"

"No! I can't do that."

"Okay, then, wait here." I ran to the bedroom and came back with the ten dollars meant for the gas and electric bill. "Here." I slapped the money on the end table, grabbed the bunch of pictures, ran back to the bedroom, and locked the door. I put the pictures next to my sleeping baby and leaned against the door.

The man pounded on the door. "Open this door at once! You can't get away with this."

"Go away!" I yelled over and over, until I heard the front door bang shut and the sound of the car as the man drove away.

Chapter Thirty-Four

The Coop

By the beginning of my second winter in Minnesota, it became obvious that Frank would not be able to buy our little house from his mother. So she went ahead and found another buyer. We moved to a small three-room house behind Mr. and Mrs. Miller's home in the middle of a field of snow in winter and tall weeds in summer.

The payments were forty dollars a month, which was thirty dollars less than what we had been paying. Knowing that we'd have those thirty dollars a month for other things made leaving my dream house a little easier. But while deciding what to take with us and what to give back to Vera, the old washed-out feeling returned to my stomach. I decided that it was because, deep inside, I felt disappointed that everything was going wrong.

I told myself time and again that things would eventually get better. Frank would find a higher paying job and quit drinking and smoking. My English was improving all the time, and when Rodney started school, I would find a job.

The little house had been cleaned and painted. The bedroom was light pink, the living room light blue, and the kitchen the color of butter. I bought contact paper that had green leaves and yellow flowers on it, because it reminded me of the hills of Puerto Rico, and I covered the cupboard shelves and kitchen drawers with it. In the gloomy days of winter, that contact paper cheered me up.

I bought some white cotton fabrics with a small flowery print for five yards for a dollar, and made curtains for all our five windows. I felt thrilled to be sewing my own curtains.

But that joy didn't take away the sick feeling in my stomach, which ultimately became another baby. I felt devastated at first. Then, looking at Rodney, I decided that a playmate would be good for him. I loved Rodney with all my heart, and I would love his brother or sister just as much.

Frank's reaction to the pregnancy was disappointing, to say the least. He just looked at me and said, "Well, I'll be damned. And I'm still making payments for the first one." The insurance he had through work had not covered Rodney because the baby had been conceived while he was still unemployed. He had been making payments to the doctor and the hospital once a month ever since Rodney was born.

In spite of Frank's lack of enthusiasm, and his inability to stop drinking, I kept myself busy all day with Rodney and my sewing. The day I hung the curtains, I stepped back and admired the little house, which appeared cozier than it had with naked windows. The floor here was made of concrete, covered with green linoleum, and had no scary basement.

Vera brought me a light blue area rug someone had thrown away. I was thrilled to get it. I cleaned it with a special soap for rugs, and put it in front of our royal-blue sofa. The rug was six feet by eight, and it made the living room look nicer, as well as a little warmer for Rodney to play on, instead of the cold linoleum.

One Sunday afternoon, Nathan and Darlene stopped by to see our new home. While Nathan stayed out with Frank, who was fixing something on the old car, Darlene stood at the door, wrapped in her brown coat, and said, "Ha! This used to be a chicken coop!" Her shrieking laughter echoed from the walls.

"A chicken what?"

"A coop, where they raised chickens."

I felt insulted. "Well, maybe it's a chicken whatever you said, but I've been happy making it pretty, and it's now our home. So don't make me feel bad about it."

Darlene squinted. "Oh, hell, don't mind me. It's a heck of a lot nicer than the dump I'm living in." Her busy eyes made their way into the kitchen. "Oh, yeah, a lot nicer. I can see that it has running water, and a bathroom, too?"

"Yes, it has everything we need, and I'm glad there's no basement."

"Well, don't get mad at me. I'm happy for you. And what beautiful curtains. You made them?"

"Yes, I did. Got the fabric on sale, five yards for a dollar."

"You did a great job. Think you can make me some new curtains someday?"

"Sure, I can. Would you like some coffee?"

"Oh, I'd love a cup. Sorry I hurt your feelings."

"I forgive you," I said, then sat across from her with Rodney on my lap. When she pulled out a cigarette, I said, "Please don't smoke in here. It plugs my nose, and it is bad for Rodney."

Darlene shoved the cigarette back into her purse, gulped down the coffee, and said, "Nathan and I are going over to Donna's to play cards." She left in a hurry, and I watched out the window. She talked with the two brothers, then Nathan followed her into their car and drove away. He never came in to see the house. But I felt glad that she had left, and that I hadn't told her I was pregnant again. I knew she would say something stupid and hurt my feelings.

When Frank came into the house, he asked, "Honey, did you tell Darlene she could not smoke in the house?"

"Yes, because she called our new house a chicken coop."

"A chicken what?"

"A coop, where they raise chickens."

"Damn that big mouth of hers," he said, then lit a cigarette.

My second Christmas in America wasn't much better than the first. Again, we had no Christmas tree or lights, no gifts, and no money for stamps to send out cards.

I spent the days taking care of Rodney, cleaning, washing, ironing, sewing, and watching my shows. I often thought of writing to my mother and Alicia, but I still had no money to send, and the truth would be embarrassing. How would I write about Frank's drinking? It would be humiliating, after I had made a point of not marrying a drunk. I couldn't handle my mother saying that she told me so. And I didn't have the heart to write to Doña Inez that she had been wrong about the American men and life in the United States. If I lied to her by writing that I was doing well, she might tell my mother, and my mother would expect money.

The visits to Frank's family became less frequent as time went on. The old Ford broke down so many times that Frank had to borrow money from the credit union to buy another old car, which was three hundred dollars and in better working condition.

By the time spring came around, I had made a little quilt and summer outfits for Rodney, and a bedspread for us, all from the old clothes Vera brought me. From the leftover small pieces of fabric, I made squares for more quilts, and pot holders to protect my hands in the kitchen. I made stuffed dogs and bears for Rodney out of all the tiniest scraps of fabric.

Frank didn't let a day go by without saying that I was "the best wife a man could ever hope to have." And his mother reminding him that he was "a lucky guy."

Chapter Thirty-Five

Troy

Rodney was thirteen months old when his brother Troy was born. I had been going to a different doctor, whom I later discovered was Catholic, and who believed that women should have as many babies as God would give them and never complain. When the time came for me to deliver, he sent me to a Catholic hospital. There, I learned that although the hospital didn't turn patients away because of religion, Catholics were treated better by the nurses, who were nuns.

No one told me this, but I saw that the Catholic women who delivered around the time I did were treated with tender love. In those days, women stayed in the hospital five or six days after giving birth. During my five days, I saw new mothers come and go. It was easy to guess which were Catholic, because the nuns talked to them for a long time, but they only talked to me when they absolutely had to. I had grown up as Catholic, but had married Lutheran, and Frank had written in the admission papers that we were Lutherans.

The woman in the next bed, who had given birth four times, received several bouquets of flowers from different relatives. Her husband visited her in the evenings. One time he brought her flowers, and another time, a box of chocolates. The woman had many visits throughout the day from her parents, sisters, friends, and in-laws. I felt abandoned in my own corner. I had no parents, sisters, friends, or in-laws to visit me.

Feeling unloved, I went to the hallway, picked up the phone, and called Vera. "Please tell Frank to bring a chocolate candy bar when he comes to see me tonight. I have to go back to bed now. Bye."

Vera would surely realize that I felt abandoned, and would tell Frank to bring me a whole box of chocolates. As a woman who had borne eight children, she would know that new mothers deserved extra love. A few flowers and a little box of candy would demonstrate love and appreciation.

I had not received anything when Rodney was born, but back then Frank had had no money. Things were different this time. He had been getting paid every two weeks, and if he gave up a few beers, he would have money to do something nice for the mother of his babies.

I waited eagerly, imagining the taste of sweet chocolate and the smell of flowers. Finally, shortly after dinner, Frank walked in with his crooked little smile, but nothing in his hands. He kissed me, then reached into his pocket, from which he pulled out a short Tootsie Roll. "Ma said you wanted a candy bar."

Astounded, I looked at him, up and down, took the pitiful little roll between my thumb and index finger, and stared at it without unwrapping it. Then, as he waited to be praised for his generosity, I threw it at his forehead.

He blinked hard and said, "What the hell's wrong with you?"

I quickly turned to face the wall and stayed like that, with tears running down on the white hospital sheets. I felt him watching me.

"What the hell was that all about?"

I didn't answer, and didn't even turn to look at him, until I heard him walk out of the room. I felt no love for him then.

The leaves on the trees had turned yellow before I left for the hospital, and five days later, on our way home with the new baby in my arms, I saw the leaves dropping down to the ground. A sick feeling of despair and sadness came over me. I dreaded having to reach our chicken coop to watch the world turn cold and white again. The snow had piled up high around the little house the previous winter, and I could not bear to think of more snow so soon after a very short summer.

I looked down and saw Troy sound asleep, so innocent and sweet, safe in my arms. I, his mother, would love and take care of him, and protect him from whatever harm might come to him through the coming years. I must have looked like that in my mother's arms so many years back.

I turned to look at Frank's profile as smoke escaped out of his large nostrils. He never talked much while driving, but this time he seemed buried in deep thought.

"I wanted a little box of chocolates," I said, "and a few flowers to cheer me up and make me feel loved."

"What did you say?" He continued to stare straight ahead. "Did you say flowers?"

"And chocolates."

"Is that why you hit me with the candy bar the other night?"

"The little Tootsie Roll, you mean."

"Okay, the little Tootsie Roll. Ma said you wanted a candy bar. She didn't say anything about a box of chocolates. Do you want me to stop and get you some chocolates now?"

"No! Just forget about it," I said, knowing that I would never forget the sick feeling of not being loved.

"I'm going to take you home first, and then go get Rodney. He probably wore Ma out already. That little stinker doesn't stay still for very long. While I'm gone, make a list of things you need from the grocery store. I borrowed some money from the credit union, paid the old bills for Rodney, paid the doctor and hospital bills for Troy, and have forty dollars left to stock up on groceries. What do you think about that, honey?"

"Sounds good," I said, feeling terribly guilty and embarrassed about the fuss I had made to feel loved like I thought the woman back at the hospital must have felt. My poor husband had been trying to do his best. I reached and touched his arm. "I'm sorry that I threw the Tootsie Roll at you," I said, my voice cracking.

"It's okay, honey. I'll get you some chocolates today."

"No, Frank, don't spend money on candy. It's not important."

"Okay, then. I'll remember to get you candy and flowers the next time you have a baby."

"Oh, no. No more babies for us for a long time. We'll be lucky if we can give the two we have everything they need."

"Yeah, I guess you're right."

Frank pulled up into the driveway, helped me inside the house, then left. I put the baby on my bed, fixed up the old playpen for Rodney, raised the mattress on the crib to the highest level like I had wanted to do for Rodney, covered it with a clean sheet, and lay my new baby on it. I stepped back and took a good look, then went to the kitchen.

I saw that we had a few potatoes and an onion in a corner of the kitchen, and a half ring of bologna in the refrigerator, so I decided to have lunch ready for Frank when he returned with Rodney. While the potatoes cooked, I wrote the grocery list.

Frank returned rather quickly. Walking in, he said, "Oh, that smells awfully good, honey. I'm starving."

Rodney looked huge to me after I'd been holding the new baby. "You grew up!" I said, holding him tight and kissing his soft cheeks a hundred times. I took him to meet his brother. Frank followed us with a lovely smile that made me feel that, if only for this moment, our cozy little family was nothing less than perfect.

That joyful moment lasted less than ten minutes. As we sat down to eat our lunch, the phone rang, and turned our plans upside down.

"Damn that stupid woman," I heard Frank say as he slammed down the receiver. "There goes our grocery money."

"What happened?" I asked.

"The damn woman who figured out the hospital bill made a mathematical mistake. I still owe thirty damn dollars."

My heart sank. "She makes a mistake, and you have to pay?"

"That's right," Frank said, then pushed the plate away. "Damn, I can't eat after that damn phone call."

I looked at Rodney in his high-chair, as he smeared fried potatoes on his head and laughed. Then I looked at Frank's mad face. "It's not right, Frank. She made the mistake, not you."

"Yeah, well, I still have to pay it. I'll still have ten dollars for baby food, anyway." With that, Frank splashed some water on his face, gave me a quick kiss, patted Rodney on the head, and left.

Frank couldn't walk straight when he returned at ten that night. He brought in two cans of milk for Troy, five jars of baby food for Rodney, two loaves of Wonder Bread, a package of bologna, and a stench of booze and tobacco smoke on his breath. I was on the sofa feeding Troy as Frank went straight to our bedroom.

I slept on the sofa. By the time he got up the next day, which was Saturday, I had a long speech prepared for him.

"I'm sorry, honey," he said after coming out of our booze-smelling room. "I just couldn't help myself. After paying the damn woman the thirty dollars, I had to stop for a couple of beers."

"No," I said, "you're not sorry yet. I ran away from my parents because they were drunks, and what did I do? I married a drunk. But I did that because I thought you loved me enough to stop drinking and smoking. You remember promising me that you would stop? Now I'm sorry I ever married you and had your sons, because you don't appreciate them or me." I heard my voice growing louder, but I liked it. "I'm never going to sleep with you again, because you don't deserve any more babies. And I don't want babies we can't afford, especially from a drunk."

Frank followed me through the house. "Please, honey, let me explain. Please believe me, I'll never get drunk again for as long as I live. And starting today, I'll go outside to smoke, and I won't let my relatives smoke in our house, either."

"You've made promises before and haven't kept any. And your drinking is why you didn't stay in the service, which is why we have to live in this chicken coop."

"No, that's not why we live in a chicken coop. And you might be glad to hear that I've been looking for a real house and will find one soon. We ain't gonna stay in this coop forever."

A month later, we moved to an upstairs apartment in North St. Paul. This was my first opportunity to become friends with someone outside of Frank's family. Karen, the lady who lived downstairs, was about my age, and she became my inspiration. She had two boys a little older than Rodney, but she still went to work every morning, while her husband watched the boys. When she got home, he went to work on the evening shift someplace in town.

Every day I watched her leave for work, and then looked forward to the evenings when she'd be home so I could go down to visit her. It wasn't often, because I couldn't always get Frank to stay with our boys. But whenever he did, I had a great time with my new friend. She was one of those people who could laugh easily, which meant every time I mispronounced words. I never thought she might be laughing at me, and even if she was, I liked knowing her too much to let my pride deprive me of a friendship that would last us the rest of our lives.

"Oh, darn, I have to iron tonight," she said one day. "I've been putting it off for so long, the pile of clothes is knee-high. I need an angel to come by when I'm at work and do it for me." She chuckled at that thought.

That night I got everything done, got the boys settled in bed, and while Frank watched TV, I carried my iron and board downstairs and ironed side by side with Karen. We talked and laughed the whole time. I told her some weird stories about the people in the hills back home, and she would light up and ask questions. I think that was how I learned how to tell a story.

Of course, I wasn't the only one who could tell stories with a sense of humor. Karen was just as good. She made me smile and wish that the ironing would last longer. I learned a lot from her. Her stories were about funny or sad things that had happened, not about gossip, like Darlene's.

Although Karen became my best friend, with whom I shared sensitive subjects, I never did mention Frank's drinking problem. Perhaps if I had, she would have shed some light on the subject, but I was too embarrassed to talk about such a thing, especially when I knew that her husband wasn't a drinker. I also feared that she would stop liking me if she knew about Frank. She was the kind of friend I didn't want to lose.

Chapter Thirty-Six

Chocolates Galore

Since leaving the coop, Frank had been coming straight home from work every day, driving past several bars. He had been smoking outside, and had told his relatives they could not smoke in our new apartment. This was great, but we didn't get many visitors after that. That was okay with me, because I could always go downstairs to visit Karen.

"I love you, Frank," I said. "Thank you for keeping your promises."

That was the beginning of the right way for us to live in harmony. Frank played with Rodney while I attended to Troy. Then we watched televison together: *The Honeymooners, Gunsmoke,* and whatever else came along.

We turned down an invitation to Thanksgiving dinner at Arthur's because Rodney was in bed with the sniffles. But I put together a nice dinner: baked chicken, mashed potatoes with gravy, peas and carrots, and pumpkin pie for dessert. I put an old tablecloth over our table, lit a short candle in a saucer, and placed it in the center. Then the two of us sat across from each other. Our little boys were asleep, and our husband and wife relationship had never been better.

"Our first Thanksgiving dinner," Frank said, his eyes twinkling, one eyebrow down and the other up. "Come to think of it, this is pretty nice – the two of us celebrating Thanksgiving by ourselves."

"Yes, it is," I said, "and it will be even nicer when the boys are old enough to join us."

Frank flashed me a look that made me feel warm all over. "You bet it will."

Life turned out pretty good after that. During the weekends, we would go visit Vera and Leo, and some of the other relatives, until the smoke got too thick for my nose. When the temperature wasn't below zero, I bundled Rodney and myself up and went to play in the snow. Frank had bought an old toboggan at the Salvation Army store, and he pulled Rodney and me in it until my nose froze, but we laughed as if we had no problems whatsoever.

That year, we bought our first Christmas tree and decorated it with aluminum foil and some ornaments Vera had given us. It was the happiest time for us, Frank singing Christmas songs while reaching to put a star made of foil on the top branch. Then we both laughed when I sang in Spanish, and he copied me with his romantic accent.

I had made look-alike shirts for Frank and Rodney, wrapped them in bright Christmas paper, and placed the two gifts under the tree. Frank had bought a gift for Rodney, which he wrapped up behind a closed door. "I want it to be a surprise for you, too, when he unwraps it," he said lovingly.

"That's so nice, Frank. Thank you." I felt so good about him then. Nothing would go wrong for us from then on. We were the perfect picture of an American family, as far as I was concerned. Rodney looked like a miniature Frank with sapphire eyes, but his blonde hair was curly like mine. Troy looked like me with green eyes, but his blonde hair was straight like Frank's. I knew that wherever we went together, people would compliment us on our gorgeous little boys.

When I got up early on Christmas morning to give Troy his bottle, I saw a box that hadn't been there the night before. It was beautifully wrapped and tied with red ribbon and a large bow. Bending down for a closer look, I saw my name on a corner of the box. I went to pick it up, and found that it was quite heavy.

I didn't want to spoil a great surprise, so I went on into the kitchen, my imagination going crazy. *What's in that box? Maybe Frank felt creative and put many things in a big box. But what kinds of things would total four or five pounds?* I felt excited enough to burst out of my skin. I had to keep myself from tearing into the wrapped box.

I changed and fed Troy, but my mind was still on the box. When Frank came out of the bathroom, I said, "I have a gift for you."

That was supposed to lead him into giving me mine. Instead, he said, "Let's have coffee first, and wait for Rodney."

I put the coffee on, then we hugged by the tree.

"Our first Christmas tree," he said, "and I even have a gift for you."

"I already saw the box. Can I open it now? What's in it?"

Frank smiled. "It's a surprise, but you can't open it yet."

I hurried to get our coffee, and we sat in front of our tree with our steaming cups and waited for Rodney. Soon we heard, "Dada, Dada!"

Frank hurried to get him out of the playpen before he woke up his brother. As soon as he put him on the floor, Rodney ran to the tree, grabbed Frank's gift for him, and trotted toward us. We watched with such joy as he tore the pretty paper, his little hands shaking. Out came a white and blue rubber duck, which made a sound like a real duck when he squeezed it. Rodney laughed and looked at us with bright eyes.

"Now you can open mine," I said, handing one package to him and another to his daddy.

"Oh boy, oh boy!" Frank said, taking his time, as if not wanting to end the surprise too soon. "Oh, honey, look-alike shirts? How nice!" He took off his pajama top and put on the shirt. "Perfect fit, honey. How did you do that?" He gave me a kiss. "Thank you, sweetheart. Now I'll give you a gift from me."

I stayed on the sofa, ready to jump with joy. "What is it, Frank? It's so heavy."

He had such a brilliant smile that I thought I would be pulling gold and diamonds out of that box. I removed the ribbon and bow carefully to save it along with the paper for the next year. Lifting the paper, I saw a corner of the red box and felt my heart dancing. As I continued to unwrap it, I saw pictures of chocolate candies in little paper baskets.

Right away, my brain went to work: *He's teasing me. He found this empty box somewhere and filled it with little gifts to make me think it's candy.* That would be a romantic idea. Slipping the rest of the pretty paper away, I felt a pang in my stomach, for I noticed that the box was completely factory sealed. It had never been opened, and it contained five pounds of chocolates.

As I read the amount, a dark shadow came over me, and I imagined what Frank had been thinking when he made such a purchase: *You wanted chocolates three months ago? So pig out!*

I kept my face down, my eyes fixed on the pictures of chocolate pieces. I had filled my brain with silly romantic expectations, only to be more disappointed than ever before. Still, if I yelled, it would be in sobs, and I might never stop. And that would send him to the bars. Either way, I would come up losing.

"What's the matter, honey?" Frank asked. "Did I do something wrong? Honey, please talk to me." He touched my shoulder. "Honey?"

"Five pounds of chocolates, Frank? Why five pounds?"

He shrank into the sofa, one eyebrow down and the other up. "Well, I remembered that I disappointed you when Troy was born, and I thought I would make up for it now. I really thought you'd be pleased, honey."

"Oh," I said, cutting through the tape. "This does make up for it, all right. Let's dig in. We'll eat candy three times a day until it's all gone."

I meant to insult him with those words, but he simply answered, "Oh, no, honey. Too much candy isn't healthy. Five pounds of candy is a lot. Just have a few pieces a day. It'll last you for months."

Chapter Thirty-Seven

Starlight Place

We made it through that winter and the spring without Frank getting drunk. He would buy a six-pack of beer every now and then and drink while watching television, but not enough to get drunk.

One day he came home with the most exciting news. He had read in a newspaper that a developer had purchased many miles of farmland about twenty miles outside the city, and was building homes to sell.

"And the best thing is," Frank said beaming, "that we can buy one of those homes with a hundred dollars down on the GI Bill, then payments of seventy dollars a month. How do you like that?"

I flew into his arms. "I like that very much."

"I think we should go check it out. Don't even cook dinner. We can get a hamburger on the way back."

It didn't take me very long to get the boys ready, and we were off. We had gone for a ride through that area just the summer before, when the land had been an open field of tall weeds. Now the ground had been shaved and dirt roads with wooden frames of soon-to-be homes on each side ran through it. Three model homes had been built with shiny hardwood floors and bright tile in the bathrooms, and linoleum in the kitchens.

We looked at all three homes and chose the number two, which had three bedrooms, one bathroom, a good-sized kitchen, and a nice basement. The price was $12,000, and our monthly payments would be $72.

Rodney turned two years old in August, while Troy turned one in September, and we moved into our new home in the last week of October. Our old furniture and refrigerator looked really old and dingy next to the newly painted walls, but we had high hopes that one day we would start buying everything new on the Sears charge account.

The new house seemed huge to us after living in a coop and an apartment. It was very light, too, with two windows in each bedroom, one in the bathroom, two in the kitchen, and a huge picture window in the living room.

The basement was bright and spacious, perfect for the boys to play in during the winter months. The furnace wasn't as big or as noisy as the one in the first house we had lived in. I couldn't remember ever feeling happier than I felt moving into that new house.

Of course, Darlene tried her best to spoil my thrill. "I think it's stupid to move into an expensive house so far from town. Think of the money Frank will have to spend on gasoline just to go back and forth to work. But it's his wallet, not mine."

"Yes, it's his wallet. And I'm sorry you're jealous, because if it were you moving into a pretty house like this, I would be happy for you. I'd never be jealous."

"Oh, pay no attention to me. Enjoy your new house. I'll get mine one of these days." Darlene never came back, and she and her husband bought their new home the next year.

As the first family to live on Starlight Place, we watched all the other newcomers move in, carrying striped mattresses and brown sofas over the heaps of snow. The men got acquainted right away while clearing their driveways, but we women didn't really get to know each other until the end of May. By then, we had finished organizing our homes, and I had made curtains for all our windows. The snow had stopped falling and the ground was drying.

We'd sit on the concrete steps and watch our little children play. This was another opportunity for me to mingle with more women who weren't related to Frank. We were all around the same age, and had two or three children each. Our conversations were plain and unsophisticated. We shared recipes and sewing ideas, and asked each other how often our children came down with sore throats and runny noses.

It was on those steps that I first heard women complain about husbands and toilet seats. I couldn't tell them that the toilet seat up or down didn't bother me, because I was happy just having a toilet. So as they talked on, I simply nodded and said, "I know what you mean."

In the summertime, we got together with our neighbors and cooked hamburgers and hotdogs in one back yard or another. The men drank beer, and the women and children drank fruit punch. Then, the men and the boys kicked footballs around, while the women talked and laughed about whatever, and the little girls played with dolls. That was our happiest summer.

In the winter evenings, the children played in the basements while the adults played cards. The couple from next door came to our house one night, and we went to theirs the next. Sometimes, three or four couples got together at the same place, and it was like a party going on every weekend, sometimes past midnight.

One New Year's Eve, we went dancing with two other couples. I wore a red chiffon dress that I had made out of a long evening gown Vera brought over from the trash collection. I didn't tell my neighbors where the fabric came from, but all the women expressed their envy for my ability to make my own dresses fit so well.

"It's the figure that makes the dress," Frank said, whisking me to the dance floor. "I'm so proud of you," he whispered in my ear.

"I'm proud of you, too," I said, thinking that he would never get drunk again.

I had often heard some people say that good things were hard to come by and quick to disappear. I understood that statement when our phone rang at dawn that same January. Dear Vera had died of a sudden heart attack.

That call put us on a fast roller coaster that would take the grace of God to slow down. Frank jumped out of bed and left immediately to be with his siblings, but came back twenty-four hours later smelling of booze and smoke.

I had been on the phone with Loretta and Nadine throughout the day and part of the night. They, like me, had stayed with their children while their husbands had run to their mother's home. After six o'clock that night, none of them knew where Frank and his brother Bill had disappeared to.

I had feared that Frank would hit the bars, since that was where Bill would be, but I had not mentioned it to my sisters-in-law, hoping that it wasn't so. I couldn't believe my eyes when Frank crawled in. He looked cold and green, his lips pressed together so tightly that all I saw was a thin line curved down below his nose. There was no point in trying to say a word to him. He staggered into the bedroom, dove into bed with his clothes and shoes on, and snored so loudly that it could be heard down in the basement. Had it been summertime, when everyone's windows remained open, all the neighbors would have needed to plug their ears. The steady sound coming out of Frank was too annoying for anyone to tolerate.

Frank's drinking didn't stop there. He got drunk again the following night, and the night after that, the night of the funeral, and all the nights that followed. He still went to work every morning, and must have done his work well, because they didn't fire him. From work, he went to the bars.

There was no point in talking to him. He waved me to step aside, and into bed he'd go. I spent those nights on the old sofa.

One Friday night I taped a note to the bedroom door. *Try sleeping on the sofa for a change, I need my rest, too.*

He kicked the door open, and before I could wake up enough to run, he was all over me, mumbling, "I'm only taking what's mine."

I had no idea that a drunk, greasy man would be so strong and so heavy. When I finally managed to slide out from under him, I went to the shower. While the warm water cleansed away the grease and the stench of booze, I practiced tomorrow's speech. My English was nearly perfect by then, thanks to the conversations with Karen and my neighbors, and the TV shows.

"I am so sorry," Frank said, coming out of the bedroom the next morning. He looked like a little boy afraid of being spanked.

"You don't know the meaning of the word. Let me tell you something, Frank. It's a good thing your mother is dead. If she were still alive, I would tell her all about her drunken son. I am sorry I kept your drinking a secret from her. She was a wonderful woman, and I had not wanted to make her feel ashamed of her son. Now she'll never know."

"No, honey. Let me explain – "

"Don't bother. Let me tell you what I'm going to do. I'm going to invite Nathan and Arthur over with their wives, along with Donna and her husband. Then I'm going to tell them what you did to me last night."

By the time I stopped yelling, he gave me another promise that he would stop drinking. But the harm had already been done. Two weeks later, the washed-out feeling returned to my stomach, and the bitter taste to my mouth.

I felt such a strong hatred for Frank then, and told him so, day after day. "I'm praying for the power to pass on my labor pains to you when the time comes. I hope you get an itch between your legs and your precious thing falls off."

Frank always said, "Oh, honey, you can't possibly mean that."

"Oh, yes I do, because I hate you. I wish we had never met."

Every day, I came up with another new word to keep Frank away from me, regretting his drinking and what he had done. But he came home from work every day and drank only the beer he bought with the groceries.

However, we would not be off the roller coaster anytime soon. On our second summer in our new home, Frank came home from work one day with an extra long face. The railroad company was merging with another, and he was one of the hundreds of men to be without a job.

"We'll lose the house," he said, his eyes heavy with tears. "I know I haven't been the best husband, but I have always wanted to give you a nice home."

I had never been heartless, so I opened my arms to my troubled husband and cried with him for a long time.

"We're not without hope," he said. "I've been offered a job in a little town west of Chicago. So if you're willing, we can move there."

Chapter Thirty-Eight

Rochelle

Five weeks after Frank's announcement, I put our sheets, blankets, and pillows on the floor of the brown 1952 Chevy he had bought with a loan from a bank. The pile came level to the seat. The boys would play and sleep there all night, the length of time it would take for the drive to our new location in Illinois.

I had shed a lot of tears during those five weeks, taking our dishes out of the nice cabinets and stuffing everything in cardboard boxes. I had moved into the new house planning to replace all our old furnishings with new ones, thinking that that would be our permanent home. I had become close friends with my neighbors: Janet, on one side of the house; Lois, on the other; Aimee, across the street; and Denise, whose back yard connected to ours. I had gotten along with everyone in the neighborhood, but those four women had taken the place of what I felt sisters should be, and I hated to leave them.

Handing the house key to the new owners was as painful as cutting my hand off. The husband and wife who bought our house had been waiting near the driveway with a pickup truck filled with patio chairs, house plants, and a lot of boxes. They knew my house was spotless, so they weren't planning to even dust the kitchen cabinets before putting their dishes in.

Before getting into our car, we said goodbye to our neighbors, the women with teary eyes and the men wishing us well. As we drove away, I felt the same knots in my throat I had felt the day I had said goodbye to my family.

Frank had met his new boss the day of his interview, and his boss had agreed to find a place for us. So Frank felt comfortable about his new boss, and about working in a power plant, doing the kind of work he had done in the Air Force. But all I knew was that his boss would have a place for us, and that it would be a rental, perhaps an old apartment. After leaving our nice new home, that thought made me feel like hiding someplace and never coming out.

Had it not been for the little guys behind me fighting with each other and calling me constantly to settle their squabbles, I would have thrown myself out of the car, solving the washed-out feeling in my stomach and whatever problems awaited me in the rest of my life.

"This will be a good move for us," Frank said, turning onto the main highway. "We'll get to know a different part of the country, and make new friends. Since we're so far from my relatives, they can't expect us to visit them all the time."

Frank had never liked to talk while driving, and I had always hated the silence. Now he was in the mood for conversation, and all I wanted was an opportunity to take a mental trip to a faraway place, and not return for days. Still, if I didn't talk, he might fall asleep, and something bad could happen to my precious little boys.

"You're right. We'll make new friends. And you'll teach me how to drive, right?"

"Wrong. You don't have a car."

I felt like clobbering Frank on the head, yet I needed him to drive carefully. "Fine. I'll get a job and buy my own car."

"You already have a job. No wife of mine is going to work for somebody else."

"You know, Frank, you sound like my father, and you wouldn't believe what happened to him."

"I don't know your father, and whatever happened to him isn't going to happen to me. I just know that I love you and want to take care of you so you'll never have to leave your home to make a living. That's all."

"Okay, but I can still learn to drive, in case you ever get sick or something like that."

"Well, I'm not going to get sick, so don't worry." He lit a cigarette, took a long drag, then held the stinky thing out the window. "No, I'm not getting sick." He kept his eyes on the road, while smoke spilled out of his bubbled nose.

Delmar, an old friend of Frank's, had agreed to move our furniture for two hundred dollars in an old truck he used on his farm. He had started out thirty minutes before us, but we still caught up with him. From then on, I watched our mattress, sofa, chair, refrigerator, the old stove, and everything we owned wiggle and bounce and collect smashed bugs, dust, and fumes from vehicles.

"Why didn't he cover that stuff? Everything's going to get dirty. And wouldn't it be something if it rains?"

"Oh, honey, stop worrying," Frank answered. "It's not going to rain. Everything's going to be just fine. Are the boys asleep?"

"Like angels," I said, staring straight ahead.

Most of our drive was through the state of Wisconsin, where flying insects splattered our windshield, and signs displayed the miles to Eau Claire, Green Bay, Madison, and Milwaukee. We rode on wide highways lined with short and tall trees, and on narrow, bumpy streets bordered by dormant old homes with dark porches. Whether it was trees, shrubs, or homes, everything displayed a lethargic atmosphere to me. Even the signs advertising tomatoes and corn by the bushel, and fresh eggs at Miller's farm, made me feel like screaming. The farther we went, the worse the washed-out feeling in my stomach grew, bringing back the hatred I had felt for Frank the night he kicked open the bedroom door.

I crossed my arms over my middle and gazed at the darkness beyond the headlights, and at the old truck bobbing and clanking ahead of us. "I'm not having any more babies after this one, Frank. I hope you know that."

Frank didn't answer, but he briefly looked at me.

I didn't turn to meet his gaze, because I knew he saw himself as "the king", and saw me as his little wife who he intended to keep under his control. I couldn't believe my luck. I married him thinking that women had rights in the United States. I kept my mouth shut and stared straight ahead from then on.

After what seemed to be longer than one whole night, the traffic gradually increased, and the highway grew a third lane.

"Ah, we're finally getting there." Frank pointed. "See the sign? Rockford."

I saw the sign, and all the others: one to Marengo, another to Chicago, to Dixon, to Springfield, but none of that mattered to me.

At daybreak, Frank turned off the main highway and followed the signs to Rochelle. By now my bottom felt numb, my legs puffy, and my back painfully cramped. Except for the few stops for gas and a toilet, we had been sitting all night. Our little boys had awakened to ask if we were there yet, and then dropped back to sleep. Luckily, there had been no rain, and the old truck and car had not broken down.

Wooden houses with green grass and sidewalks lined both sides of this road, which soon took us through the center of the town. I saw a hardware store, a drugstore, a yardage store, a post office, a fire department, and a white sign shaped like an arrow that read *Hospital*.

Chapter Thirty-Nine

A Picture on a Postcard

Frank pulled up to a public phone and called his boss. I watched him scribble on a piece of paper. He then returned to the car with a wide smile.

"Not only did he find us a place, but he asked the owner to have it ready for us, and we can go directly there. Didn't I tell you we'd be just fine?"

It sounded great to me, too. By then, I was ready to stretch out even on the floor. Rodney had awakened and was jabbing at my shoulder. "Are we there yet?"

Frank gave the instructions to Delmar, and then we followed him down the main street through the town and merged onto a highway. Five miles later, we turned onto a narrow street which ran between many acres of corn fields. A few miles later, we left that paved street and drove the rest of the way on a gravel road. A cloud of dust grew between Delmar's truck and our car. I smelled the dust, and knew our things would be so dirty we'd end up throwing everything away.

After a mile on gravel, Delmar turned into a long, dirt driveway. At the end of the driveway stood a two-story wooden house with green grass separating it from more corn fields. White with a blue roof, the house looked like a picture in a postcard. My first impression was that this home had for years housed many joyful moments and a lot of laughter from a large family. I saw it as a dream come true to its owner and hoped that it would bring us peace and happiness. To me, everything looked promising in the summertime, so I didn't even imagine the place in the middle of winter.

"Gee, my new boss wasn't joking when he said this place was out in the country," Frank said, parking behind Delmar's truck.

I had always found moving from one house to another exciting, so the location of this place didn't bother me right away. After sitting in that car all night, all I wanted was to get inside and stretch out my spine.

Delmar stepped down from his truck, scratching his head, and asked, "Who the hell did you say found you this forsaken place?"

"My new boss. But I didn't know it was so far out of town." Frank looked up the road. "Here comes somebody now, probably the owner."

A blue pickup truck pulled in behind our car, and a stout man wearing a cowboy hat and boots stepped out.

"Howdy, folks," he said in a deep voice that didn't seem to belong to him. "I'm Joe Peters. Glad to make your acquaintance." He extended a thick hand. "You must be Frank."

"I am. And here's my wife Jackie, our two sons, Rodney and Troy, and over there is our friend Delmar. He was kind enough to help us move. But hey, I didn't know this place was way out in the sticks."

Mr. Peters didn't seem interested in details. "I beg your pardon, but this tranquil part of the world is not what I would consider 'out in the sticks.'"

Frank's face looked sad. "No offense. I was only joking."

"Oh, it's all right." The man softened. "You might say I'm a little sentimental about this place. My old man built it, and he just passed on less then two months ago."

"Sorry again," said Frank.

"Oh, well, that's life." Joe dug into his pocket and pulled out a ring of keys. "I'll let you in. The place looks better on the inside."

We followed him up three wooden steps and onto a porch that still had two weathered rocking chairs side by side.

"I'll haul those away," he said. "Unless you want to keep them for the little guys."

"Oh, yeah," one of the boys said, and they each climbed up on a chair and started rocking, with dust flying up around them.

"I guess that answers my question," Joe said, while attempting to unlock the front door. He turned the knob, but the door would not open until he lifted up on it then pushed. He said that in fifty-five years the house had settled considerably.

"A 55-year-old house," Frank said. "I'll be damned."

"Yeah, my folks came here as newlyweds, and without much carpentry experience, they started on this house, one room at a time. Six years went by before they finished it. They raised nine kids here. No wonder the floor is sloping. Imagine all those feet thumping around constantly."

There was sentiment in Joe's face as his eyes wandered from one side of the living room to the other. I imagined him as a small boy playing with his siblings on this wide board floor that had been painted glossy brown.

"Now, folks," Mr. Peters said. "These windows have tilted to one side, and it takes a man to pry them open. But that's why you're paying fifty dollars a month rent. A house this size in perfect condition would cost you an arm and a leg, and you'd probably have to hire people to clean it before moving in. As you can see, this place is spotless. The wife and I spent the whole day yesterday cleaning. And by the way, little lady, the wife will be making you folks a pot roast so you don't have to cook tonight."

"Why, thank you. And please thank your wife for me," I said, anxious to hurry through the rest of the house so we could move our things in. Our boys had already discovered the stairs up to the second floor and were having fun running up and down, giggling and arguing.

We stepped into the dining room, the best room in the house. Its floor was level, and both windows opened and closed easily. This room had a high white ceiling, and the walls were papered in a soft lavender, with bright pink and white roses and green leaves. The curtains on both windows were of sheer white, with ruffles that appeared brilliant in the early morning sun that was now shining through.

The three bedrooms upstairs were large, with high ceilings and papered walls. Each room had two windows, without curtains, so I would be busy sewing for some time. The bathroom was also large, and the bathtub stood on dog paws, which the boys found hilarious.

"Oh, Mommy, can we take a bath now?" Rodney asked.

"Yeah, Mommy, with bubbles," Troy added.

I convinced them to see the rest of the house first, and we all hurried back down to the kitchen. It was the most rundown part of the house, with rusty metal cabinets, a bumpy floor, and a metal tub for a sink. Our stove would not be hooked up until Frank could go to a hardware store and buy a device that would convert it from natural gas to propane.

"Now here's another thing, folks. There's a phone here, but you'll be sharing the line with seven families. That can be a pain in the neck sometimes, because some of them people have teenaged girls, and when them girls get on the phone and start talking about boys, they hate to give up the line. But if you tell them it's an emergency, they'll hang up quickly, because they know that's the law. Got to be going now, folks. Give me a call if I can be of further assistance."

When Mr. Peters left, I made Spam sandwiches and coffee for our breakfast. Then Frank and Delmar hauled our furniture into the house while I went over the cupboards with my cleaning rags, removing whatever dirt the Peters' might have overlooked.

When the men finished, Delmar went upstairs to sleep for a few hours before heading back to St. Paul, and Frank drove to town to buy the part for the stove.

I opened a few boxes and got busy putting my kitchen things away. Meanwhile, the boys discovered an old tire hanging from a tree in the back yard, and soon they were swinging each other, their laughter and yelling waking the countryside.

Frank returned within an hour and was hooking up the stove when Delmar came down.

"Heck, I can't sleep in the daytime, so I might as well start back." He had another cup of coffee, wished us well, then left.

Later, Mrs. Peters, a short, smiling lady with small blue eyes, came by with her pot roast. "I'll come by tomorrow, pay you a short visit, and pick up the pot," she said. Giggling like a little girl, she trotted back to her car.

At last the four of us sat at the table for our first meal in our new-old home.

"I'm sorry we had to leave our nice new home, honey, but we'll buy another as soon as I can qualify for a loan."

"It wasn't your fault," I said. "And this old house isn't really that bad."

"I know it isn't bad, but we deserve better." Frank's eyes were all sparkles, and I thought that if he gave up drinking for good, we could still be a happy family.

Frank helped me clean the dishes and unpack a few boxes that night. We even laughed when the boys chased each other up and down the steps, Rodney dressed as a cowboy and Troy as an Indian.

"We should go to bed early," said Frank. "We are expected at my boss's for lunch tomorrow. We can leave here early and drive through town first, to get ourselves oriented."

"Sounds good to me," I said. We went upstairs like a happy couple, got the boys into the bathtub, then went to put sheets on the beds.

"I'm nervous about meeting my new boss again tomorrow," Frank said, sounding so sincere that my heart went out to him.

"I'd be nervous, too," I said. "But I'm sure you'll make a good impression. It's not like you've never met him before."

"No, it isn't, but that won't stop me from lying awake all night worrying about it."

I should have suspected that he had something else in mind. But wanting so badly for our relationship to improve, I gave him a sympathetic look and offered myself to him, knowing that sex always helped him fall asleep fast.

"Yeah, that'll help me sleep like a baby, all right. But I'll tell you what. I've got to sit down with a cigarette and unwind before I can do anything else. Get the boys out of the tub and into bed, then take your shower and go to bed. I'll be back up here in no time, and I'll take my shower, then join you under the sheets." He winked at me with a sexy smile and headed downstairs.

I knew that Frank hadn't brought whiskey or beer from St. Paul, and he had only been to the hardware store, so why would I suspect anything else? I hurried to do as he had suggested, and while tucking the boys into bed, I told them not to start making noises as they usually did before falling asleep. Their daddy needed a good night's sleep, for he had an important day tomorrow. Both boys looked at me with eyes like their father's, and I felt more eager to get under my own sheets. I kissed and hugged my sons and headed to the shower. I even hummed as I lathered myself.

Frank was still downstairs when I came out of the shower, but I smelled the cigarette smoke, and knew he was still trying to relax. Lifting the covers, I quickly stretched myself on the clean sheets, my spine stretching after being cramped for so long. I waited to hear the squeaking of the stairs, which would be followed by the sound of the shower. I pictured the suds on Frank's chest, trickling down to his pubic hair. I imagined him scrubbing himself, fast, anxious to bang his body against mine.

Embarrassed for wanting my husband after being mad at him and after a sleepless night, I scolded myself. Still, I tuned one ear toward the steps and waited.

Chapter Forty

Wait Until Tomorrow

Frank's side of the bed was still cold and smooth when I awakened. Daylight was coming into the room through the uncovered windows. I saw cracks on the yellow ceiling and realized that this was not our St. Paul home. I had slept all night, but where was my husband?

After the usual stop at the bathroom, I headed downstairs slowly, my eyes scanning the dark corners of the room ahead for Frank or anything that might startle me. After two years of waking up in a new, one-story home in St. Paul, this old house gave me the feeling that I was walking through a dark house of ghosts and monsters. In spite of my careful steps, as soon as my foot touched the floor, one screech after another sent chills through my skin.

I hurried through the dining room, because it was darker there than it had been upstairs.

As I reached the front room, I found Frank slumped in the old chair, cigarette butts standing on a heap of ashes in an ashtray on the armrest. I was right: he had been tired and fell asleep unintentionally.

Then the stench of booze hit my nose, and I saw the almost empty bottle of Seagram's 7 on the floor to his right. A heavy blow hit the pit of my stomach, and several thoughts poured into my mind. I felt like clobbering him on the head with something heavy, but he looked so pitiful. His face was oily and yellowish. His hair, also oily, looked like he had been scrubbing it without water. I wanted to scream so loudly that he would bounce high off the chair and crack his head on the ceiling. That would drive some sense into him.

Still, I backed away quietly and went to the kitchen, where I covered my face with a towel and sobbed away my frustrations and fears. I hated that I couldn't take the boys and leave Frank. He was my only provider, and there was no place I could go, with no money, two small children, and another on the way.

When the tears finally stopped, I made a pot of strong coffee.

Holding a steaming cup in one hand, I shook Frank until he opened his bloodshot eyes.

"Gee, I guess I fell asleep," he said. The smell of whiskey rose from his mouth like polluted fog.

"So that's how you are going to meet your new boss, with a hangover and a yellow face?" My voice reached the ceiling and beyond, but I liked it. "Did it take getting drunk and passing out to calm your nerves? Or was the nerve story only an excuse to drink a whole liter of whiskey?" It was hard to keep from dumping the hot coffee on his head. "How could you do such a thing, Frank! How could you?" This time I spilled some of the coffee on my foot, but I shook the burning pain away and kept on yelling. "I have never been more disappointed in you than I am at this moment. I don't think I can put up with your drinking for much longer. You are a disgrace!"

"Oh, yeah," he finally mumbled, looking down at the bottle. "Sorry, honey. I couldn't help myself."

"But that's the problem, Frank. You don't need to help yourself. Booze usually does that for you!"

"Oh, shit. Don't get smart!" He stood up, gulped down what was left of the coffee, and went to the stove to refill the cup. I watched him stagger away, and then I ran upstairs to wake the boys.

I stayed up there with them to give Frank time to make himself presentable. I had always tried to keep the boys from seeing their father drunk or with a hangover. I wanted them to love and respect their father, not fear or dislike him the way I had feared and disliked mine. As time passed, that became more difficult. The boys seemed to know when we had a problem. I feared that one day they might call their father a drunk, and call me stupid for loving him. Just the thought of hearing those words from them made me want to disappear.

Frank was coming up the stairs when we were going down, so luckily, this wasn't the place for him to play quick-draw with his sons, as they usually did every morning.

"Good morning, my sons," he said, barely moving his lips. I knew he was trying to keep his booze-smelling breath from the boys, especially from Troy, whom he often accused of having a nose as sensitive as mine. By the time the boys returned the greeting, they were at the bottom of the stairs, arguing about which show they would watch, *Roy*

Rogers or *Popeye.*

I fried eggs and potatoes, thinking that a solid breakfast would bring back the healthy glow to Frank's face. I would be embarrassed if he showed up to meet his new boss with a yellow face. If the boss guessed that the yellow was from drinking, Frank might lose the job before starting it.

Frank came down all showered and clean-shaven, dressed in his blue shirt and black slacks that had always made him look smart and attractive. He kept his eyes to the floor, but I still could see that the color had returned to his face. I didn't let him see that I felt relieved. I could tell that he wanted to apologize to me, but wouldn't dare in front of the boys. I also knew that the boys could see that something had changed since last night, but they, just like their parents, didn't know the right words to say. That kind of chill feeling had hung around us before, and on that day, as we prepared to begin all over again, the chill felt heavier and sharper than any other time.

In our five years together, Frank and I had learned how to put on a good front. We knew how to sneer at each other and smile at others in the same breath. That day, after we finished breakfast, I got myself and the boys ready, and we left the house as we had planned — except that, unlike the night before, we were all quiet and preoccupied.

Frank drove through some dirt roads, aiming his gaze left and right, showing us the cornfields without saying the words. I kept my remarks to myself for fear that I might not be able to stop yelling if I started. The swaying cornstalks took me back to my early years, when my parents had kept me in the fields ripping off the husk-covered corncobs. It made my stomach churn to think that I had run away to escape the cornfields and drunken parents, only to find myself years later surrounded by cornfields and a husband who had been drinking all night.

I saw myself in a sealed barrel, spinning around the world, unable to see clearly, yet the whole world could see me. Perhaps I had been standing still all this time, with the world racing away from me. In the long run, I would find myself tired and old, no longer able to reach my goals.

I was suffocating, with a huge lump at the bottom of my throat, by the time we reached the paved road. I wanted to explode, to reveal my feelings and regrets to my husband. But our little sons were in the back seat, giggling, whispering, and punching each other. Besides that, we were expected somewhere for lunch. We needed to appear trouble-free, healthy, and happy.

Frank's lack of words – the right words, or any words for that matter – was maddening. It made a little problem grow much too big too fast. He knew I hated silence, yet he drove on, his nose aiming at the road, his eyes darting everywhere but my way.

He turned right on Main Street, stopped twice for red lights, and then were in town. We passed a drugstore, a bank, a beauty salon, and a barber shop. Next came the fabric store, a five-and-ten, the hardware store, and The Liquor Barn. Frank looked at everything but the liquor store, as if realizing that I now knew where he had stopped the day before.

I didn't care where he had bought his booze. The fact that he had had to drink it was what bothered me. I knew that he could be a better husband if it wasn't for his drinking. I didn't understand why he still chose to drink, knowing that it would eventually ruin our marriage.

Chapter Forty-One

New Ideas and Hope

A group of people talking and laughing had always helped me forget my problems and move on with hopes that things would eventually get better. But this time, forgetting was more difficult in spite of the nice people we met.

Joseph Johnson and his wife Mildred saw us pull up in front of their house and were at the door before we knocked.

"Good to see that you made it here okay," Joseph said, standing tall and slim, with twinkling brown eyes and a jolly laugh. "This is my wife Millie. You must be careful, because she'll spoil those little guys."

Mildred was short and stout, with dark blue eyes that closed when she smiled. She reached for me with one hand, and for the boys with the other, and whirled us into the living room where two other couples waited. They were introduced as Kent and Nancy, and Fred and Julie. They had arrived in town a few days earlier.

After the introductions were over, the men began talking about their new jobs, and we women drifted into the kitchen.

"I'll take the boys down to the basement where they can watch cartoons with Nancy's little girls," Millie said with a quick one-two tap, as if we were having a party rather than a get-acquainted lunch. "And by the way, Jackie, you'll be glad to know that Nancy lives only a mile from your place, and she has a daughter who babysits. If you ever need to get away for a while, you know who to call." Her last words rang from the bottom of the stairs.

The other women chuckled. "She's putting ideas in your head, Jackie," said Nancy.

"I need ideas," I said, then took a seat across from the two women. I listened as they talked about the experiences they each had during the move from their homes in Minneapolis. Like Frank, their husbands had lost their jobs with the railroad company, and both couples had had to sell their homes just as we had. Julie and her husband had no children, so they had rented an apartment in town. But Nancy and Kent had five children, so the only place they could find was out in the country.

Millie returned from the basement with gleaming eyes. "Oh, Jackie, your little boys are so cute and well mannered."

My chest grew bigger as I thanked her. Nothing pleased me more than hearing compliments about my boys.

Millie opened her refrigerator and placed a large plate of ham and cheese sandwiches, and one of cut-up vegetables, on the table with glasses of water and cups for coffee. Julie and Nancy stood up and offered to help, but Millie waved them away. "No, no, sit down and talk. I have everything ready."

She gave Nancy and me each a tray of little sandwiches, chips, and Kool-aid to take down to our children, who were sitting hypnotized in front of the TV set. They all reached for the Kool-aid first, ignoring our comments that they should eat their food first.

"Oh, well, as long as they're quiet," Nancy said, then started up the steps. I followed her, thrilled that my boys were not fighting.

As we reached the top of the stairway, Millie called the men to the table, and they walked in like four mustangs ready to take on the world. Their steps rumbled from the living room to the kitchen, and their voices roared. I wondered if Frank was the only one with a drinking problem, and what the other men would say if they knew our secret.

Joseph led the blessings, thanking God for the food, for new friendships, and asked for guidance as he and his employees would soon begin their new jobs. Everyone said "Amen," and the conversations continued, man to man, and woman to woman. Everyone had something to say, and laughter followed their words.

Frank gave me a hint of a wink every time his eyes met mine, which meant that I should forgive him because he still loved me. But I still had the picture of the empty Seagram's 7 bottle in my mind.

He had often said that I never let him forget his mistakes. He was right. I had no intention of acting as if nothing disgusting had happened. After all, his list of mistakes was rapidly growing.

It was easy for him to forget, because he lived for the moment. Life was great when he saw me smiling, or heard me humming. It meant that I had forgiven him, and our problems were all behind us.

As I observed the other couples, I felt sure that, although they might have their ups and downs, none of the other three men at that table had drinking problems. Their wives couldn't have possibly been just putting on a good front.

I did feel better by the time we left there, because I had met Nancy, and I left looking forward to seeing her again. She had more children than I had, and lived farther from town than we did. I would not feel so alone way out there, and the boys would have some playmates.

Hopefully, Frank would realize that he was jeopardizing his marriage by drinking, and would quit. If nothing else, he would discover that he was the only drinker in the new group, and would not want to risk losing his job. That was probably wishful thinking, but I still had hopes.

"We're going to be just fine," he said as he turned onto Main Street. "Those guys I'll be working with are very nice. I finally am going to do the kind of work I like. That's what I was trained for in the Air Force, not cleaning oily engines and floors." He gave the steering wheel a quick sweep with the palm of his hand, then reached into his pocket for a cigarette.

"Yes," I said. "But what if . . . never mind." I didn't want to start an argument and destroy the good moment.

"I know what you're thinking. But don't you worry, I'm done with the booze."

"You said that before."

"Yeah, but this time I promise."

"Promise what, Daddy?" Rodney's face came forward, his chin resting on the ridge of the backrest of our seat.

"Never mind, son. I'm talking with your mother."

"You mean it's a secret, right, Daddy?" Troy had joined his brother. I felt his soft breath on my shoulder, and love filled my heart. *Life would be much nicer if it weren't for Frank's drinking.*

He didn't answer Troy's question, but lit another cigarette.

Chapter Forty-Two

What About Santa?

We stopped at the grocery store on our way back home, but I could not concentrate on the things we needed to buy. Too many thoughts about Frank and his drinking occupied my mind. I had learned from watching the "soaps" that a man who drank a lot was an alcoholic. But what would Frank do if I told him that he was an alcoholic who needed help? Would he yell at me and head for the nearest bar? That thought made me feel like punching the cans of peaches and Campbell's soup as we walked between the stacks. If it hadn't ben for my fear of getting in trouble with the manager, I would have done it just to show Frank that I was still mad about his drinking. Still, Frank walked around as if nothing serious had happened. I kept looking for a sign of remorse on his face, but he seemed totally at ease.

I picked up a few things and headed out of the store while Frank was still in line to pay the bill. I didn't even look at him when he finally came out. And on the rest of the way home the boys chattered and teased each other in the back seat, but Frank and I didn't speak a word. I was wondering how to fix the drinking problem..

Once we walked into the house, Frank said, "How about a group hug?" He knew that I would not refuse because the boys loved group hugs. They heard him and came running with their little arms stretched open. I could not resist their enthusiasm and the wet kisses they spread on my face. But Frank could not see that my response was to the boys, and not to him. His eyes were on me as he hugged his sons.

"Will you play with us, Daddy?" Rodney asked.

"Not now, son. I'm going to help your mother unpack. I go to work tomorrow, and she can't do all that by herself."

That touch of consideration was so phony it made me sick. It was for his own special interest. I had done plenty of work by myself in the past, while he had spent his free time in the bars.

"Maybe you should go kick a ball with them while I make supper,"

I said, "since you'll be gone all day tomorrow. You can help me unpack later."

Frank's face fell. "I was hoping that we could go to bed early tonight."

"We went to bed early last night, don't you remember?"

"You're not going to forgive me for that, are you?"

"Yes, I am. You are forgiven. Go play with the boys."

There wasn't anything else Frank could say. By then, the boys had found their old football and were tugging at his trousers. "Yeah, Daddy, come on, let's go outside."

Frank did not give up easily when there was something he really wanted. He was back in fifteen minutes with a sweet smile and love spilling from his eyes.

"This is going to be a great place for the boys, honey, just wait and see. There's plenty of room for them to run and yell. And it's going to be good for us, too. I'll be making more money than ever before, which means that one day I can buy you an automatic washing machine, and maybe even a dryer. And with the rent being only fifty dollars, we can get a better car and start saving for a new house."

He appeared so convincing and enthusiastic that I tightened my lips and brushed aside the drinking problem. "That would be good, Frank. I want nothing more than happiness for us. Now call the boys. Supper's ready."

Frank winked. "I couldn't have asked for a better wife."

The boys ran in raving, "Spaghetti, yummy! Mommy made spaghetti! Yummy, yummy!"

We sat together like the perfect family again, Frank at one end of the table, and I at the other, with the boys across from each other. That way they could make faces at one another, but could not really reach to start a fight.

"Think we'll be able to buy some fabric, Frank? So I can start on the upstairs curtains?"

"No, honey. That has to wait until payday."

Rodney put down his fork and stretched open his eyes. "And where are we going to go for Halloween, Daddy?"

Frank's gaze met mine, but Troy came up with a more important question.

"And, Daddy, are you going to tell Santa that we moved? If you don't tell him, he'll give our toys to other kids when he shows up at our house and we aren't there."

"I already told Santa that we moved, Troy. And, Rodney, don't you worry about missing Halloween. I'll drive you boys to a neighborhood near town so you can get your treats."

The boys' smiles lifted my spirits, but what their father said next sent chills through my bones.

"Now, honey, I need to tell you something important. The basement here is just a hole under the house. The only way to get to it is from outside. The two panels bellow that window is its only door. I want you and the boys to stay away from there. If you try to go in, that old door can come down and trap you guys down there. The only thing there is an old furnace . . . and I mean *old*. It's the kind that uses oil instead of natural gas like we had in St. Paul. But anyway, I don't want you three down there because I won't be here to let you out."

Frank could not have given me a more frightening warning. I felt spooked. A deep, dark cave was under our house, and I was being told not to check it out. How would I live knowing that there was something dark and mysterious under my floor? But I couldn't express my fear in front of the boys. All I could do was give Frank a warning look, which he missed.

"Daddy, are you sure a big monster isn't down there?" Troy looked startled.

His brother joined him. "Yeah, Daddy. Did you check it out?"

"I checked everything out. The space under the house is only big enough for the old furnace. No monsters can fit in it." That seemed to satisfy the boys, but it didn't take away my fear.

Frank was a bundle of love that night. He even helped me with the dishes. We unpacked a few boxes, bathed the boys, and tucked them into bed. Finally, we took our showers and crawled under our sheets.

He apologized for the previous night, then promised to give up the drinking, with the exception of a social drink every now and then. I was the best little wife a man could ever have, and he was going to do his best to make me happy.

Chapter Forty-Three

When the Rats Moved In

The days would have been painfully lonely if it hadn't been for Nancy. She was an energetic women, tall, with short brown hair, small dark eyes, and cinnamon-colored skin. She walked fast and talked even faster, and her language was filled with bad words in every sentence.

She knew how to keep her husband from controlling her. Several times a week, she drove him to work and kept the car just to go for long drives on the country roads, or to do her shopping, or to take her children to the park. She often invited me to come along with my boys.

During one of the drives, we came to a place where some women had gotten together and were selling old clothes and household items outside a garage.

"Good!" Nancy said, pulling off the road. "A garage sale. Let's see what kind of junk people sell out in the sticks. You kids stay in the car." Nancy's words weren't disputed even by her teenage daughter.

I had heard of garage sales before, but had never been to one. I saw all kinds of dishes, clothing, knick-knacks, an iron, a dust pan, and two end-tables.

I saw a table loaded with old books, some for as little as ten cents, but I didn't even have a nickel. Next to the table I saw a set of Junior Encyclopedias. I wondered if I would ever be able to buy anything like that.

"That's a good deal for five dollars, Jackie." Nancy had seen me running the tips of my fingers over the spines of the books. "I'll loan you the money if you want to buy it. You'll need it for your boys later on, anyway."

Tears rushed to my eyes. *She knows that I haven't any money.* "You will? I sure would appreciate that. And I'll pay you back next week."

Nancy winked, "No problem, pay me whenever you can."

Walking back to the car, I felt this wind-like feeling growing up my legs and into my stomach. I would read every word on those books. One day, I would find books on how to be successful. "Nancy, that set of Encyclopedias is going to change my life for the better. I have to do something for you in return. You are so good to me. If you ever need some sewing or alterations done, I'll be happy to do it for you. That's one thing I can do well."

She looked at me and smiled. "You've got a deal! I can't sew a straight stitch. But you aren't obligated to do it. All I did was loan you five dollars."

"And you got us out of the house. It's awful to spend the long days with only the company of my two little boys. They have each other and they know I'm there when they need me."

Nancy chuckled. "I know what you mean. Kids keep you busy, but they aren't much company."

Kids could not keep a secrete either. When Frank got home that day, our boys met him at the door and blabbered about the books Mommy had bought.

"Books! With what?"

"With five dollars that Nancy loaned me," I interjected. "And I promised to pay her back next week. So don't forget to give me five dollars when you get paid."

"Why would you spend five dollars on books?"

"It's a set of Encyclopedia, which the boys will need once they start school."

"So why not wait until then to buy books?"

"Because I am going to read every word on those pages before the boys."

"Well, I'm beginning to think that Nancy has a bad influence on you. She wears the pants in her family. I don't want you to become like her."

I didn't reply to his stupid comment. And the next day, the boys and I went to the park with Nancy and her children. We took sandwiches, chips, and soda pop with us. While the children ran around, the two of us talked on a blanket.

"You can't raise kids out here without a car," she said.

"I know, but Frank will never teach me how to drive. He says that no wife of his is ever going to drive him to and from work."

"Hell, don't pay attention to that crap. What would you do if one of the boys got sick or hurt during the day while Frank's car is in a parking lot fifteen miles away? And what about the new baby? You have to rush babies to the doctor when they get sick. Anything can happen while you wait for Frank or someone else to give you a ride into town. Just the thought of something like that scares the shit out of me."

"Yes, but how will I learn if Frank doesn't let me use his car?" I felt small and stupid telling her that, but it was true.

"Oh, hell, I'll teach you."

"You will?"

"Sure I will. But it's got to be before school starts. That would be better for you, too, because next spring you'll have the new baby. You're due in March, right?"

"Yes, in March."

"I'll tell you what. Next week I'll bring Kent to your place in the morning, and he can ride to work with Frank. You can learn with my car. It's an automatic, which is what Frank's driving, and you can learn faster than you would with a standard. Just don't tell Frank until after you get your license. If you do, he might refuse to give Kent a ride, and I won't have the car as often."

"Don't worry, I won't tell him."

For the next three weeks, Nancy dropped Kent off at our house every other day, and as soon as the men drove off, she took the boys and me with her. My boys stayed with her children, and I didn't tell them about the driving lessons. They would blabber to their daddy, and that would be the end of my lessons.

"I didn't tell my kids, either," Nancy said. "They don't need to know every step I take. I like secrets!" She pulled off the dirt road and told me to get behind the steering wheel. "Just relax," she said. "This is a good place for you to get acquainted with the car because there's no traffic, and I won't let you go into the cornfield."

"This is so strange for me, Nancy. If I learn to drive a car, it will be my biggest accomplishment. I'll be grateful to you for the rest of my life."

"Oh, that's no big deal. You'll learn fast, you'll see."

I didn't learn fast on my first lesson. I kept turning the wheel too sharp, confusing the brakes with the gas pedal, and wiping the sweat off my hands.

"It's okay," Nancy encouraged. "The first time is always the worst – like sex, you know? The first time is a waste, but then it gets better with time. The more you do it, the better you'll learn."

"I know what you mean," I said, but I didn't. The thing about intercourse was still a problem for me. Actually, it had become something I could not understand. In my mind, sex was embarrassing, and forbidden. A few days earlier, I had seen on a news report about President Kennedy that his wife Jacqueline was pregnant. I sank into the blue sofa and whispered to myself, *"They do it, too? Even our new president and his wife do it?"* So there I was with two sons and a growing belly, yet no one would hear me say that I was pregnant, or that I'd be giving birth. It sounded better to say that I was expecting a baby.

Nancy kept her promise, gave me two lessons a week, and even brought me a driver's handbook. "Read it every day and memorize everything," she said.

One morning, Nancy sat on the passenger side seat of her car while I drove to Ashton, a small town where they had the kind of parking spots you could pull right into, so I wouldn't have to worry about parallel parking. On that fateful morning, I was granted a temporary driving license – the permanent one would come by mail from Springfield, Illinois.

"I have a driving license," I said to Frank two days later.

He nearly fell off the kitchen chair. "How did you manage to do that?"

"By passing a test. See?" I showed him the little card with my name on it.

He rubbed his chin. "I should have stopped that friendship at the beginning. Just because Nancy wears the pants in her family doesn't mean you're going to do the same. I'm hiding the extra car key so you don't get tempted to drive some day when I'm asleep."

"If I had known that you were going to act like that, I would have driven away one day without telling you. What would you have said then?"

He stared at me, then realized how stupid he had sounded. "Well, I'll see how well you drive before letting you take the car out on your own, especially with the kids in it."

The next Saturday, we went on a picnic with Kent, Nancy, and their children. Frank was bubbly the whole time, and never even hinted anger toward Nancy for teaching me how to drive. That was the way my father had been. He would make angry remarks about someone in front of his wife and children, then treat that person with good manners and friendliness.

On the mornings when Nancy didn't keep her car, the boys and I stood outside and watched Frank back out of the driveway and drive down the dirt road. Then the boys played outside, and I hurried into the house to do my cleaning and laundry so I could read from the encyclopedia. After lunch, while the boys napped, I sewed or baked bread and cookies, then read some more.

It was easy to learn how to read these books. I chose a subject, looked it up in the index, then opened that page. My reading was slow, for I tried to pronounce the words carefully. According to the sentences, I figured out their meanings. During my readings, I remembered Doña Luisa saying, "You'll learn English in no time." Then my brain reached way back to my godfather's words when I was six. "You'll become a fine writer someday."

Those memories became boosters to my energy, and I sounded the words out loudly so they could reach the heavens, where my godfather and Doña Luisa were listening and smiling.

When the fields came due for harvest, the boys and I watched Mr. Peters cut the dried corn plants with his machine and rapidly suck the corncobs into a box-like trailer. We watched from the downstairs windows, then ran upstairs, because from up there the view was wider and longer. The area that had appeared large before, now went on as far as our eyes could see. All the green plants that had made our house appear cozy when we first saw it had disappeared, and now our home stood naked in the middle of many miles of dried and dusty flat land. I thanked God for Nancy, for she had made living way out here tolerable.

About two weeks after Mr. Peters had cleared his crops off the land, I went downstairs one morning and spotted some black beads on the dining room floor. A whole trail of them ran across the floor and into the kitchen. I followed the beads, hunched down to see better, and discovered something I had known as a child on the old farm in Puerto

Rico — something I had hoped never to see again.

"Frank!" I shrieked.

He came running. "What the hell's the matter?"

I pointed to the dark trail on the floor, my heart pounding so hard I could not speak.

"Damn! That's rat shit. The man harvested the corn and left the field rats without food."

"Are you sure they are rats, Frank?"

"No doubt in my mind. It's pure rat shit, all right! I'll get some D-con on my way home from work and wipe out that problem fast."

That was my most miserable day in Illinois. Any little noise I heard from then on was a rat. I worried that those rats would eat all our food, and chew on our furniture. And the worst thought of all was that the rats would bite the boys. I thought back to the stories the hill people of Puerto Rico had told. "Rats ate the babies' toes, the babies developed fever, and then the babies died."

By noon, I had read all about rats in my new books, and I felt so nervous I had to call the landlord. Mrs. Peters and her husband came right away.

"My dear, we're so sorry," Mrs. Peters said. "Those little creatures usually run out of the fields after the harvest."

"But don't you worry none," said Mr. Peters. "I'll take care of that for you. The little beasts will be gone soon."

That sounded so reassuring I invited them to stay for coffee and cookies.

Mr. Peters sat Rodney on his knee. "What are you going to be when you grow up, young man?"

"A farmer like you, that's what!"

Troy ran to Mrs. Peters. "I'm going to be a farmer, too." His green eyes moved from his brother to me, as if letting us know that he was somebody, too.

That precious moment erased the rats from my mind. I pretended that Mr. and Mrs. Peters were my parents, and my boys were being loved.

Chapter Forty-Four

When Darkness Came

It turned really cold on the first week of October, so I turned on the old furnace for the first time since we had moved in. A cloud of dust poured into the house through the little vents, and we all started choking and coughing. I turned off the dinner I was cooking, opened the doors and some windows, and ran outside with the boys.

From outside, we saw the dust rolling out of the house. I imagined that the old furnace had accumulated a lot of dust, and we would be breathing it in all winter. I felt so devastated then. There seemed to be no end to the horrifying obstacles. What would we do if that wasn't something that could be fixed?

By the time the dust had stopped spilling out of the windows, we were freezing. Still, as we walked back in, I noticed a terrible stench which grew stronger when I closed the doors and windows. I suspected there was something rotten under the house, but never thought of the rats. Mr. Peters had said that the rats would be gone. He didn't say they would die there.

That night, we moved upstairs with the television set, the electric frying pan, the coffee pot, and some of the dishes. The gravity-heat from the old furnace did not reach upstairs, but neither did the stench of the dead rats.

Every morning, I ran downstairs with a towel over my nose, grabbed the milk, cold-cuts, or ground meat, and ran back up again. And since there was no heat upstairs, we put on our winter coats first thing in the morning and kept them on all day. On sunny days, even though it was cold, the boys and I stayed outside for hours to escape the stench. Bundled from head to toe, we kicked the football and ate peanut butter and jelly sandwiches and bananas.

If Nancy came by to take us to the park or just for a ride on the country roads, we met her by the driveway so she would not smell the stench. On Frank's days off, we packed a picnic and blankets and went to the park where we stayed until late afternoon. One of those times, we stopped to see Fred and Julie, but we didn't mention our problem with the bad smell. Frank didn't want his boss to find out about it and feel bad for getting us a rat-infested house.

It took over a month for the stench to clear out of the house. By then, the first snow of the season had whirled down over and around us. From then on, we looked in all directions to see nothing but miles and miles of snow. A snowplow cleared our gravel road once in the morning and again in the evening. But we learned that only those who absolutely had to use that road ever did. Therefore, a car or pickup truck passing our place became a rare thing to see. Of course, most of the time our downstairs windows were covered with ice, and we couldn't see out anyway.

Frank was always able to drive out in the mornings, for the plow had just gone by. But after work he would get stuck before reaching home, so he waited for the plow, which would reach our place between 7:00 or 8:00 in the evenings. Frank found the bars to be a good place to wait. He didn't come crawling home at two o'clock in the morning, for he knew enough to follow the snowplow, but I knew he would stay later once the snow stopped coming down. I also knew that he would never give up drinking completely, no matter how many times he promised to stop.

On clear nights, while the boys watched cartoons, I often went upstairs and stared at the flat miles of white, glistening snow through the window that faced the road. My eyes followed the dirt road, and every now and then I could see the headlights of cars going up or down the paved road. Occasionally, an old pickup truck rode down toward our place, and I would get a jolt of joy thinking someone was coming to visit us. Then, as it passed our house, it left me feeling more lonely than I had been before. I usually stayed at the window and thought back to my years of struggling.

I couldn't understand why my dreams of becoming American had turned into such a nightmare. I had never expected to end up with a drunk husband in a place of rats and mice, surrounded by miles of snow-covered fields. Feeling as if something had scraped out my insides, I would turn from the window and go downstairs to read about a place where it never snowed.

When Frank was scheduled to start work at four o'clock, he left the house at three. Loneliness and hopelessness came over me each time he drove away. He would have a soft smile, and a cigarette dangling from his lips. He'd wave as the boys and I stood watching. I knew he felt powerful, being the man, the husband, the father, and the one leaving to do an important job. He operated a power plant which produced the electricity a city and its county depended upon.

In the early hours of those evenings, I had my books to read, and the company of my little boys. The sound of their funny words and laughter, and sometimes fights, made the house seem warm and friendly. But once I tucked them into bed, the floorboards squeaked louder, the walls appeared colder and meaner, and the outdoor darkness threatened to swallow the house with us in it. I would go upstairs then, knowing that Frank would come home around one o'clock. Sometimes he did, but sometimes he didn't show up until after two, smelling of smoke and whiskey or beer.

When his schedule was to start work at midnight, he left the house at eleven. By then, I had been fighting to stay awake for two hours, for it was my duty to pack his lunch and see him off. Fear of the dark hit me the minute he drove away. The old house grew larger and turned colder, and there was a long way between the back door and the second floor where my little boys lay asleep. Each night, I trembled all the way up the stairs. If I left the light on downstairs, the darkness would look in from outside and see me scared. If I turned the light off, the darkness would creep up behind me.

Every night, I reached the bedroom with my heart in my throat, which made me more nervous because the pounding blocked the sound of possible footsteps coming up the stairway. I always checked on the boys before going to my room, but I held my breath to slow down my heartbeat. Sometimes I choked and coughed, and the echo startled me even more. Finally, I would tiptoe to my room, where my fear grew even more.

The loud click of the light switch made me jump when I turned it on, and later when I turned it off. Everything kept me jumping. I sat in bed, pulled the covers up to my chin, and with my eyes wide open, listened for any sounds that might come up the stairs.

I wondered if all the rats and mice had really died with the D-con

Mr. Peters had put in the old basement, and what I would do if one came upstairs. Would I have the nerve to kill a rat? And what would I do if rats bit my boys?

One night I left the bathroom light on and its door open so I could look into a lighted area. If the stairs squeaked, I would see whatever might be coming up before it entered my room. I lifted the covers slowly and stretched out on my bed, feeling sure that I was finally controlling my fear of the dark. I gathered the blankets and quilts tightly around my body while, so that nothing could creep up on me if I did fall asleep. I lay facing the lighted area outside the door so I would not have to turn if I heard the floorboards squeak.

To take my mind off the fear, I thought about my baby, who I felt swimming inside me. *It has to be a girl – a precious little girl with blue eyes and curly blonde hair, like Rodney. I'll make pretty dresses for her, with ruffles and lace. I'll comb her hair so that her curls will bounce when she walks.*

During those few moments, I fell asleep and dreamed that my boys were blowing in my face, going away and coming back to blow again. Finally, I woke up and heard a strange sound. My heart thumped, and I opened my eyes, only to see nothing near my bed. *It's only a dream. Oh God! Why did I dream such a thing? Now my loud heartbeat will keep me awake the rest of the night.*

I stayed still, clasping the thick bundle of covers. Soon I heard a strange sound: *Thrrr* . . . I felt the cold air over my face. *Thrrr* . . . I heard it again, and felt the air. After the third time, I stared toward the lighted doorway and saw something flying into my room. I covered my head, knowing that my heart would soon stop, and would never start up again. I would soon be dead, and then what would become of my little boys?

Sweat grew under my covers, and I felt a quivering in my womb. My poor unborn baby was suffering. Slowly, I uncovered one eye and stared toward the doorway. I heard the *thrrr* sound again, and a beast entered the room, flying over my face, then turning around and flying out of the room again. I uncovered my other eye and saw the flying beast return. It looked like a rat flying under a dark umbrella. As it turned toward the doorway, I saw the bathroom light sparkling in its beady black eyes, like small diamonds in the sun.

"It's a bat," I whispered and pulled the covers over my head.

I remembered a woman in Puerto Rico who almost went crazy trying to get rid of a bat that got tangled in her hair. Not only did she end up having to cut off her hair, but the bites from the beast almost killed her. She had lain in bed for many weeks, burning with fever, twisting and screaming with muscle cramps.

I had to go to the boys' room before the bat found them. But how? I uncovered one ear and counted from one when the beast left the room, and made it to ten before it returned.

The next time the bat flew out of my bedroom, I pushed the covers off and launched out into the boys' room, slamming their door shut behind me. I leaned against it, gasping as Rodney lifted his head and then put it down again. I wanted to tell him that it was only me, but I was mute, and struggling to breathe.

Through the closed door, I could hear the sound of the bat's wings every time it flew in and out of my bedroom. I would not open the boys' door again, but I would not cuddle next to them, for fear that they might wake up and decide they needed to go to the bathroom.

I waited for my heart to slow down. Then, with only the little light that reflected into the room from the snow outside the window, I went to the boys' closet and took out their jackets and the extra quilt and pillow we had. I put down the jackets and the pillow against the door, wrapped myself in the quilt, and lay there, shivering, and hearing the bat flying on the other side of the door.

I heard the boys mumbling in their sleep, and the sound of the bat's wings, a vehicle's horn far away, the vague cry of cows in the distance, and the night breeze moving the bare tree branches outside the window. I heard my heartbeat, and felt the movement in my womb. I rubbed my belly and prayed that the trauma would not hurt my baby, and that Frank would come right home from work. I listened, shook, and listened some more.

Chapter Forty-Five

Lucinda

Frank came home at about 8:30 in the morning. By then, the sound of the bat had stopped. The boys had awakened and were downstairs watching cartoons. I could hear Donald Duck and Mickey Mouse. I had climbed into Troy's bed, but was still too shaky to sleep.

"Honey, what's wrong?" Frank stared down at me, his eyebrows meeting at the bridge of his nose.

"Bats," I said. "There are bats in the house, and I hurt from shaking. I hate bats, rats, and mice, and I hate this house, and your boss for getting it for us. And I want to move far away from here."

"No, honey, not bats in the house. My God! You're cold and so pale. Didn't you sleep at all last night?"

Those were the words I needed. I became a little girl again – this time in the arms of a loving daddy who held me against his chest and allowed my tears to soak his shirt. This was a privilege I had never had as a child – but it didn't stop today's sobbing and trembling.

"I'm taking you to the emergency room," Frank said, and I didn't agree or disagree. He practically carried me downstairs.

I don't know when Frank had told the boys what was happening, but there they came behind us, dragging their jackets down the stairs. "What's wrong with Mommy, Daddy?" I heard one of them ask. And that made me cry even more.

"She's just a little nervous, son," Frank answered. "But she's going to be all right soon."

I ended up having my baby a month early, and stayed in the hospital for eight days. Luckily, the doctor found the baby healthy and normal, and at five pounds three ounces, I could take her home with me when I left the hospital.

I felt doubly blessed during those days, because Nancy kept the boys so Frank didn't have to miss work. Better yet, she saw to it that he would watch them during his times off. That, I believed, kept him away from the bars. Still, I never asked him if he got drunk during that time, for fear that he might admit doing so. I wanted to believe that he had been concerned enough about the children and me to give up the drinking.

The doctor's diagnosis was that I was anemic, too nervous, and needed more sleep. I also needed to learn how to kill bats, rats, and mice. Most important of all, I needed to take better care of myself. If I didn't, I would not live long enough to see my children grow up.

I named my beautiful baby girl Lucinda. She had hazel eyes and reddish, curly hair. She would sleep as close to my bed as I could bring her crib, for I didn't want bats or rats biting her pink little toes and fingers. And, she would also be the last baby I would ever have even if it meant divorcing her daddy, who didn't believe in preventing babies.

The day I came home from the hospital, in mid-February, was the coldest and gloomiest day of that winter. Even the darling baby in my arms and the sweet little boys could not lift my spirits. I just sat on the ugly blue sofa and stared as the boys reached to lift the corners of the blanket that cocooned their little sister.

Frank sat next to me, put his arm around my shoulders, and began one of his long promises.

"I have made a decision, and this time I'm sticking to it. After all, with the best wife a man can ever have, and two sons and a daughter, it's time I clean up my act. I'm giving up the drinking. From now on, I'll go to work and come right home to my little family. Let's save every nickel we can and get us a better house in town. What do you say, honey?"

"I say that you'd be smart to do that, and that I'll wait to see you follow through with your commitment." With that, I carried my baby to the freezing room upstairs, and stayed with her in my bed the rest of the day and night. Frank had no choice but to take care of the boys and bring me some Campbell's noodle soup and coffee.

I didn't sleep much that night, afraid that I might roll over the baby, but the next morning, life looked a little brighter.

We had a near-perfect spring and summer that year. Frank came home after work every day without stopping at the bars. When he worked from seven o'clock to three, if the weather was nice, he took us for rides on the country roads and then stopped at one of those fast food restaurants where the waitresses came on roller skates to wait on us. We would have hamburgers, French fries, and ice-cream floats. Afterward, we would go home to watch *Gunsmoke* and *Have Gun, Will Travel* on TV.

When he worked from three o'clock to eleven, I waited up for him while reading the encyclopedia, or sewing outfits for the boys and pretty dresses for Lucinda. I even made shirts for Frank, and swimming shorts for the boys so they could turn the water hose at each other while playing on the green grass in the hot summer days. Our lifestyle had taken a turn for the better, and if we moved to a better house before another winter, our hard times would be behind us.

Everything went incredibly well for us until a phone call interrupted us one night in September. Frank's brother Bill had died from liver disease. Frank jumped off the bed and walked around in circles, moaning and scratching his head. Nothing I said could comfort him. By four o'clock that morning, he was backing out of the driveway on his way to St. Paul.

"I'll call my boss from a public phone in a couple of hours," he said, and left.

I didn't realize until hours later that he had taken even the milk money, and all we had in the refrigerator was a half gallon of milk and one loaf of bread. I thought he would realize that and turn around, for he would not abandon us without money or enough milk for the babies. By the end of that day, it was apparent that he wasn't coming back anytime soon. So I got busy and made bread, and then called Nancy and had her pick up some milk for us when she went to the store.

When she brought the milk, I had to tell her that I would pay her back when Frank got home, for he had taken all the money.

"If Kent did anything like that to me, I'd hit him on the head with my iron frying pan, I guarantee it," she said.

"I might end up doing that myself," I told her.

"You'd better, or else he'll lose respect for you."

"I think he already has." With that, the tears came.

"Well, you're too good for him, if you ask me. Just give me a ring whenever you need something else."

I watched her drive away and wished to be like her. Then I wished she had taken us to spend the night at her house.

That night, I could not go to sleep. For one thing, knowing that Frank wasn't coming back for days scared me. Then came another thought: *What if he stops for a few drinks and gets killed? What would become of me with three little children?* I grabbed my pillow and blanket, took Lucinda out of her crib, and spent the rest of the night on the floor in the boys' room.

The next day, I took the crib apart and moved it into the boys' bedroom. Then I made a bed for myself on the floor. As soon as it got dark every night from then on, we took a jug of milk, a jug of water, and a box of crackers upstairs, where I whispered stories to the boys until they fell asleep. I kept the door closed and my ears tuned to the stairway, always expecting to hear the squeaking of the steps. Every once in a while, I heard a vehicle crushing the gravel on the road. I saw the streaks of light on our walls, and as they disappeared, I heard the sound of the tires fade away.

I practiced in my mind what I would say to Frank when, and if, he came home. He needed to know that he wasn't worth all the misery I was going through.

Chapter Forty-Six

Kissing a Stranger

Three days after Frank left, I carried the playpen outside so Lucinda could get fresh air while the boys played on the grass. I sat on a blanket near the playpen, trying to read, but my mind kept going over the things I needed to tell Frank. He had not bothered to call us even once.

At seven months, Lucinda had been crawling, reaching for everything, and talking in her baby vocabulary. But that day she lay in the playpen with sad eyes and sucked her thumb. I decided to take her back into the house. Maybe the sun was a little too warm for her. I changed her diaper and tried to give her some baby food, but she kept turning her head. I took her upstairs and put her in the crib, thinking she would be okay after a nap.

Hurrying back downstairs, I called the boys to lunch. While they ate in front of the TV, I lay on the sofa for a short rest. I hadn't had much sleep in the past three nights, and I felt worn out. But my frustrations with Frank, and my concern about Lucinda, made relaxing impossible. I had to go back upstairs and make sure she was all right.

Lucinda's face was the color of strawberries, and I heard a strange sound in her breathing. I touched her face and it felt hot.

Fear threw me off balance like a sudden gust of wind. Neither of the boys had ever felt that hot. I ran downstairs to call the doctor.

"My baby is sick!" I cried. "She is really hot and has a strange sound in her breathing."

"Bring her in," the woman on the phone said.

I hung up and called Nancy for a ride into town, but there was no answer. I hung up and dialed Mrs. Peters' number. However, there was no answer there, either. Now I felt panicked. I really needed help, and there was no one I could turn to.

I ran back upstairs. Maybe this wasn't happening. I would find my baby awake and smiling. But no . . . she was still sleeping, and her curls were wet.

Desperately, I ran back to the phone again. Two girls were on the line, talking about Troy Donahue and Connie Stevens.

"Please, hang up the phone. I need to call the doctor. My baby is very sick."

"Take it easy, lady, we just got on," one of them said, and they both laughed.

"Please, my baby is very sick," I cried. The girls laughed even more.

Wanting to strangle those girls, I turned to the window and saw a red pickup truck coming down the road. I slammed the phone hard, hoping to break their eardrums, and ran out the front door waving my arms. The driver, an older man, hit the brakes, and a cloud of dust rose into the air.

"What's the problem?" he asked.

"My baby is really sick. I need a ride to the doctor's office." I ran back into the house, and the man followed me through the living room and up the stairs. I never looked at the boys, but I heard them running behind us.

The man looked at Lucinda. "Oh, yeah, that baby's really hot. Sounds like she's got asthma. Who's your doctor?"

"Dr. Zack," I said, picking Lucinda out of the crib. "My little boys . . . I can't leave them alone!" I cried.

"We'll take them with us," the man said, heading downstairs. "I know Dr. Zack. He's a good doctor. Come on, boys, your little sister's gonna be all right."

I followed the man and my boys, with Lucinda wrapped in a blanket. When we reached the living room, the man turned off the TV.

"Come on, boys. I'll give you a ride in my new truck." Any other time, the boys would have clapped and cheered, but that day they seemed puzzled as they followed the man.

"It's okay, boys," I said. "The nice man is going to help us. Your little sister is sick." Everything happened so fast it all seemed like a blur. There was no time to fear a stranger, or to comfort my confused little boys.

"By the way, I'm Matt," the man said, trying to fit all of us into the only seat of his pickup truck. "I'm your landlord's brother."

"Pleased to meet you. Thank you for stopping. But what's asthma?"

"Oh, nothing your doctor can't fix. Most kids who live out here get asthma."

I turned Lucinda's little face up so she could breathe better, and I felt too choked up to speak. Neither of the boys had ever gotten that sick, and all I could think about was that she might die.

"She's gonna be fine, your little baby," Matt kept reassuring me. "I'll drive you right to the door, then I'll go park my truck. Don't worry about the little guys. I'll watch over them."

I felt too overwhelmed to question the man's kindness. But he must have known that this was serious, because he grasped the steering wheel so hard his knuckles turned white. He sat straight, as if leaning back would slow him down. I saw the black needle on the speedometer climbing steadily higher.

He pulled up in front of the doctor's office, helped me out of the truck, then drove away with my little boys. I hurried inside without a word to Matt or the boys, a suffocating pressure in my throat.

"Bring her right in," a nurse said as I walked through the door.

I followed her, so scared I could hardly breathe.

"Dr. Zack," she called out, then proceeded to take Lucinda's temperature. "A hundred and four," she said as the doctor walked in.

I stood staring, my mind blank, my baby's hot little hand in mine.

The doctor looked in her mouth. "Sore throat, too." Next he listened to her little chest. "And possibly asthma."

I backed out of his way, my eyes on my baby. Her little chest was rising and falling. Her legs were long and slim, her arms down and still. This was the worst thing that could ever happen to me. I would die if I ever lost one of my children.

"Is asthma a serious illness?"

"It can be," the doctor answered. "You'll have to keep a dust-free home, and keep her from crabgrass and all sorts of vegetation. I'll give her something to bring down the fever, and I want to see her again in a week."

Lucinda screamed when he gave her a shot. The doctor said her scream was a good sign, but I felt a long, sharp pain right through my stomach.

"Give her some of this every four hours and bring her back in a week," he said. "But call me if the fever isn't gone by tomorrow." He gave me a little bottle of a red liquid and patted my shoulder. "And don't worry so much. She'll be just fine."

I thanked the doctor through the blockage in my throat, picked up Lucinda, and went to find my little boys. Matt was reading a children's book to them, and both boys were hypnotized. That brought even more tears to my eyes. Here was a stranger doing something for the boys that their father had never done.

And at that moment I wondered, if my children still had a father. For all I knew, he could have gotten himself drunk and could be dead in a ditch off any road between St. Paul and Rochelle, Illinois.

That day, I hugged and kissed a stranger for the first time in my life. It was the only way I could thank Matt for coming by when he did, for driving us to the doctor's office, for the fatherly care he had given the boys, and for bringing us home.

"Oh, it's all right," he said, a little taken aback by the hug and kiss. "I have a family, too, and have seen my wife all broken up over the young ones whenever they get as much as the sniffles. Give me a call if anything else comes up, and my wife or I will come right away." He wrote his phone number on a piece of paper and handed it to me. Then he shook the boys' hands, bowed to me, and left.

The boys ran to turn on the televison set, so I took Lucinda upstairs, put her in her crib, then went into the bathroom, where I pressed a towel over my face and sobbed until the towel got soaked with tears.

Frank returned close to midnight on Saturday. He had been gone five days, and had not called once to see if we were still alive. I heard him when he unlocked the kitchen door, closed it again, and locked it.

I walked out of the boys' room quietly, and went downstairs ready with my speech. Then I saw him coming toward me with his lips puckered.

"Stay back!" I shouted, smelling booze and tobacco smoke. "I came down to tell you something important, but you are too drunk – gone for five days, and then come home stinking like a beer barrel on fire. Don't bother coming upstairs. I don't want the boys to see you drunk."

"Oh, honey, I'm sorry. My brother's death has been hard for me. I had to stop for a few drinks. I couldn't stand the sadness. But believe me, honey, I am done with that stuff for sure."

"You almost had a second funeral to attend, had it not been for a nice stranger who happened to be driving by when your little daughter stopped breathing! And I, like an idiot, have been anxious for you to get home so I could explain what happened. Well, I'm not going to explain anything to a drunk. And don't tell me that you're done with drinking, because I am done listening to you."

I ran back upstairs into the boys' room, and locked the door. Minutes later, Frank knocked on the door.

"I just want to see the kids."

"You'll see them tomorrow when you're sober." I heard his steps going into our bedroom.

The next morning, the boys discovered their daddy, and ran to him, cheering, "Daddy's home, Daddy's home."

Frank turned over. "Oh, my sons, my sons."

I carried Lucinda downstairs and sat her in the old highchair. If her father had not awakened with a hangover, he would soon develop one. I had been going over my speech all night, the anger growing stronger, like a storm that would sweep away the countryside. *He's going to find out that I am no longer the naive little girl he married.*

I cracked an egg on the edge of the mixing bowl, pretending it was Frank's head. Only half of the egg's contents ran inside the dish. The other half slid down into the countertop. I cleaned the slippery mess, then cracked six more eggs. I beat the yolks with a fork so furiously the mixture formed bubbles. *Oh if it weren't for the children, I would take off running and never stop. All the years with Frank have been a waste of my time.*

While slapping the strips of bacon on the hot frying pan, I heard the shower turn on upstairs, and then the squeaking of the steps as the boys came running down.

"Daddy's taking a shower," Troy announced, flying past me, and Popeye's voice soon rang from the TV. *He's in the shower. Soon he'll be down here with puckered lips. I'll make his head spin today.*

At the sound of the squeaky stairway, I glanced up and saw him. He looked sparkling, clean-shaven, with puckered lips. I turned and shoved my head into the refrigerator, reaching for the bread, the butter, and the milk. He got the hint and moved on to join the boys.

"Breakfast is ready," I announced, and the three came running. Even though I wanted to explode at Frank, I talked to the children with motherly love. "Here you are, sweetheart," I said to the boys. "Eat the bacon, Dumpling. It's good for your teeth. Oh, Lucinda, darling, don't smear the eggs in your pretty hair."

From under my brow, I could see Frank's smiling face. I was loving his children. How lucky for him. But he was wrong, because I wasn't loving his children. I was loving *my children*, for I did not want them to remember my angry face and bitter words as I had to remember my mother's.

The boys swallowed their last bites on their way to the living room to their cartoons. Now I could confront Frank. But he jumped ahead of me.

"I feel bad about my brother's death, and about upsetting you last night, honey. Can you forgive me?"

"Yes, but I made a decision which you must hear, so forget about everything else and listen. This is what I decided. We'll spend another winter in this horrible house, and save money. But we will not move to another house anywhere near here."

"Why not?" Frank did the thing with his eyebrows, one up and one down, but I didn't find it cute anymore.

"We'll use the savings on a new start somewhere else."

"What are you talking about?" He reached for a cigarette.

"Don't light that. You can't smoke in the house anymore. Lucinda has asthma. Just be still, and I'll tell you. Or would you rather run to the bars?"

"Don't get smart. I'm not going anyplace."

"Good, because you need to listen to my plan. See, I don't want to leave you because of our children. But I'm not willing to live snowed in with rats, bats, and mice, and a man who will never stop drinking."

"Don't keep throwing that shit at me. I gave you my word that I'm quitting."

"I know you gave me your word, but your words are bubbles of air. All it takes is the death of a relative, and you forget all about me and our little children. You drive away in *your* car and take all *your* money with you, leaving us stranded and without milk for the babies."

"That only happened once, and it ain't gonna happen again."

"Maybe so, but I'd be stupid if I sat back thinking it wouldn't happen again! I need to think of my children, because obviously you don't."

Frank sprang from the kitchen chair. "Are you saying that I'm an unfit father?"

"Back away, Frank! Before you make a mistake."

"I already made a mistake," he said. "I went home for my brother's funeral, and now you're punishing me!"

"I'm not punishing you, Frank. I'm working out a compromise that will be good for all of us. But if you aren't willing to listen, all of us will lose."

He drew a steadying breath. "All right then . . . talk."

"We'll spend this winter here, then in June or July, we'll sell our junk, pack our sheets and dishes in the car, and drive to California."

"California! What the hell are we gonna do there?"

"We're going to live there. I have been reading about it. California has job opportunities and a dry climate, which is good for people with asthma. And we would not be snowed in for six months every year with a heater going day and night and still freeze. Better yet, the houses have no basements for rats, bats, or mice to hide in."

"You're getting too smart for me," he said. "I gotta go out for some air." He hurried to his car and drove away.

Chapter Forty-Seven

The Dream

We made it through another stench of dead rats, and when Christmas came along, we bought a tree so tall it reached the ceiling. I made the boys cowboy shirts, and bought them Roy Roger hats. We were able to buy each a toy car and truck, and a doll for Lucinda. I had made Frank some new shirts, which I wrapped and put under the tree. And to make our Christmas the best ever, Frank surprised me with a ten dollar camera. Now I could take pictures of my babies, paste some on our walls, and send my mother some if I ever found the nerve to write after so many years.

Although Frank did not get drunk, he bought his packs of beer and drank a few every night. Then, once the children were asleep, we got into the same argument in the bedroom.

"You've got to wear that thing, Frank. I don't want any more babies."

"That's like taking a shower with a raincoat on," he would say. "I shouldn't have to wear such a thing to make love to my own wife. That's enough to drive a man to drinking."

"Why would it? It didn't stop you from drinking before. Besides, I shouldn't need to explain to you why we can't have any more babies, when we can't afford the three we have."

"Oh, don't give me that shit. I knew a neighbor who had nineteen kids, and none of them starved to death."

"You don't expect me to have nineteen babies, do you?"

"Of course not, but we shouldn't stop at three, either."

"Okay, we won't stop. But just be prepared to give birth to the next one yourself, because I'm not going to do it." At that point, I would grab my pillow and leave the room. He would fall asleep, and the next day apologize, only to repeat the pattern again.

As if having to fight my husband off wasn't bad enough, one afternoon while ironing after he left for work, I felt a sharp pain in my right ankle. I shook and wiggled my foot, thinking it was from standing, but the pain continued. I turned off the iron and stretched out on the old sofa to watch cartoons with the boys. The pain didn't go away, but another started on the knee of the same leg. It was a cold pain, as if I had ice in my joints.

I went to the kitchen to prepare the evening meal for the children, limping, while the pain grew more intense. I took some aspirin and struggled through the meal and the cleaning afterward.

I had no idea what the pain might be, but I feared for my little children. What would become of them if the pains were due to something like polio or cancer? Tammy, in one of the "soaps," had had similar pains. She was diagnosed with leukemia, and died a short time later. I imagined my poor little children with a mean stepmother who would not let them have a drink of water before going to bed. Even if they ended up with any of Frank's relatives, they would suffer because I knew that no one in the whole world would love them as much as I did. Before long, the tears began to spill out because of the horrible thoughts.

"What's wrong, Mommy?" Troy asked, tiny creases forming between his little eyebrows.

I wiped my tears and faked a smile. "Oh, nothing's wrong, sweetheart. I was just remembering something sad that happened a long time ago."

"Tell Rodney and me about it!" Troy said. "If it's that sad, tell us!"

"It's getting late, and it's a long story. I will tell you another time." I knew he would forget about my tears once he returned to the cartoons.

By the time I bathed Lucinda and got her into bed, another pain had settled in my right shoulder. Now I knew that whatever was traveling up my right side would probably kill me during the night. I felt really scared then. If I knew that the doctor would give me a shot or some kind of pill and cure me instantly, I would call him. But what if he sent me to a hospital?

I took four aspirin tablets and went to bed once I had tucked my little ones into their beds, kissing and hugging them, but holding back a stream of tears that finally gushed out in my pillow.

"It's probably from sleeping on the floor," Frank said when he got home. "Stay in bed tonight, and you'll feel better tomorrow."

"I worry about dying and leaving my little children for someone else to mistreat, Frank."

"Hey . . . uh, honey. Just because you have pain in your joints does-n't mean you're gonna die." Frank held me for a long time, whispering, "You're going to be all right, honey. I'm done with the drinking. I'll take care of you and our kids."

I felt so good in his arms, but I knew that he would turn that sym-pathy into quick sex. Getting pregnant now would be devastating for me. I pulled away and turned toward the wall. By morning, I had the icy pain in every joint of my body.

A series of visits to the doctor began the next day and continued for over three weeks. Different kinds of pain relievers were prescribed, but none took away the pains, and some burned my stomach. I had blood taken out of my arm so often that I began to wonder if I would soon run out.

"You have symptoms of rheumatoid arthritis, but it's not showing in the blood," the doctor said. "I want you to go see a doctor in Rockford. He'll be able to help you more. There is nothing else I can do for you here ."

We spent another three weeks going back and forth to Rockford, where more blood was drawn, and x-rays of all kinds were taken. Then the doctor said, matter of factly, "Yours is a strange case. I can see that you're in pain. Your descriptions sound like rheumatoid arthritis, but your blood shows nothing. So at this point, my dear lady, my advice is that you buy yourself a wheelchair and move to Arizona."

That was the heaviest blow I had ever felt to my stomach; it actual-ly knocked the wind out of me.

"Your problem can be due to something else," the doctor contin-ued, expressionless. "Maybe it's the cold weather. Or maybe you miss your relatives, or even the warm climate of Puerto Rico. I just don't know."

I walked out of his office with weight on my soles, wanting never to reach the waiting room where Frank and the children were waiting. The report of my diagnosis would probably send Frank to the bars. But how long could I keep such information from him? He was the only person

I had to count on. The thought of having no one to turn to, except for a man who found his comfort in the bottle, was enough reason for me to run for my life. Yet I knew that living apart from my little children would be a death sentence. And taking them with me would mean starvation for all of us. I envisioned a dark grave at my feet, and my words spilled out through sobs.

"The doctor suggested I buy a wheelchair and move to Arizona."

"Arizona! What the hell did he mean by that?"

"I don't know! You should have gone in with me."

"How could I, with all these kids? But you want to move to California, anyway. I'll bet those pains will go away once we reach a warmer climate."

Hearing Frank say that we were moving to California sounded great, but the pains in my joints didn't let up. I could hardly get out of the car and walk into the house when we got home that day. From then on, I took a dozen aspirin tablets a day to be able to take care of my children.

One early morning after Frank left for work, I experienced the worst of all pains. He had brought me four aspirin tablets and a cup of coffee with milk and sugar. In approximately thirty minutes, I would be able to go downstairs and tend to my little ones. I had my ears tuned to the sound of the TV downstairs and thought that all three children were down there watching cartoons.

Instead, I heard a loud thud at the top of the stairway. I turned my head just a little, and listened, frozen, as my darling Lucinda hit every step of the stairs. There were bangs and booms and plops all the way down to the dining room. There was no way I could have jumped out of bed in time to save her.

Her loud shriek as she hit the bottom step claimed my heart. I let myself roll off the bed and out the bedroom door. At the top of the stairs, I sat with straight legs and went down on my seat, for my knees were frozen stiff and would not bend. By the time I reached my bruised little girl, Troy was comforting her.

"She cut her lip, Mommy, but she'll be okay," he said, and through my tears I could see the pain in his eyes.

I stayed on the floor, my arms wrapped around both of them, our tears and Lucinda's blood dotting the green linoleum.

I ached from head to toe and deep inside, seeing Lucinda's black and blue legs, arms, and face, and realizing that Troy was sensitive enough to understand what his sister and I were feeling.

Later that afternoon, while Lucinda slept on the sofa, I sat down to write a letter to my mother. This time I intended to tell her everything that had gone wrong for me since leaving Puerto Rico. So what if she wrote back telling me that I had made my bed and I should sleep in it? Maybe she would realize that I deserved better than this, and would say some prayers for me.

When I went to write *Dear Mama*, I wrote *Dear God* instead. This was chilling, but it looked good on the white sheet of paper. Had anyone ever written a letter to God before? So what if I was the first person to do such a thing? Would it hurt anyone?

I have been lost and confused for a long time, dear Lord, but I always kept my faith in you. Somehow, I have often been able to solve my problems, but I don't understand why I deserve these icy pains in my joints. And although these are the most severe physical pains I have ever had, seeing my little babies suffering hurts me even more. I don't expect you to drop everything just to help me, for I am not better than all the other people in your world. But I'm asking you to give me the knowledge to find ways of fixing my own problems.

Faithfully yours,

Well, you know who I am

The sheet of paper had more teardrops than words when I finished writing. Then, realizing that I didn't have God's address, I folded the paper in four and wrote *To God* on one side and placed it under the doily of my dresser.

A few nights later, after taking several pain pills, I fell asleep and had the weirdest of all my dreams: I was playing hide-and-seek with Lucinda in an open field in a strange land. The sun was bright and quite warm. There was no breeze, and the earth was made of small dry granules that stirred as we walked, but no dust rose from it. There were no green grass or flowers on this flat surface. And the trees, which were far apart from each other, looked like arms with crooked fingers sticking out from the granule-like soil.

One minute Lucinda was there, and the next minute she was gone. I ran around calling her desperately, the granules slipping from under my feet, making me stumble as if someone was pulling me back and someone else was pushing me, preventing me from finding my little girl. I tried to yell, but my voice had been taken from me. I kept reaching for something to pull myself out of this. I cried, but no sound came out of me. Suddenly I felt hot and unable to breathe. I gave myself permission to die, *But oh, Lord, please not before I find Lucinda.*

A voice called out to me from somewhere, and then I saw the brown, hairy legs of a man from the knee down coming from behind one of the deformed trees.

"Look only at my feet," the voice said, and I stared at the two feet which were inside worn brown leather sandals. "She's right over there," the voice continued. "She's sleeping peacefully on the warm desert sand."

I reached to touch the short black hairs that draped over the sandal strap, but found myself sitting straight in my bed, soaked in sweat, my heart pounding in my eardrums, the vision of the brown legs and sandals vivid in my mind.

After changing my wet gown, I went to check on my children. They were sleeping peacefully under their covers. I went back to my bed, but instead of sleeping, I read about the deserts of California in the encyclopedia. I saw a picture of a deformed tree and the word cactus written under it.

I knew then that our move to California would solve all our problems, and my dream had been the answer to my letter to God. That was a peaceful conclusion.

Chapter Forty-Eight

Westbound

One morning in May, I awakened without pains in my joints. I had slept all night for the first time in months. I turned on my side, still no pain. It was incredible. I had been healed over night, praise The Lord!

"Frank, my pain is gone. I can bend my arms and legs."

He raised his head from the pillow. "Are you sure? Just like that and the pain is gone? It must be a miracle."

"Whatever it is, the pain is gone. "Now you can give your notice at work. I want to leave this place before more bad things happen."

Frank stayed quiet for a while. Then he said, "How about the first of June? I want to see if I can get a better car first."

"The first of June will be fine," I answered, walking out of the room the way I had walked before the pain. Even the stairway seemed brighter that morning, as my feet landed on one step then another. *What a great feeling, to be able to bend my knees.* For the first time since we arrived at this part of the country, I felt like shouting that spring was really here and we'd be heading to the westcoast. I didn't think about jobs or money. We were leaving, and I could picture the ocean breeze, palm trees and flowers. Instead of putting the coffee on, I went to the calendar, wishing to flip the pages and put us in the month of July.

"Don't get too excited yet," Frank said when he came down.

"How can I not get excited? I'm bursting with joy. My pain is gone, and we're moving."

"Well, better pray that we are not making a mistake."

"Don't worry. I've been praying, and will pray a lot more."

"Good! We'll need all the prayers we can get."

I didn't continue the conversation for fear that he'd go to the bar. But two days later, with Nancy's help, I found a man in Ashton who owned a used furniture store. He offered me two hundred dollars for our old furniture, the refrigerator and stove, the washing machine, the old vacuum cleaner Vera had left for us, and the sewing machine, and he would not claim anything until we were gone. I agreed to this, but kept what was left of the buttons, which I would use in the coming years.

Frank bought a $1,200 station wagon, with his old car as a trade-in, and monthly payments to a bank. On the first day of June, he gave his one-month notice so his boss could find another engineer to replace him. In spite of his drinking, Frank had been able to do his job well and make friends with his boss and all the other workers.

"I felt bad," he told me that night, his face flushed as if he were ready to cry. "They all hated to see me go."

"You'll make new friends again," I said, feeling bad, for it was my fault that he had to leave the job he liked so well.

The night before we left, Nancy and her family came by to say goodbye. Frank and Kent shook hands and forced themselves to smile.

Nancy and I hugged each other. "Write to me once you get settled," she cried.

"You have been a great friend," I told her, brushing away my own tears. "I'll never forget you."

We watched them drive away, and I felt the same sadness I had felt saying goodbye to my friends in Minnesota, and years earlier to my family in Puerto Rico.

A couple of hours before Nancy's visit, we had said goodbye to Mr. and Mrs. Peters, and I had cried when they hugged the children. "You won't become farmers in California," Mr. Peters said to the boys.

Mrs. Peters chuckled. "No, they might become movie stars."

"I'm going to be a cowboy," Rodney said.

"Me, too," Troy added, and the couple laughed. But I could not stop my tears from flowing. My children might not find another couple like Mr. and Mrs. Peters in California.

That night, as I stretched out in our bed, I said, "It's sad to say goodbye to nice people, but I'm sure we'll make new friends wherever we go."

"Yeah, it's sad, all right," Frank said. "But not as sad as it is to leave this old bed. It was Ma's bed for many years."

That, too, made me feel bad. "I know it's sad, but we need a new beginning."

"Well . . . uh, but first we have to get back to normal." The old bed squeaked as he turned toward me, his lips puckered and a look in his eyes.

"We have a long way to go before we can find whatever you consider normal." I kissed the side of his face and quickly turned toward the wall.

"Oh, shit!" Frank said, turning his back to mine. But he was snoring within minutes.

I stayed awake for a long time, praying that the move would strengthen my love for Frank, and that together we could lead our children to a better future.

The next day at dawn, on the fifth day of July, we loaded the station wagon with clothes, sheets, pillows, blankets, towels, two boxes of dishes, and the Styrofoam cooler with milk, cold cuts for sandwiches, and a package of ground meat for that night's hamburgers in some campground along the way. In a cardboard box, we had bread, chips, cookies, and hamburger buns. We would stop in grocery stores when necessary to refill the cooler.

The boys, who were singing, "California, here we come," occupied the back seat with their few toys, and Lucinda with two dolls rode in front with us. We were off by nine o'clock that morning.

When we reached the paved road, we saw the used furniture store owner and his son in a pickup truck. They were on their way to pick up our furniture, which he had paid for two days earlier. I couldn't hold back my tears then, but Frank patted my hand.

"We'll be okay, honey."

I nodded, then took a deep breath of that manure-smelling country air.

We drove away with a total of six hundred dollars to our name. "I'm less likely to lose it," Frank had said during a dispute over who would budget the money.

"What if someone grabs you in a gas station bathroom?"

"Nobody's going to grab me," he had answered.

"You need to start treating me like I'm an adult, Frank."

"What the hell does that mean?"

"It means that you carry half of the money and I'll carry the other half. If one of us gets robbed during the drive, the other one will have money to get the children to a safe place."

"You've been watching too much TV," he said.

I had said nothing else because I didn't want a fight. But eventually he gave me half of the money, and the responsibility of budgeting it.

I figured one hundred dollars for food and gas, one hundred for cheap motels along the way, and one hundred would go to any car breakdown we might have. With three hundred left, we would rent a house for under a hundred, and have two hundred dollars left for food until Frank found work. It would be my challenge to spend less and end up with more than three hundred dollars upon reaching California. I knew I could do it if none of us got sick along the way.

For days before leaving, I had studied the maps Frank had brought home. We would head south, then connect with major highways leading to Los Angeles.

"No," Frank had said. "We're heading north, and then taking the route leading to Sacramento, which is the capitol of California."

"It's warmer in the southern part of the state, Frank."

"Yeah, well, I know more about geography than you do."

I had to avoid another argument, but I had read about California more than he had. I knew that the state ran alongside the ocean all the way to the Mexican border. It had sandy beaches, flowers everywhere, and in the southern part we would never be snowed in. We'd be close to Hollywood, too, where anything was possible according to talks I had heard on TV, and close to Disneyland, which my children would enjoy.

"We should try to enjoy this drive instead of fighting, Frank. It's not every day that people like us can drive across the United States."

"Well, I hardly consider this a vacation," he said.

"No, but we can pretend, can't we?"

I made a mistake by saying that, because from then on, he could hardly wait to reach a motel so that once the children fell asleep, we would play honeymooners. It always turned into an argument, however. And the next night he would start the problem all over again. In the first place, I didn't want to get pregnant, and secondly, it didn't seem right to have sex in the same room with the children, even if they were asleep.

The thing about intercourse was still a mystery to me, even after three children. I couldn't understand why Frank enjoyed it so much, when all I ever got was another baby. It wasn't that I hadn't heard about sex before. Nancy and my old neighbors back in St. Paul had talked about it often – although they called it *screwing*, not intercourse. I always listened, but never volunteered any information, because I believed that such topics should be private between a man and his wife. I also believed that only married people who were old enough to accept responsibility were entitled to sex. I never expected it to become an open subject, or something anyone could do in any old place and at any age.

Frank had never been one to talk much, especially while driving. But on this long drive, he didn't have a choice. The boys asked him questions all the time. And I had questions, as well as suggestions.

I knew that Frank liked me better when I let him have his way in bed, and when I didn't know much about anything. Still, he needed to know that the naive little girl he had married was learning to watch out for herself, even if that made him feel less powerful. If I knew the answer to one of the boys' questions, I wasn't going to keep quiet while Frank took his time with an answer.

"Well," Frank said, "just because you read a few books doesn't mean that you know everything."

"I'm not claiming to know everything, Frank."

"Then don't jump to answer a question addressed to me."

"I didn't jump. You were too slow."

"The problem is that you're getting too smart too fast."

"Are you afraid that I might become smarter than you?"

Frank took a deep breath and said nothing.

"Is that why you don't want me to read the map?" By then, he had pulled off the road several times to run his index finger over the fine green and red lines on the map.

"Of course not! But it's my responsibility to get us there without ending up in Mexico or Canada. After all, you haven't been reading maps for very long."

"It doesn't take a long time to learn how to read a map!"

"Okay, well . . . I'm the man in this family, anyway."

I let that remark fly by, too, because I needed him to get us to

California. But I didn't like to be treated as if I didn't know anything, just as I didn't like it when he had turned to the bottle after losing a member of his family or a job.

At some point, on our third day on the road, Frank made a wrong turn. We ended up in Denver in the late afternoon when people were getting off work and many cars were pulling onto the crowded streets.

I turned my head slightly and saw the movement in Frank's right temple. He was biting hard on his teeth, trying to find a good place to turn around.

"I knew you were making the wrong turn," I said.

"Fine! But don't rub it in!"

My plan had been that every day, before twelve, we would keep our eyes open for a park. I would prepare our noon meal there while the children ran and stretched their legs. Then we would sit under a tree and watch them play a little longer. That way, they would take long naps in the car.

"Well," Frank had said. "The more stops we make, the longer it's going to take us to get there."

"Yes, but you can't expect three little children to sit all day in a cramped car."

"Why not? It's only for a week."

"A week is a long time for children."

"Well, you always have the last word, so be it!" He dragged hard on the stinky cigarette, his nose seeming to grow bigger each time the two streams of smoke spilled out. That was an indication that he needed a few drinks. "You know, Frank, the longer I know you, the more you sound like my father . . . and you won't believe what happened to him."

"I'm not trying to be like your father. I never met the man." Frank punched the steering wheel. "Shit!" He stepped on the gas and continued on a winding road that eventually led us to Salt Lake city.

I took over the map then, and saw something that might make him feel better.

"The turn you made back there could turn out to be a blessing," I said softly.

"Oh? How is that?"

"There is a big base on the Mojave Desert, and this highway leads to it. You might be able to find a job there."

"Yeah, well, if you're talking about Edwards Air Force Base, that's in Sacramento, not in the Mojave Desert."

"No, no, Frank. See, I have my finger on it. It's in the Mojave Desert."

"I knew a guy who was stationed there for four years, and he told me it's in Sacramento. That's why we are going there. The base has its own power plant, and I am hopping to apply for a job."

"Why didn't you tell me that before? It would have kept me from worrying."

"Because I didn't want to give you false hopes. It would be a government job, and I might not qualify. "

I shoved the map under the seat. "You're right, Frank, it is in Sacramento. But I'm not too disappointed in myself, because you know more about everything than I do." I crossed my arms, threw my head back, and closed my eyes.

"Well, honey, I grew up in this country, so I should know more than you. But that doesn't mean you're stupid. In fact, I think you're pretty smart . . . sometimes even smarter than yours truly."

I didn't say another word on that subject, but I knew that for the first time, he was right. I was smarter than he was. I felt good knowing that he had realized it.

Frank drove for three more days, stopping in parks and rest stops and sleeping in cheap motels near the main highway. By then, he had yelled at the boys many times for arguing and punching one another.

"Well, Daddy," Rodney said a few times over his dad's shoulder, "you're not so smart."

"Yeah, Daddy." Troy stood next to his brother. "If you were smart, we'd be wherever we're going already."

"Better sit back and shut up before I pull off the road and spank you guys."

I said nothing, but hoped that he would not do such a thing. I wanted our children to grow up with the freedom to express what they felt. One day they would learn that their parents were not the brightest people in the world. They would also learn that our ignorance created them, and *they* were the only good outcome of it all.

Chapter Forty-Nine

One Wrong Turn

Frank exited the freeway and followed the signs to Sacramento as if he knew exactly where he was going. Then he pulled into a gas station and asked the attendant for directions to Edwards Air Force base.

"Edwards! That's on the other side of Bakersfield."

I felt embarrassed for Frank. He stepped out of the car seeming confused, and with a patch of sweat on the back of his shirt. Still, I crossed my arms and stared straight ahead at the green trees and grass a few feet away, my right foot tapping the floorboard of the car.

"Damn!" Frank said as he got back into the car. "Son-of-a bitch sent me out on a wild goose chase."

"Who sent you on a wild goose chase?" I asked, a burst of laughter breaking inside my throat.

"That damn friend who told me Edwards was in Sacramento."

"You should have looked at the map," Rodney said, squatting down behind me.

"Yeah, Daddy, you should have listened to Mommy," Troy added, then leaned back on the seat to escape Frank's hand. I felt too sorry for Frank to say what I thought.

He drove away slowly at first, then stepped hard on the gas and headed toward the highway. "I don't want to hear a damn word from any of you. We're going to a town called Lancaster for the night."

Lucinda sucked her thumb and stared at her dad until her eyes closed. But the boys stretched and complained. "Are we ever going to get there?" Rodney whined.

"No!" Troy answered. "Daddy doesn't even know where he's going!"

Frank drove on, a cigarette in his lips, nose straight ahead, smoke steadily coming out of his nostrils. I sniffed, rubbed my eyes, and waited.

We pulled into Lancaster at midnight, and found *No Vacancy* signs at every motel. At one of those motels, a man called other places for us. "Sorry folks," he said, "but I don't think you'll find a place in this town. It's Friday night, and there is a motorcycle race in Tehachapi. There are people from everywhere in this town and in Palmdale. Every motel is bursting at the seams."

Frank looked as if he had been hit. Even the next cigarette didn't comfort him. "I could easily pour a whole damn bottle of whiskey down my throat, and I'd probably still feel like a big piece of crap!" He clobbered the steering wheel, then turned the key to start the engine. "You tell me what the hell to do, because I haven't a damn clue."

I wanted to explode, but instead I said, "Okay. First of all, stop being mad, and don't even think about whiskey, because all that would do is turn you into that piece of you-know-what you don't want to be. And secondly, drive down one of those wide streets and find a place to park. We'll spend the rest of the night in the car."

Frank didn't say a word, but backed up and drove down a narrow street, then turned onto a four lane road, Avenue L. About a half mile down, I spotted a bright light over a low building on our left. As we came closer, a sign with an arrow read *Highway Patrol.*

"Turn in there," I said. Frank did, and I pointed to a parking space near the back door of the building. "Park over there." This had not been planned; it had just happened. The sign had appeared, and I told Frank what to do, but I had no idea what to expect from the Highway Patrol building.

Within seconds, a tall, uniformed man came out and walked toward us. I told Frank to let me do the talking. He nodded.

As I rolled down the window, the officer asked, "Need some help?"

"Yes, we do," I said. "We just arrived in town, but all the motels are full, and we need to spend the rest of the night in the car. I thought this would be a safe place, if you can let us stay."

He peered inside the car and saw the boys like rag dolls twisted around each other. "Where are you coming from, and where are you headed?"

"Coming from Illinois. My husband will be working at Edwards Air Force Base." I worried that Frank might cut in and admit that he didn't have a job waiting. If he did, the officer might think we were drifters and chase us away.

"No problem," the officer said. "You'll be fine here. And we have some blankets you can use. How about some coffee, and chocolate for the kiddies when they wake up? Feel free to use our washrooms, too."

Frank stepped out and shook hands with the officer. "Thank you for your understanding. It's been a long drive, and I feel small and incapable at the moment."

"No need to feel bad," the officer said. "We see this kind of thing happening often. We're glad to help. This is much better than having to assist someone in an accident."

Frank followed the officer inside, and I stayed with the children. I realized how fortunate we had been. A whole week on the road and no accidents, not even a flat tire. *Someone up there is watching over us.*

Frank and the officer came back with blankets and a small tray of hot coffee and doughnuts.

"Come in to use the washroom whenever you need to," the officer said. "In the morning, bring the little ones in for some hot chocolate."

"Thank you very much," I said, looking at the kindest face I had seen since Don Felipe back in Puerto Rico a long time ago. I couldn't hold back the tears as the officer walked away, and old memories flooded my mind. So many things had happened to me since I ran away from home all those years ago. I had been hoping to find a good place in which to spend the rest of my life, yet it had all seemed to be an endless struggle.

"Thank you for not getting mad at me for making that stupid mistake back there," Frank said with sad eyes.

I sipped my coffee. "Forget it. You got us here safely. That's the important thing."

We held hands over Lucinda, who slept soundly between us. The parking lot of the Highway Patrol office was home for our first night in the state of California. But we would not talk about this to anyone. We would never mention it to Frank's family, not to mine, and not even to our children. If they realized upon waking that we had spent the night here, we would admit it to them. Otherwise, we would let this memory fade away.

Chapter Fifty

The Beginning

"Thank you for your hospitality and understanding," I said to the officer the next morning when we took the children in to use their washroom facilities. Frank and I had agreed to pass on the coffee, chocolate, and doughnuts. This would save us from humiliation, for we knew that the boys might say something, and we would end up admitting that we were actually chasing a dream. It was bad enough knowing that we would be in a heap of trouble if Frank didn't find a job right away, so having to tell the people of our new town about it would be too painful.

We drove east on Avenue L from the Highway Patrol parking lot.

"Mommy, was that a police station?" asked Troy.

Rodney jumped to answer. "No, dummy, that was a jail!"

"That was a Highway Patrol station, Rodney," I said. "Don't call your brother a dummy. We stopped there for some information when you guys were asleep. They let us use their bathroom because you were nice boys."

The boys looked at each other and smiled. I would tell them the whole story some day when they were old enough to understand. I wasn't ashamed, but I didn't want them to develop a negative image of their parents.

A short distance from the Highway Patrol building, we came up to a shopping center which had all the major stores, including Sears and J.C. Penney.

"Good old Sears," Frank said, giving the steering wheel the little sweep with the palm of his hand.

"We'll charge only the bare necessities," I said. "Even if it means sleeping on the floor for months."

"Well, you just pray really hard that I find a job soon."

"I don't believe in praying for things like that, but I'll pray for good health and the ability to do whatever it takes to get us a better beginning."

We stopped at a family restaurant near the shopping center, where the children and I had pancakes, and Frank had eggs and bacon for the first time since we had left Rochelle, Illinois.

From the restaurant, we stopped at a gas station for a map of the city. Then we drove up one street and down another, where homes looked expensive and well-kept. After leaving that area, we crossed Sierra Highway, and turned into a community where the homes looked like those of low-income people. We drove down one street after another and saw several signs in the front yards of homes for rent, but they were all a hundred dollars or more.

We kept looking. Finally, we saw our house – a two-story house in the middle of the block with tall grass and weeds all around it. Taped on the inside of a window was a white piece of cardboard with big black letters that read, *FOR RENT.*

"Pull in there," I said to Frank. I hurried out of the car and to the sign on the window. *Four bedrooms, two bathrooms, eighty dollars a month, you clean it.* I shielded my eyes from the sun with my hands and looked into the living room. The carpet looked faded and worn in spots, and pieces of paper and beer cans had been swept into a corner. But the place looked cleanable.

I hurried back to the car, intending to go find a pay phone and call the number listed. But as I reached for the car door, a young woman came out of the house next door.

"I have the key to that house, if you want to see it," she said with a smile. "My name is Judy. I volunteered to show that house because the owner lives down in Long Beach, and I'm tired of seeing it empty. My husband has been mowing the lawn, but he hurt his back. That's why the weeds took over." Judy was blonde with blue eyes. She was about my age, had three children, and was expecting another.

I knew immediately that I wanted the place. For one thing, I could see that Judy and I would become good friends. The other reason was that I had liked living in a two-story home. This one was newer than the one in Illinois, and it was bound to be warmer in the winter.

Judy's oldest boy, Tommy, was Rodney's age. Before we even entered the house, the two boys were running through the tall weeds.

Her daughter Linda looked like a doll, with big blue eyes and blonde, curly hair. She was close to Troy's age, and she stood making eyes at him while he took his time coming out of the car. Then the two ran after the other boys. Judy's youngest boy was one-year-old Billy. He stared at Lucinda, but she sucked her thumb and showed no interest in him.

We made a quick inspection of the house. It had carpet only in the living room. The rest of the house had beige and brown vinyl tile. It was ugly, but easier to clean than an old carpet. The kitchen cabinets needed repairs and a good cleaning, but I knew that was something I could do. The stairway to the second floor was made of wood that could use a few coats of varnish, something Frank could handle.

The two rooms upstairs were bright, with two windows each. There were no curtains, but I could make some. The floor up there was wood, with narrow boards like the ones in our new house in St. Paul, but they also needed varnish. The bathroom was only a toilet and sink; the shower and tub were in the bigger bathroom downstairs. We hurried through, checking the light switches, closets, and water faucets.

"We'll take it," I said.

Judy clapped. "Good! I'll help you clean it."

"Oh, thank you," I said, "but we can do that ourselves. But if you have a vacuum cleaner I could use, that would be great."

"I'll go get it," she said and hurried out the door. By then, the boys and Linda had been to the back yard and up and down the stairway, yelling as if they had known each other for years.

Judy came back with a vacuum cleaner, a plastic bucket, a mop, soap, and a bunch of rags. She insisted on running the vacuum cleaner, so I mopped the floors. Meanwhile, her husband Marvin had come out of the house, groggy with nerve relaxers, and told Frank he could use his weed-whacker and lawnmower.

It all seemed like a dream to me. There I was needing a good night's sleep, yet scrubbing a filthy floor, a young girl I had just met helping me, my boys running around with new friends – and Frank, also needing sleep, mowing and raking grass someone else had neglected. No money had been paid up to this point, yet we were all assuming that this would be our home for some time.

I had not volunteered any information to our new neighbors about our furniture or jobs. They simply concluded that Frank had a job waiting at Edwards Air Force Base. All I had told Judy was that we had come here because Frank would be working there. I hadn't said that he had a job waiting, or was going there to look for work.

By two o'clock that afternoon, we had cleaned the place inside and out. Marvin had ordered pizza for all of us, and had refused to let us pay for half.

"We'll make it up to you," I said.

"You bet we will," Frank added. "Not only have we been blessed with finding this place, but meeting you is more than we could've hoped for."

"We've been hoping for a family to move here for a long time," Marvin said. "The last tenants were a couple of crazy guys that made our lives miserable."

It was good to hear that our new neighbors had a good reason for wanting us there, but of course, I didn't tell them that. We paid them one month's rent, thanked them for all their help, and excused ourselves, for we needed to go shopping.

"If there's anything else we can do, just let me know," Judy said as they walked out.

We drove to Sears, where we charged sleeping bags, air mattresses, and a bigger cooler. From there, we stopped at a grocery store and bought ice, milk, corn flakes, bread, peanut butter, strawberry jam, and ground meat. We would eat light until Frank found a job.

Back at the house that night, after a light snack and baths, we made one big bed on the floor of one of the upstairs bedrooms. Frank and I lay next to our children, and I whispered that we were far away from home, vacationing in a small campground where everything was good, clean, and beautiful. Neither of us knew who fell asleep first.

I was the first to awaken to the sounds of California birds, children, and cars. I went to the window and smelled the desert air. It was dry, cool, and refreshing. It made me feel good all over, as if I had reached a heavenly place and all my problems were behind me at last.

I went downstairs to turn on my electric coffee pot. Then, while the coffee brewed, I opened the back door and stepped outside. A cool breeze wrapped around me, and I knew that the California air had magic, and I had opened a huge window to the world. Now I could reach beyond my dreams. I could breathe better than ever before, and a boost of energy traveled through me. This was a new beginning, a place where I would be able to grow, unrestricted by freezing air or snow. In this California location, I would find ways to earn some money while caring for my children. There was no doubt in my mind that Frank would find a job – if not on the base, then somewhere else. And if there was a way for me to earn some money, I would do whatever I had to do to find it.

I inhaled deeply, filling my lungs with fresh desert air. Then I went back inside and carried two mugs of coffee to the second floor. I stood quietly at first, one mug in each hand, and stared at my husband and three children sleeping so peacefully. I had taken the right steps to bring us here. Frank might never tell that to me, or to anyone else, for that matter, but I knew who had motivated this move, and that was the important thing. I had stated what I wanted, and he hadn't disputed the idea.

I sat near Frank's head and placed the mugs on the floor. "It's time to wake up," I said softly. "It's time to get up and smell the fresh California air." Soon I had four pairs of eyes glaring at me.

"Oh, yeah, we're in California," Troy said, yawning. The silence was broken. The three children had gotten enough rest and were ready to take on the neighborhood.

"We'll pack some sandwiches and an old blanket and go check out our new town and its surroundings," I said. "What do you think, gang?" I had learned words like "gang" from Nancy back in Illinois.

Rodney sprang from under the cover, his curly hair aiming in all directions. "If you're planning to keep us cramped in the car all day, then I'm staying here and playing with Tommy." Not waiting for a reply, he pulled up his pajama bottoms and dashed off to the bathroom.

"That kid is growing up too fast," Frank grumbled, then sipped his coffee. "So, what are you planning?"

"Come to the kitchen and I'll tell you," I said.

"Can we go, too?" Troy asked.

"No, it's going to be a surprise, so stay here until I call you down to breakfast." Rodney would have protested, but Troy just smiled and nodded.

Downstairs, I explained to Frank that staying around the house all day would give us too much time with the neighbors, and we might end up telling them that he would be looking for any kind of job, doing anything to keep us from starving.

"I gotta hand it to you, honey. That's a damn good idea. I just hope that I can find the job you think is out there waiting for me."

"Well, if you don't find a job right away, I might be able to do some cleaning for one of the local motels. Cleaning is something I can do, and I would probably get paid each day, or each week. In any case, we're not going to starve."

"You're right, honey. But I'd rather work at a gas station than see you cleaning motel rooms."

"You're going to work for a gas station?" Rodney had come down and was standing at the doorway, hands on his hips, dressed in his play clothes.

Frank stood square in front of his son. "Get back upstairs until we call you, young man!"

Rodney turned and went to the living room window. "We should have stayed in Illinois!"

When Frank went upstairs to get dressed, I hugged Rodney and whispered that his daddy and I really needed the help of our oldest son. "You can help us by keeping your brother and sister from running around. We need to see where the parks with swings and games are in this town, so I can take you guys there when your daddy's working. And before we come home today, we can stop in one of those fast food places and have hamburgers and ice cream sodas. What do you think about that?"

"I think it's good, Mommy. But this time I want my own French fries that I don't have to share with anyone, and tomorrow I want to play with Tommy all day."

I squeezed him tightly and took a deep breath. "You've got a deal, sweetheart."

When we walked out with our cooler and the old blanket, Judy came out. "Did you all have a good night?"

I told her that we had, and that we were going to check out the town. "We may be back late. If so, we'll see you tomorrow."

"Check out the park," she said as we backed away.

"You should have told her that you had planned that already!" Rodney said.

"You're right, Rodney," I said. "But we can make her feel good when we thank her tomorrow for giving us the idea."

"Good thought, Mommy," Troy said.

Frank smiled and winked at me, and I felt that California was the right place for us.

Chapter Fifty-One

Cactus Trees

We drove toward the center of town, then through its main street, past a Salvation Army store, the theater, a drugstore, and a fabric store. From there, we stopped at a nice park across from the civic center.

After the children swung on the swings and slid on the slides, we drove north. At two different gas stations, we saw signs that read *Help Wanted*. Frank would come back tomorrow. We kept going north, toward Edwards Air Force Base, on a lonely road with cactus trees on each side.

"Oh, what crooked trees," Rodney whined.

"Those are cactus," I explained, feeling proud for knowing that information. "They grow in the desert, and some have water you can suck out if you are stranded."

"How do you know that, Mommy?" Troy asked over my shoulder.

"She read it in the encyclopedia." Frank answered quickly.

"Did you read that, too, Daddy?"

"I read it a long time ago, Troy."

Rodney grasped the ridge of our seat and pulled himself forward. "You mean you read it in the old days, right, Daddy?"

"All right, son, enough with the wisecracks!"

I burst out laughing. "Serves you right for answering a question addressed to me." Frank said no more and drove on.

The base stretched for miles and miles left and right, a cluster of buildings here, and another there, with patches of grass and shrubs and some flowers in between. Huge open spaces of concrete or blacktop ran from one cluster of buildings to another, and every now and then we found a patch of sandy soil that appeared as dry as old bones.

We read the gold letters with arrows on the blue metal signs posted in street corners: *Hospital, Mess Hall, Personnel Office*, and many others.

Frank pointed to a high chimney way out in the distance. "Power plant. See it? I would be lucky to find a job there." His eyes lit up. "Civil service, good health insurance, and four weeks vacation a year." He gave the steering wheel the old sweep with the palm of his hand. "Yup, I would be so lucky."

"So, are you going to check it out tomorrow?" I asked.

"Well . . . uh, I think one has to write first."

"If I were you, I'd show up here first thing tomorrow in my best outfit and with all my papers that have information about my previous jobs. If they turned me away, I'd write the letter and take a temporary job elsewhere while I waited for an answer."

Frank got up early Monday morning, dressed in his best shirt and trousers, and drove back to Edward Air Force Base with his folder in hand.

I could have said a special prayer that he would find the kind of job he wanted. But I left it all in the hands of fate. If it was meant to be, he would find the job.

I visited with Judy that morning and asked her questions about the neighborhood, while our children played in her back yard.

"The people on our street are down-to-earth and friendly," she said. "The husbands work, and most of the women stay home with the kids. That one in the green house across the street is the only one you'll have a hard time getting to know. I've been here seven years, and have talked with her no more than a dozen times. She has six kids and is expecting another sometime after Christmas. She has never mentioned this, but most of us neighbor women believe that her husband beats her."

"He beats her?" I was shocked. "I didn't think American men did things like that."

"Sure they do," she said. "But the women are too ashamed to talk about it. They hide until the bruises fade away."

I changed the subject because I didn't want to know if she had ever been beaten. "So, what's available in this town for a woman who might want to earn a few dollars without having to leave her children alone?"

Judy was quite helpful. By late afternoon, I had two plans made for myself. I would order a telephone, charge a sewing machine at Sears, run an ad in the local newspaper, and take in sewing. According to Judy, the only dressmaker in town had moved to Fresno. "You'll be swamped with work in no time," she said.

If by chance the sewing idea didn't work out, I would take in ironing. Judy said that women like school teachers and nurses paid someone else to do their ironing. This was before polyester and knit fabrics, so everything needed ironing. I had never minded having to iron for hours, and I was very good at it. Earning a little money at it would make the job more pleasurable.

I cooked the ground meat we had bought the day before, and added onions and tomato sauce. We would eat it between slices of bread as soon as Frank got back, then we would leave for the shopping center.

I could tell that Frank had gotten the job when he drove up the driveway with a smile. I ran to the door. "You got a job, didn't you?"

He took me in his arms. "Starting next Monday. How does that grab you?"

"It grabs me just fine. Tell me all about it."

"It's really incredible how it happened," he said, bubbly, his hands shaking. "First, I was turned away at the door by a security guard behind a desk at the entrance of this huge building. He said I needed an appointment to apply for a job. Then, as I was on my way out, a door behind him swung open and a large woman appeared. She asked him something. He answered in a low voice, but she called me into her office. Mrs. Andersen – that's her name – asked me about a dozen questions. Why was I there, and did I have some recommendations? How long had I been working in a power plant, and did I have a family, and so on. I answered everything and showed her my papers. After a while, she said I should come back after twelve. Meanwhile, I asked if I could go see the power plant, and she gave me a pass.

"At the power plant, I met some of the guys working there. They are very nice and knowledgeable. Then the head man told me that one of their workers who had been there for a long time had found out he had cancer, was in the hospital, and was not expected to come back. I felt really bad for the poor man, but that explained why Mrs. Andersen had called me into her office. Evidently, they needed someone to replace the sick worker, and miraculously I walked in. I swear, honey, you must have ESP."

"What's ESP?"

"Extra sensory perception." Frank winked at me with a sweet smile. "If you hadn't thought of us coming here, we would have grown old in Illinois."

That made me feel good about myself, but I still told Frank about my plan. After supper, we went to Sears and charged the sewing machine. We went to the phone company the next day and ordered our phone. From there we stopped at the Salvation Army store and bought a chest of drawers for six dollars. It had five drawers, one for each family member.

While I cleaned the drawers and put our clothes away, Frank went to a lumber yard and bought two sheets of plywood and some four-by-fours. He spent the rest of the week making our dining table and a longer table for cutting fabrics.

Our phone was installed on Friday morning, and the minute the man left, I called the local newspaper. My first customer called on Tuesday, and I was in business. From then on, I had something to sew every day.

Things were working out incredibly well. Frank left for work every morning, and the boys played with Judy's children and met many other friends. Every home on this street had at least one child, some had five or six. With the playing came some squabbles. Troy kept a distance from them, but Rodney was usually a participant. I became a referee at times.

Through Judy, I met the other neighborhood women, and all but the one in the green house would run over every now and then for coffee and a quick chat. I had no difficulty talking and laughing with any of them. Still, Judy and I seemed to have more in common with each other. She helped me keep an eye on my children when I had a customer, and I watched hers when she went to the doctor for her pregnancy care. And when she had her baby in mid-November, I watched her three children.

Of all the neighborhoods I had known in the United States, this became my favorite. Each day, I learned something new from one woman or another. They were all homemakers living on tight budgets with working husbands – some who smoked and drank beer, some who bowled with a team, and others who went hunting for deer and rabbits in the mountains.

I also learned that some of these ladies got into arguments over each other's children and dogs. Two women who lived next door to each other across the street even fought over the smell of dog poop. One of them decided to get even by scooping the poop with a shovel and throwing it over the fence onto her neighbor's side yard. "It's yours, so *you* smell it!" she shouted. Soon, the other woman got her shovel, and through our window we could see the poop fly back and forth over their fence. Eventually, one of the husbands appeared and broke up the fight.

I kept a friendly distance from such women, and warned my boys to stay on our side of the street.

Two of my customers also became my friends. One was Mrs. Shoemaker, a plump older lady who needed large dresses made specially for her. The experience I had obtained sewing for my big sister-in-law back in St. Paul benefitted me in Lancaster. I made dresses for Mrs. Shoemaker that fit her better than anything she had ever bought at the store.

"You're a genius, young lady," she would say. Soon she was stopping by just to say hello, always with a basket of fruits and cookies for my children. "You can call me Grandma," she told them with a grandma smile that won my heart.

The next lady was Mrs. Asher, another stout woman with fitting problems and the need to be a grandmother. At last my children had two substitute grandmas replacing the missing ones. Although I told my children who their real grandmothers were, it felt good to pretend. "Come to Grandma," the ladies would say to Lucinda, who was now going on two and needed a lot of attention. And I, who had work up to my ears with the children, the housekeeping, and the sewing, needed the wisdom of an older woman now and then.

Rodney started first grade that September, with children who had attended kindergarten, which he had missed in Illinois. This became a problem for him, especially knowing that his brother started kindergarten before his fifth birthday.

I didn't get to walk them to school for their first day, because Lucinda had been in bed with a cold, which I feared would turn into an asthma attack. Feeling overwhelmed, I stood outside, and through tears watched them walk away with Judy and two of her children. My little boys had become of school age while I was still struggling to have a happy life. It was more like they had grown up and were on their way to the Army.

I felt such an emptiness in my chest. *My babies are on their way to school. A short time ago, I was searching for my place in the world. Now I'm striving to keep what I have found, but I'm not sure it is the place. Meanwhile, I have three little people who count on me. They probably think I'm old, as I thought of my mother. Yet I feel like a little girl, still starving for love and affection.*

The emptiness in my chest eased a little when Troy returned at 11:30, but it didn't go away completely until Rodney arrived, close to three o'clock in the afternoon.

It took me a long time to get used to having school-aged children. And while the other mothers went places during school hours, I kept sewing to earn our grocery money. Frank's check was hardly enough to cover the rent, the car payment, and all other expenses.

Frank's schedule was the same as the one in Illinois. He started on the eight to four shift, and changed every three weeks. Each morning he drove away in *his* car, so if I needed to go someplace, I had to wait for him to come home so he could play chauffeur.

"No wife of mine is going to drive," he insisted.

"Let me drive to the grocery store," I said one morning when he came home from the midnight shift.

"I'm wide awake. I can drive you."

"I'm the only woman in this neighborhood who is not allowed to drive, Frank. How do you think I feel about that?"

"Well, I don't know how you feel, but you should feel glad that I want to take care of you."

"One day you're going to realize how stupid you sound when you say things like that, Frank!"

"I'll cross that bridge when I come to it. But right now, I'm going to take care of my family the only way I know how. I do the driving, I write the checks, I pay the bills, and everything else. That's my responsibility."

"Okay, Frank, but one day, you're going to be sorry for treating me like this."

"What the hell is that supposed to mean?"

"I don't know, but I'll bet you can figure it out for yourself if you try." I walked away without another word. He went to bed, and was snoring within minutes. *His* car sat in the driveway all day.

The other women in our neighborhood drove their only car when the husbands were sleeping and on weekends. And those women not only wrote the checks for their groceries, but for all their bills, too. Watching them come and go made me feel owned, but I didn't make a big issue out of it as long as Frank stayed out of the bars.

We had a great Christmas that year. By then, we had bought a bed for us and one for each of the children at Sears, on our charge account. We had picked up an old sofa and two chairs at the Salvation Army, had ripped off the old covers, and with fabric I bought on sale and Frank's help, I had made them look brand new.

We had a few extra presents under the Christmas tree for the children, thanks to Mrs. Shoemaker and Mrs. Asher, who brought them each a toy wrapped in red and green paper. I had made new outfits and pajamas for them, which I wrapped in Christmas paper and tied with red ribbons. I made cookies shaped like Christmas trees and Santas for my family, and some for Judy and her family.

After putting aside the bad feelings about not being allowed to drive or write checks, things ran pretty smoothly, except for the old problem behind our bedroom door. Every night when Frank was home, and at two o'clock in the morning when he worked from four to twelve, I had to fight in order to get some rest and keep from getting pregnant.

I never told him that he was being a pig about the intercourse, but I believed that he was exactly that. I had heard Judy say that about her husband, who had to mount her every single night. I didn't tell Judy that Frank was the same way, but I lived in fear. If I denied myself to my husband, he would head for the bars.

Yet he made his first visit to a California bar on New Year's Eve. He got off from work at midnight and went straight to a club outside the base. He staggered into the house after 3:00 a.m., the stench of tobacco smoke and booze surrounding him like a thick cloud.

Chapter Fifty-Two

Forever Drunk

Frank didn't visit the bars every night after that New Year's Eve, but often enough to keep me disgusted and to squeeze our budget. Sometimes he spent more on drinks for himself and his friends in one hour than I earned in a whole day of sewing. It was like pouring water into a bucket that had a huge hole in its bottom. We would never catch up with our bills. Yet he insisted that the money he spent drinking came from his wages, not mine.

As the days turned into weeks, and the weeks into months, our situation grew worse. I finally stopped trying to reason with him. I kept busy and tried to act as if nothing was wrong, because I didn't want to argue or appear angry in front of the children. Of course, I often had to remind Frank that it was an act, not an invitation to bed.

One day I decided to teach him a lesson. It was a Sunday afternoon in mid-September, when the leaves were beginning to fall. I had been angry and lonely, for he had gone fishing with a friend on Saturday and had returned home close to midnight, then slept until noon. He had breakfast for lunch, then announced that he had to change the oil and rotate the tires on the car.

Too mad to ask him if he planned on spending some of the weekend with the children and me, I watched him through the living room window as he opened the trunk of the car and took out his tools. He didn't appear to be thinking of us.

I went upstairs and took a shower. The whole time, I thought about how sorry I would make him feel by the end of the day.

I hurried out of the shower, wrapped myself in a big towel, then went to look out through the boys' window. Frank was reaching under the hood, and the boys were playing cowboys and Indians nearby. *Good! They'll be busy for a long time.* I went to my closet, pushed hangers around, and pulled out a peach-colored blouse and a tube-tied navy blue skirt I had made long before meeting Frank.

Lucinda had gone down for her nap a little late, and was sound asleep, so I tiptoed while getting ready. I tied my hair into a ponytail with a red ribbon, and put on a little lipstick. I wore an old pair of black high-heeled shoes that were dried up and stiff because I hadn't worn them for years.

I headed downstairs quietly and out through the kitchen, hoping to avoid the boys, but Rodney spotted me.

"Mommy, where are you going all dressed up?"

That got Frank's attention. "Yeah, what's up? Going somewhere?" He stood holding a greasy piece of metal, his hands covered with black oil.

"Yes, I am. And you're in charge of the children. And don't forget Lucinda. She's still sleeping." I talked and walked, never looking back. Since his car was up on the jack, he wouldn't come after me.

I took quick steps with my tube-tied skirt and stiff, high-heeled shoes. I wasn't eighteen anymore, but I felt brighter than ever before. I had learned a lot from the "soaps" on television, and from the friends I had made in different neighborhoods. The afternoon was beautiful, with clear skies and a mild breeze that made the tree branches wave and the tall grass sway gracefully.

I turned right on one road and left on another, heading toward the main street of the town where I would look in every window of every store, and eventually end up at the movies. My feet were hurting, but it would boost Frank's machismo if I turned back because my old shoes were rubbing the skin off my toes.

I thought back to 1952, the year I moved to the *barrio* near the base in Puerto Rico. Mentally, I didn't feel any older, but my old skirt was a little tight around the waist and hips, so I knew that I looked more like a woman than a girl. But since this was my first time out without Frank, I let my body find my old walking style. For this short time, I wanted to feel single and free, even if it meant getting into a fight with Frank later.

In my mind, however, I was doing something wrong. *What will I do if Frank gets really mad at me when I get back? And what if he puts the car together and comes looking for me, leaving the children alone? Something might happen to them, and the world will see me as an unfit mother.* Such thoughts made my heart pound in my ears. Still, I had to teach Frank that he wasn't the only one who could go places alone. And he needed to know that unless he quit drinking, I would keep on learning, and one day leave him. Perhaps he couldn't see that his drinking would affect the future of our children, but I knew differently. I wanted them to grow up in a better environment, without booze and arguments.

As I got closer to town, I noticed more people and cars on the streets, but never saw anyone familiar. This was good because I didn't want to tell anyone why I was out by myself.

I had left the house around five o'clock, and I reached the theater just as the movie started. The bright screen blinded me momentarily, so I sat on the second seat in one of the side rows. When my eyes adjusted, I glanced around before looking at the screen. I was the only one in this section of the theater. *I should have sat more to the center,* I thought. Yet I didn't know if it would be okay to move. *Why am I such a coward? And what is Frank thinking? How mad will he be when I get home? Darn! I should have stayed home.*

All I would ever remember about the movie was the loud music and a man in a white suit singing and skipping down a sidewalk between two hedges of pink, yellow, and white roses.

Then my adventure turned into a nightmare. One minute I was by myself, and in the next minute, a creepy guy who smelled like something rotten came and sat next to me. I gasped and turned to see a fat belly, thick beard, and dark eyes. He smiled and showed a line of brown, broken teeth. I was shocked, but didn't know what to do. Then I felt a hot, sticky hand on my knee.

I bolted out of my seat like a cat that had been poked with a sharp object, and hurried across to the center of the theater, where a few couples sat with some children. I looked back in the direction where the man had been sitting, but he had disappeared. The movie went on while I trembled, perspired, and bit off all my fingernails.

The man smelled so rotten. He'll be waiting for me outside the theater. Maybe after a while he'll get tired of waiting and leave. But if I go out now, will I come face to face with him outside the door?

My fear intensified with each breath I took. I couldn't concentrate on the movie. My heart was pounding so hard it hurt. *Why didn't I stay home? Why did I try to get even with Frank? Lord, what shall I do?*

For the longest time I thought, shook, and prayed. And instead of waiting for the movie to end and leave with everyone else, the fear got the best of me, and I walked out shaking and looking left to right. The sun had gone down by then, and I would soon be walking in the dark. Now the man would follow me and I'd be dead.

A fast walk was impossible with high heels and a tube-tied skirt. I imagined the stinky man around the next corner, waiting to snatch me as I struggled past. I could hardly breathe.

And if that wasn't bad enough, an old black convertible with three young guys with black hair, and dressed in dark clothes, turned from another street. The minute they saw me, they slowed down and started yelling. "Hey, baby, you want a ride?"

I looked straight ahead, trying to run. They laughed and drove the car so close to the curb I could feel the heat of the engine on my legs. Their arms reached for me. I ran in short steps as close to the buildings as possible, my eyes darting everywhere, searching for another car, or a person, anyone who might come to my rescue. There was no one else on the street at that moment, and the stores were closed because it was Sunday. I had been scared many times before, but having to run from three guys who looked drunk didn't compare to any of my other fears.

"Come on, sweetheart, talk to us, we'll be good! We'll take you any-place you want to go." Clapping and cheering, they laughed and called out, "Come on, sweetie, give us a little loving!"

I saw a phone booth on the other side of the street, so I dashed across behind the car. The guys clapped and laughed, and then turned around at the intersection and brought the car close to the sidewalk again.

"Come on, gorgeous, let us give you a ride."

In my fright, I pulled on the door of the phone booth, instead of pushing it in. I gave up on the booth and tried to run again, away from the reaching hands, the brown faces, and the glimmering dark eyes.

Finally, I reached the next intersection. It was a one-way street, so I crossed there, knowing that if they made a left turn, they would be going against traffic. I heard them clapping and yelling as they went straight ahead. I turned left on Date Street and headed for home, my heart racing so fast I feared that it would stop before I could get there.

It was really dark by the time I reached our street, and I was worn out, gasping and sweating. Every leaf that rustled on the ground made my pounding heart jump higher. All I wanted then was to throw myself into Frank's arms and cry.

I saw that the lights were on, so I went around to the kitchen. Through the window, I saw Frank washing his hands in the sink. I took a deep breath and walked in.

"So there you are," he snapped. "Wanna tell me where you've been? I've been worried sick about you!"

I could see that he was mad, so I hurried past him, went up the stairs, and straight into the shower. The flow of tears was greater than that of the water coming through the shower head. I couldn't believe my luck. I had started out trying to teach my husband a lesson, but instead, I had learned one myself.

I finally came out and got the children into their beds. Frank waited in his chair in front of the television set, a cigarette between his fingers and a mug of coffee in his other hand.

"So what the hell is going on?" he asked when I came down.

I looked at him, then sat on the sofa, across from him and said nothing.

He ran a hand through his hair, brought one eyebrow down, and raised the other. "Are you gonna do the shit with the silent treatment? Or are you gonna tell me what's gotten into you?"

"Okay," I said. "I'll tell you what's gotten into me. You are what's gotten into me. And before I say anything else, I want you to stop using those ugly words like 'shit' and 'hell.' If you don't, I'll stop talking to you for good. It's not the kind of language I want our children to learn."

"I don't talk that way in front of the kids. And don't threaten me again. Just tell me why you ran out this afternoon."

"I didn't run out. I went to the movies by myself, since you have forgotten that I need to get out every now and then."

"Why didn't you say so? We could have all gone with you."

"Because I wanted to show you what it is like for me when you go fishing early in the morning and come home late at night and drunk."

"Don't start with that shit about drinking again."

"You know, Frank, if you keep acting like that, I'll have no choice but to leave you."

"Leave me?" His eyes stretched wide open. "And where would you go?"

"I'll have a place by the time I leave," I said. While he stared at me, I stood up and started up the stairs. "From now on, I'll concentrate on preparing myself to live alone. I will not spend the rest of my life with a man who thinks more of the bottle than of his wife."

As I reached our room, I heard Frank walk out, and the car engine roaring down the street. He needed the booze.

Chapter Fifty-Three

A Wicked Neighbor

There were no ways I could escape turbulence in my life. One day, Judy came to my door in tears. "Marvin got a higher paying job in Bakersfield and we're moving there in three weeks. I don't like Bakersfield, but we need the extra money."

A sick feeling swept through me like a storm. "What are you saying? I can't imagine living here without you next door."

"I know what you mean," she said. "I might never have another neighbor as nice as you. But maybe we can visit each other someday."

Like with everything in my life, I had to accept the fact that my nice neighbor was leaving. Maybe I would get lucky again and another nice couple would move in next door. I spent as many hours as possible with Judy, helping her pack while our children played in her back yard. And on the day they moved out, I stood at my door watching through a fog of tears. Her husband drove a U-Haul truck filled with their belongings, and had their oldest boy along for company. Judy followed him in their car with the other three children. When they disappeared around the corner, I went back inside, and stayed in mourning the rest of the day, and for weeks afterward.

The house next door stayed empty for two weeks after Judy left. Then a big woman with three rough-looking boys moved in. I knew difficult times were coming with one look at the boys. The very next day, one of those boys said to my Rodney, "Put one foot in our yard, and I'll break every bone in your body."

When I heard the angry words, I ran out, but the boy went back inside. I kept my boys in for the rest of the day, then waited until the woman came home late that afternoon. When she did, I went to her door.

First, I would welcome her to our neighborhood. Then, in a friendly way, I would tell her about what her son had said to mine. I figured that if we were going to live that close to each other, it would be healthier for all of us to get along and watch each other's children, instead of living in fear.

I knocked on the door gently, and heard a strong hand grab the doorknob and pull on it at the same time. The sound made me jump back. "Yes?" the woman demanded. A mop of reddish black hair surrounded her puffy face, and her dark eyes stared at me. "What is it?" A foul smell of booze and smoke made me take another step backward.

"I'm sorry to have bothered you, but I just came to welcome you to the neighborhood."

"Well, thank you," she said, as if wanting to bite me. "But come back another day, 'cause I don't have time to visit with you right now." She closed the door.

"Wait!" I yelled. "There's something you need to know." I had smelled booze on her, but I didn't think she was drunk.

Her door swung open. "What is it!"

"It's about one of your boys. He threatened to break my little boy's bones, for no reason at all."

She peered at me. "Well, honey, boys will be boys."

"Maybe so, but if my boys talked like that, I'd wash their mouths out with soap."

"You raise your boys your way, and I'll raise mine my way. And you might as well get rid of that phony accent, 'cause you ain't fooling me." She slammed the door shut, leaving me startled with an open mouth. I hurried back to my house and locked myself in with my children.

When Frank finally came home, I poured him a cup of coffee and told him what had happened. I didn't expect him to go out and punch the woman on the nose, but I wanted to hear something comforting. Perhaps he would even suggest that we find another house and move.

However, he sipped his coffee and said casually, "Better stay away from people like that."

I wasn't too surprised, because he smelled just like the mean woman next door.

I could hardly sleep that night. I thought about where we could move to. Finally, I remembered hearing about San Diego, a town close to the Mexican border, where it never snowed, and flowers bloomed all year. Since Judy was gone, and a mad woman with mean boys lived next door, this was a good time for us to relocate.

San Diego would be good for me because Lancaster had been cold and dry in the winter, and too hot and dry in the summer. I had developed allergies I had never known before, and the doctor said it was due to the desert air. And wouldn't it be nice to live in a town where flowers bloomed all year round?

Frank had a one week vacation coming up during Easter week, when the boys didn't have school. It didn't take me long to talk him into driving down to San Diego.

"I have always wanted to see the Mexican border, anyway," he said. "And I also heard about a power plant near there. I might be able to get a tour of it, too."

My heart thumped. "Oh, do you suppose you could get a job there? Wouldn't that be nice, Frank? Imagine living in a place where flowers bloom year-round, and where we won't have to wear heavy winter clothes!"

"Well, don't get too excited. I work for the Air Force, and that's the Navy down there. Besides, didn't we move here because of Lucinda's asthma?"

"Yes, but she hasn't had an attack of asthma since the one in Illinois. It was probably a one-time thing."

"Well, I hope so, because we can't keep moving every two or three years."

We bought a cheap tent at Sears, and on Friday morning we headed down to San Diego on our first real vacation. The car was packed with the tent, the sleeping bags we had bought when we came to Lancaster, and our Styrofoam cooler. We would have the best time in our whole married life.

We talked, laughed, and joked all the way to a campground by the sea in Carlsbad, a short distance north of San Diego. The boys were like two little men, willing to help set up the tent and watch Lucinda. We had packed weiners, buns, chips, sodas, and big marshmallows. After smearing sunscreen on the children and ourselves, we all dipped our feet into the ocean water. The children shouted, "Cold!" but refused to back away.

I watched them and their father, who had never looked happier, and I knew that a place in San Diego would be a better beginning for us. I was still expecting Frank to give up the booze. Our marriage meant everything to him, and he would want to be a better husband and father. Such hopes I had, even after years of disappointments.

Chapter Fifty-Four

Down El Camino Real

The next day we headed down to San Diego alongside the ocean on a road called El Camino Real. It was like a dream. The scenery was breathtaking, with flowers everywhere, and the breeze smelled romantic. Our beautiful children were chatting and teasing each other in the back seat, asking often, "Are we there yet?"

"Soon we'll be," Frank answered with a loving smile. "Just relax and enjoy the ride."

"Are we going in the water again, Daddy?"

"Yes, Lucinda, we're going to go in the water. That's if it's okay with your mommy."

"Are you going to let us, Mommy?"

"Only if you all behave."

Three little voices answered, "We will!"

The children had never sounded sweeter, and they looked absolutely precious when I glanced back. My heart was singing. There was something magical and invigorating in the ocean air – something that made everything and everybody seem perfect.

We ended up in Chula Vista, a small town south of San Diego. It was not very crowded for a Saturday afternoon. We went up one street and down another, noting the stores, the cracked sidewalks, and of course the people. Frank drove slowly.

"Lots of Mexicans," he said.

"You'd have a chance to practice your Spanish if we moved here," I pointed out.

"Yeah, but will I like living among Mexicans? I've heard they are kind of strange."

"How strange, Daddy?" Troy brought his chin to the backrest. "Are they bad people?"

"No, son. They are good people, but they are different, that's all."

"Well, Daddy, *everybody's* different." Rodney sounded frustrated. I thought it was because he had never liked being in a car for a long time. But it was because he was growing too fast.

"You're so right, Rodney. Everybody is different." Frank turned onto Avenue L, and headed toward the ocean. This pleased the children. They clapped and cheered, "Goody! We're going to the beach. Are you going to let us play in the water, Mommy?"

"Yes, Lucinda, I am going to let you play."

We came up to another little town, Imperial Beach, and found a motel that had rooms available for nine dollars a night. Frank signed for two nights. It was so close to the beach that we could walk out a back door and step right onto wet sand. I thought the children would go crazy. "A back yard of sand? Wow, Daddy, no grass for you to cut!"

Frank looked at me with a smile that sent my mind back to when we had met nine years earlier. So much had happened since then, and I still thought that things would get better.

Later that day, we went to a supermarket and bought more ice for our cooler, ground meat, hamburger buns, milk, bananas, apples, and more chips. We spent the afternoon and evening running in and out of the water, cooking our hamburgers over burning charcoal, and roasting marshmallows.

"It can't get any better than this," Frank said, with love in his voice and eyes.

I nodded, then thought, *It can get even better, if you don't start drinking again.*

We drove down to the Mexican border on Sunday morning, then to the San Diego Zoo in the afternoon. The next day, we left the motel and drove to the little island of Coronado. Later that afternoon, we would return to the campground in Carlsbad for one more night, then head back to Lancaster on Tuesday.

Just before reaching Coronado, Frank spotted the high chimney of the Navy's power plant. "I sure would like to see that place," he said, turning right on that road. "Will you wait in the car with the kids, honey?"

"I will, but make sure you ask for a job application."

As we approached the building, we heard the rumbling sounds of the engines and boilers that made electricity. Frank pulled up to a parking space, and before he could get out of the car, a tall man came out through the wide-open door. He was the foreman.

Frank introduced himself and the family. Minutes later, we were all walking into the noisy power plant. Frank tried to explain to us what all the engines and belts did, but Lucinda became frightened, so I took all three children out to a patch of green grass where they chased away the pigeons and seagulls.

While the children ran after the birds, I hoped that Frank was the worker the boss had been looking for, and Frank would come out with a bright smile and announce that he gotten a job offer and we'd be moving to San Diego. This feeling was like a little hurricane whirling in my stomach which made me feel like flying with the birds. It was one of those things that I wanted so badly, and it hurt to think we might be going back to Lancaster without even the hope of ever coming back to stay.

Frank finally came out of the building, lighting a cigarette, and not looking any happier than he had an hour or so earlier.

I hurried to meet him. "Did you ask about a job?"

"Yeah," he said, motioning for us to get in the car. "But they aren't hiring now. And like I told you, this is the Navy. I work for the Air Force." He started the engine. "Everybody ready?"

It was the way he said it, like it didn't matter, that knocked the wind out of me. I looked at him as he backed out of the parking space, and something hit me like lightning.

"Frank, wait!" He slammed on the brakes. I bolted out of the car and ran back to the power plant.

The boss saw me and came forward. "Is something wrong?"

"Yes, but it's too noisy here."

Looking confused, the man opened a door to a small office, motioned me to enter, then stood tall and serious. "What's the problem?"

"You see, I need to move to San Diego because I'm allergic to the desert air. It makes me sneeze all the time, and look at my eyes. They itch so much I scratch day and night. All my eyelashes are coming off, see?" I blinked at the man while he peered at me as if wondering whether I was crazy. "So please, if you need a good worker, give my husband a job. Thank you for listening, and goodbye." I pulled open the door and ran back out with my face and ears burning hot.

Frank was waiting for me outside the door. "What's going on?"

I flew past him without words. As I reached for the car door, I heard the foreman say, "You have a remarkable wife there, Frank Wilson."

I didn't hear Frank's reply, nor did I look at him as he got into the car. "In God's name, what was that all about?" He drove slowly. "Honey?"

I took a deep breath. "I can't explain it, Frank! It's like something flew me in there to tell the man to give you a job so we can move to San Diego."

"You did what?"

I stared down at my knees.

"She said she told the man to give you a job," Troy said, from behind his daddy.

"I know what she said, so sit back!"

Lucinda got to her feet. "Well, Daddy, if you knew what she said, why did you ask, 'You did what?' with a mad voice?"

I looked at Lucinda. "Thank you, sweetie."

Frank drove quietly for a few minutes. At the light, he said, "I don't need my wife asking anybody to give me a job. I can do that myself."

"Yeah, Daddy," Rodney said, "but the man told you they were not hiring, remember?"

"I think you kids better sit back and keep your mouths shut before I head for the highway and put an end to this vacation!"

Not much was said after that. As we toured Coronado, we barely noticed that its beach was nicer and cleaner than the ones we had seen so far. The children could not go in the water here, for they would be wet on the drive to Carlsbad. Knowing that, and the fear of having to go home sooner than planned, kept them almost disturbingly quiet.

Unable to stand the silence, I said, "I'm sorry I ruined the good time, but you should have told the man why we needed to move here, Frank!"

"How could I? I don't even know the reason myself!"

In the tent that night, I whispered, "I want to move to San Diego, where I'll see flowers all year and we won't need heavy winter clothes, and where there is no desert air to make me sneeze and scratch my eyes."

"I understand," he whispered back. "But the Air Force isn't going to transfer me to the Navy just because you sneeze and scratch your eyes."

"Maybe not. But I picture us moving here before the heat of summer. And I'm good at predicting things."

Frank said no more, and soon began to snore. I listened to the waves, and imagined living this close to the ocean.

Chapter Fifty-Five

Near the Border

One week after school closed for summer vacation, while I was preparing Frank's lunch, the phone rang. He answered it, and I heard him say, "Is that right? Well, I'll be damned. How soon? Well, okay then, I'll see you in about an hour." He hung up the receiver, and his face broke into a wide smile. "Can you beat that. I have been transferred to the Navy base in San Diego."

"San Diego!" I jumped up and down and screamed so loud the children came running and joined in on the excitement. It was hard for me to even finish making Frank's sandwich, because I wanted to start packing right away. I knew the angels had been hard at work because I had prayed for other things since coming back from San Diego, but had left the move in the hands of fate.

I gave Frank an extra hug and kiss before he left. He had been drunk only twice since the vacation, and I was still dreaming of happiness.

The next Saturday, we drove back to San Diego to look for a house to rent. If we didn't find a house, we would rent a storage space for our furniture, and stay at the cheap motel in Imperial Beach until a house became available. But the angels were still at work. After calling several numbers from the classified ads in the Chula Vista newspaper, we spotted a repossessed home for sale.

One phone call led us to the real estate office, and by five o'clock that afternoon, we had ourselves a house. We would pay rent until the necessary papers were filed and recorded in our name. It was a simple house with three bedrooms, one and a half bathrooms, and no fancy gadgets or pretty carpets. But we'd have a roof over our heads, and things would get better with time.

In the first week of July, Frank, with Rodney to keep him company, drove a U-Haul truck with everything that we owned to Chula Vista. He unloaded the furnishings and returned to Lancaster to drive us down in *his* car.

When Frank came home from work on his first day at his new job, he said to me, "My boss asked me a question this morning that I haven't been able to figure out."

"What was it?"

"Well, it hardly made sense. He walked up to me and asked, 'Did I save your wife's eyelashes by having you transfer here?' I looked at him like an idiot, and didn't know what the hell to say. You didn't tell him that your eyelashes were falling off in the desert, did you?"

"Oh, sure I did. And thank God he listened."

"You never told me that your eyelashes were falling out."

"If I had, would you have heard me?" I didn't get an answer.

I spent the next four months cleaning the windows, making curtains, scrubbing walls and cabinets, and pulling the tall weeds that had taken over the yard. On Frank's days off, we patched the wall cracks, painted inside and out, and replaced doorknobs and broken faucets.

We met the neighbors on each side of our house, but neither would become our friends. They were older people and claimed that they liked being by themselves.

A couple two houses down, however, had three little boys and were delighted to meet ours. And a couple two houses up on the other side had a little girl, Penny, who was the same age as Lucinda. The two girls became inseparable.

When school started in September, the boys left together in the mornings and came home at the same time. I ran an ad in the local paper and started sewing again. With the boys in school all day, and Lucinda playing at the neighbor's house, I put in a lot of hours sewing. And I put away most of the money I earned to give my children a big and happy Christmas.

That year I prepared my first turkey for Thanksgiving dinner. It wasn't easy, but I wanted the children to learn the American tradition. Before stuffing the turkey, I put on a light blue dress with a white apron, and tied my hair back into a ponytail. It was my way of being sanitary. I scrubbed the kitchen sink with Comet and rinsed it over and over to wash away every trace of the cleaning powder.

I took the turkey out of the plastic bag and put it in the clean sink, where I scraped the skin with a sharp knife, removing the small lumps left by the feathers. I turned the bird so that the drumsticks were pointing to the ceiling, took out a couple of packages that contained the neck, the liver and other things that made me gag. I scraped out from the large cavity all the maroon-colored clots with a spoon. Then I turned the turkey and scraped the other cavity, where the stomach had been. When I could look through one cavity and see out the other, I cut off all the skin that hung around both cavities, and the chunk of yellowish fat left from the tail.

Frank walked in as I was making the final inspection.
"Holy smoke. There ain't much left of that darn turkey. For heaven's sake, you must have used fifty gallons of water. Were you trying to wash the darn thing down the sick? And you should see your face."

I didn't need to see my face. I had been squinting so hard that my vision was distorted, and my skin burned when I finally relaxed my face.

Maybe I had cleaned the poor turkey too much, but the dinner turned out delicious, and I ate some of the white meat soaked in gravy and found it quite tasty.

We even said grace before that feast, and I felt proud of myself and my little family. It all seemed so normal then, as if we had finally gotten on the right track. Frank had been drinking his beers at home, but had not been drunk since Lancaster.

For Christmas, we put up a big Christmas tree, decorated it with new ornaments, and put more packages under it than we ever had before. Everything had been running smoothly since the move from Lancaster.

Then Frank's schedule changed everything. He'd get home around nine o'clock in the morning and go straight into the shower. From there, he came out clean-shaven, and with *that* look in his eyes. Whether I was trying to finish a garment which would be picked up at noon, or whether Lucinda was in the house, Frank wanted me in bed with him.

"You can still get that done," he'd say to me, turning off the sewing machine and pushing the fabric to the side. To Lucinda, he would say, "Wanna go watch *Sesame Street* with your little friend Penny?"

Once he said that, Lucinda wanted to leave, and I had all I could do to convince her and her daddy that it was too early for her to go knocking on the neighbor's door.

"Excuses and rejections, if you ask me!" he would bark, then go to the refrigerator for a beer. If by chance Penny's mother called, asking Lucinda to come up because Penny had been asking for her, Frank's face lit up and I had to put down the sewing and go with him. Each time, we would have the same argument.

"You have to wear that thing," I insisted.

"You sure don't sound like the sweet girl I married!"

"That's because I am not the same dumb girl. Now I am an overworked, tired wife and mother in need of real love and understanding."

"Well . . . uh, love is what I'm offering you."

"No, it isn't, Frank. You want to use me, not give me love."

"Oh, hell!" He would turn on his side and growl like an animal. I'd leave the room and go back to my sewing.

Chapter Fifty-Six

An Honest Job?

When Lucinda started kindergarten, I said to Frank, "Next year, Lucinda will be in first grade. I'll be able to find a part-time job somewhere, where I can earn more money than I do sewing all day. What do you think?"

"That's a great idea," he said. "Just four blocks down the street is a little Chinese laundry. I have often seen *Help Wanted* signs in the window."

I nearly fell to the floor. "You want me to work in a Chinese laundry?"

"Why not? It's an honest job, and it's within walking distance."

"Well, I was thinking more like in a department store like J.C. Penney's."

"How will you get there?"

"By car. I think it's time you bought me a little car – a used one, four or five hundred dollars, something like that."

That developed into our first serious fight in Chula Vista.

"First, you want a job far away from the house, then you want a car, and God knows what else after that."

"What are you afraid of, Frank?"

"I'm not afraid. I just want to be the breadwinner around here, that's all."

I had felt like less than a speck of dust several times in my life, but after those words from the man who claimed to love me, I felt invisible.

"You used to be such a good little wife," he went on. "Now you don't let me make love to you, and don't even want to have my babies. Soon you'll tell me to find my pleasures with someone else."

I had struggled for the right words to express my hurt, but my brain woke up after that statement. "Now that's a great idea, Frank – the best idea you ever had. Go ahead and divorce me, and marry someone who might be willing to give you a dozen children."

"I'm not talking about a dozen, dammit."

"Can't you understand that we can do more for three children than we could do for six or seven? They need things like dental care, and a better education than their parents had."

Both of Frank's eyebrows went up and quickly down this time. "That's a hell of a thing to worry about! The boys will go into the service at eighteen, get their teeth fixed, and have job training. You don't need to worry about them."

"And what about Lucinda? Is she going into the service, too?"

"Lucinda will get married, like her mother, and her husband will support her."

The memories of my parents claiming that girls didn't need an education flashed through my mind, and I paced the floor in a rage. "You are disgusting, Frank! And I am stupid. I married you because I truly believed that you would be a much better man than my father. But if it weren't for the color of your skin and the different language, you would pass for his son. How could I have been so stupid! The fact that you were American made me think you were perfect!"

"Yeah, well, you had a lot to learn!"

I felt the tears building up, but I swallowed hard, because I wasn't going to cry in his arms this time. Having his helpless little woman crying in his arms would give him pleasure. "I had a lot to learn, you said? Well, there's a lot more I still have to learn. And I just realized that I'm not going to learn it here with you, Frank!"

"What the hell is that supposed to mean?"

I leaped to the door, grabbed the knob, and said through clenched teeth, "You're smart, figure it out!"

I heard him say, "Damn!" as I banged the door shut behind me.

Walking around the block several times, I thought, fumed, remembered, and wondered what to do. I didn't want to go back into that house before the children returned from school. I would be madder if I found Frank in his chair, smoking and drinking, and I'd be totally disgusted if I found him snoring.

I headed down toward the school, planing to wait around for the children and then walk home with them. At an intersection, I met up with a woman who seemed in a hurry. I nodded hello.

She smiled, "It's my day at the library, and I'm late," she said, without slowing down.

Increasing my pace. "Where's the library?" I had no idea that schools had their own libraries.

"At the school, the school library . . . I'm a volunteer."

A volunteer? How does one volunteer? I followed her to the small building next to the school. "I came to see my little girl during recess, but I'm early. She's in first grade, and I worry. You know how it is with the youngest one."

"Oh, I know," she said. "I have three."

"Three girls?"

"No, one girl and two boys. But the girl is the youngest. That's why I volunteer here, to be nearby, just in case. Know what I mean?"

"I do. Mind if I wait around here?"

"Not at all, be my guest." She began to shuffle books around from a pile on a high counter. I watched her curiously.

"My name is Jackie. What's yours?"

"Oh, I'm sorry. I forgot my manners. My name is Debby. It's nice to meet you. Are you new in town?"

Debby and I became friends. When the recess bell rang, I ran out to see Lucinda, then went back to the library.

Debby was about my age, petite, with blonde hair and blue eyes. Her husband was a distributer for the Oroweat bread company, and she had been a stay-at-home mom since her first child had been born. But in the coming January, she would be returning to school to obtain a teaching degree.

Our conversation went from one subject to the next, she up on a ladder, and I handing her the books as if we had worked together before. She said that the school library needed more volunteers, so I signed up before leaving. I would work every Wednesday for three hours, and a Mrs. Martin would train me on my first day.

"It's an easy job," Debby said. "You'll learn a lot about books, and even have time to read some, if you enjoy reading."

I didn't tell her that I couldn't read much English; it would be too embarrassing. But on the way home, I felt smart, and more than just a "little wife." I had taken my first step toward learning.

Chapter Fifty-Seven

Downhill from There

In my day-to-day struggle, I had held onto the old dream of being a wife to a man who would appreciate me, not use me or take me for granted. But by the mid- sixties, I had learned that while most of the men in God's world were probably civilized and knew how to appreciate a good woman and their children, the rest of the men were like my Puerto Rican father and my American husband. Such men grab what they want and do as they please without regards to the damage they leave behind.

As I came to realize such facts, I had to wonder if my luck would ever change. Was it my destiny to always find myself in the hands of men made from the same ingredients as my father? This was a scary scenario, which left me no choice but to take control of my life once again. I would do whatever was necessary to turn my situation around.

The 1960's were difficult times for couples who were trying to raise children under certain principles. There was rock-and-roll and Beatles music, marijuana and LSD, psychedelic colors and groovy hippies, the Vietnam War and the flower children.

Frank, who wanted control, suddenly found that his world was turning upside down in front of his fat nose. His wife had met Debby, a woman of great knowledge who encouraged her to vote, convinced her that she wasn't too old to return to school, said it was okay to become a school teacher, a nurse, a social worker, and even a writer.

Rodney, who hated school, claimed that his parents were too old-fashioned, and that attending school was a waste of time. He would rather hitchhike to London and join the Beatles. Frank coped with that by reaching for more beer and whiskey.

"I'm going to work where I can earn more money to help us, Frank. Can't you see that? We'll be able to buy a better house and start saving for the children's college, which I think would be an investment."

"Investment? Where the hell did you learn that kind of talk? Oh, never mind. I already know where that comes from. You have managed to attract some sophisticated friends, school teachers and nurses! Chicken shit, in my book, putting ideas in your head!" Frank was referring to Debby and two of my sewing customers: a schoolteacher, Amanda, and a nurse, Joanna.

"I don't need anyone to put ideas in my head, Frank. I have a brain, too. And I love my children enough to worry about their future!"

Frank drove to the nearest bar after every argument. He kept a pack of beer and a bottle of bourbon for the times when the bars were closed.

When his schedule changed to the seven to three shift, he would stop in the bars on his way home two or three times a week. Each time, he would stay a little longer. Then he'd call about 7:00 or 8:00. "Honey? This is Frank."

"I know it's you, Frank, because no one else calls me honey!"

"Oh, yeah . . . I wanna tell you to go ahead with dinner 'cause I'm gonna be a little late. I stopped for a beer, and got to talking."

"We had our dinner two hours ago, Frank, and the children are already going to bed. Were you too drunk to see the clock?"

He usually hung up at that point, then got home between midnight and two o'clock in the morning. I'd take my pillow and a blanket and move to the sofa.

"You're rightfully mine," he would say with a smirk as I walked out.

"I wish you had stayed in the bar the rest of the night."

"Well, honey, wish in one hand and piss on the other, see which hand will fill up faster."

"One of these days you're going to be wishing that you had treated me with respect."

"Yeah, yeah, wish, wish . . . "

Through all the ups and downs, I managed to work at the library three hours a week. I learned how to file books on shelves according to author and title. Then I went home to cook, then sewed until eleven o'clock at night. The rest of the week I cleaned and ironed, baked and cooked, then sewed until eleven.

One day Frank came home from work sober, and with a smile and bright eyes. "Hey . . . uh, honey. This guy I work with is having a New Year's Eve party, and we are invited. Think your friend would watch the kids? We haven't gotten dressed up since St. Paul. How about it?"

"No. You'll end up getting drunk and embarrassing me."

"Oh, no, honey, this time I won't get drunk. I promise."

I had been wanting an opportunity to wear a red dress I had made out of new fabrics, so I became really stupid and agreed to go. I even fantasized about dancing in a large room with dim lights, beautiful music, and dressed-up people.

On the day of the party, I colored my nails and pinned my hair so it would look like it was permed. I got all my work done early and prepared a nice dinner. At six o'clock, I walked the children to Debby's place and came back to get ready.

"Wow! Look at you," Frank said as I came out of the bedroom in my red dress and black shoes. "Mother of three and still looks like the girl I married. It's time we start going out dancing, honey, while we're still young. Don't you agree?"

"I do. I would like that very much, but only if you don't get drunk."

"Don't worry, I won't get drunk. I'll only have a few drinks. I think you should, too. You can't have any fun if you don't drink."

"Drinking is not necessary to have fun."

"Yeah, well, I'm gonna have a few drinks, but I won't get drunk."

Maybe Frank meant that, but the drinks were free, and gradually he saw to it that not a drop would go to waste. Two hours into the party, he was yellow and sweating. Still, he insisted on dancing, pressing his wet cheek against mine and whispering in my ear.

"I'm so turned on by you, sweetheart. I'm aroused, and can't wait to get home."

I had my left hand on his shoulder, but he kept moving it onto the back of his sweaty neck. I suffered the whole time, for if I tried to get away, he would cause a scene, and his co-workers would realize that he was a drunk. Meanwhile, I felt terribly embarrassed, with a wet face and messed up hair.

"He'll be okay," one of the women said to me. "He just had a little too much to drink." She wasn't walking very straight herself, so why would she say anything else about Frank's drinking.

As the evening neared midnight, I realized that I was the only one drinking Dr. Pepper and 7-up, and the only one not having fun. Then, to top it all off, just as people were counting down the minutes to midnight, Frank threw up on the dance floor. The warm beer and whiskey splashed up the legs of the men and women around us. The men put up their fists, and the women backed away yelling and looking down at their splattered nylon stockings.

I didn't wait to see what would follow. I ran out the door and headed for home on foot. I would never want to see any of those people again. I didn't even wonder what would become of Frank if all the husbands of the splattered women started beating on him. I felt too embarrassed to worry or to be afraid that some other drunk would come by and drag me to some strange place.

I never found out how Frank got away, but he caught up with me a half-mile down the road. I kept walking as fast as I could, but he drove slowly next to me, calling, "Honey, please get in the car. I'm sorry for disappointing you, but we'll be just fine. This old car knows the way home. I'll drive slowly, please get in."

I was too far away from home to be walking at night, so I had no choice but to get into the stinky car. I was fuming, mad and trembling, but I knew not to argue with a drunk. Instead, I prayed that a police car would show up, and that my little children would not end up orphaned.

By the grace of God, we made it home that night. Frank staggered into the bedroom, but I slept in Troy's bed.

The next day I packed a picnic, and as soon as the children came home, we got into the car and went to Balboa Park. I left Frank a note: *I took the children to the park in your stinky car. Be ready to talk divorce when we return.*

"Are you sure you can drive?" Rodney asked.

"Yes, and I'll start out slowly, so don't be afraid."

"Why didn't we wait for Daddy?"

"He needed more sleep, Rodney. Now don't keep asking questions, just help me watch for signs, okay?"

"Okay, but you should have waited for Daddy."

Not only did Rodney look like Frank, but he thought and acted like him. I knew that if I left Frank, I would be the bad guy in Rodney's eyes. But I also knew that Troy would take my side. Which parent would Lucinda choose?

When we returned home, Frank met us at the door as if nothing had happened. He eyed the car which I had parked in front of the house. "Didn't put a few dents in it, did you?"

I marched past him. "Come, Lucinda, I'll help you with your hair." We both got into the shower. To cool off my anger, I talked to Lucinda. "You are so precious to me. I want nothing but the best for you and your brothers. That's all I want, the best for the three of you."

I didn't want to argue with Frank in front of the children, but waiting for a convenient time would be impossible. I knew that one more nasty remark or joke from him would make me explode. For the moment, I hoped he was asking the boys where we had been and what we had done, because I would not tell him if he asked me. That was not what I intended to talk to him about.

"Okay, boys, your turn," I said when Lucinda and I came out. She went to her room, and I to mine, where the stench from last night still lingered. Later I went into the kitchen to start supper. Frank stayed in his chair smoking. After a few minutes, he walked into the kitchen with cat-like steps and sat at the table.

"You got my note, right?" I asked.

"Yeah, honey, but – "

Lucinda came in. "Daddy, can you untangle this?"

From the corner of my eye, I watched his hands shake as he tried to loosen the knots in his daughter's blonde curls without hurting her. Memories of my father combing my hair on my first day of school, so many years back, flashed through my mind. *What is in alcohol that makes men lose their common sense – that causes them to destroy love and lives? What has happened to the man I thought of as gentle and loving? What is in alcohol that made the two men who should have loved me turn into unlikable beasts?* I felt like throwing the onion I was chopping to the floor and crying my eyes out. But I had to be strong and blame the tears on the onion, which was now receiving a brutal attack from my sharp knife.

Frank kissed Lucinda's shoulder when he finished, and she walked away with bouncing curls.

"Honey, I'm sorry about last night. I'm so ashamed."

I swallowed a hard knot. "Are you ready?"

"Ready for what?"

"To talk about divorce. You read the note, didn't you?"

"Honey, you can't mean that!"

I saw Rodney come out wrapped in a towel, and the argument would have to wait. This was worse than labor pains. I was ready to burst, but had to go on as if nothing horrible had happened. My children would not witness anger between their parents.

"Oh, honey," Frank said to me later that night. "You're not going to join the women's liberation movement, are you?"

I hadn't heard the term before. "What's a liberation movement? And what does it have to do with your drinking problem that's breaking us up?"

"Everything," he said, blowing smoke. "Women nowadays file for divorce for any little thing."

"Getting drunk the way you do is more than a little thing, Frank. I'm not looking for reasons to divorce you, and you're not looking for ways to save our marriage. That's the problem."

"Well, now, that kind of talk can drive a man to drinking."

That was another one of his jokes, and the slight smile was supposed to indicate that our problem wasn't a serious one.

Chapter Fifty-Eight

Under-Qualified

I saw an ad in the paper about the opening of a fabric store on Avenue J and Broadway. They were hiring women who knew about fabrics, and I knew I could do the job. I would make more money than sewing at home, and I'd finally get to use my mathematics.

The next day, I put on a yellow skirt and jacket which I had made, and left the house at the same time as the children. Two blocks away, they turned right and I turned left.

"Good luck, Mommy," said Rodney, and Lucinda copied him. But Troy winked and said, "I know you'll get the job, 'cause you're smart and pretty." We threw kisses at each other and parted.

It took me twenty-five minutes to get there. I then waited an hour for the manager, only to be told that they wanted only highschool graduates. I returned the blank application form and left with the most humiliating feeling twisting my insides so hard I could not draw a breath. I wanted to fly home and crawl under the bed and never come out again. Everything in my whole life had gone wrong. I had no one I could turn to, yet the future of my children was really up to me. They could not count on their father to lead them.

My feet suddenly felt too heavy, and it would take me forever to reach home. Why had I thought that someone would hire me, a woman from the hills of Puerto Rico without a highschool diploma? I remembered Troy's wink and vote of confidence, and my tears hit the sidewalk like raindrops. I felt this huge storm whirling in my stomach, and the sobs blared out with great force, but I didn't care who heard me. The sounds that were coming out of me were scraping my throat, and my body bent down so far I nearly rubbed the sidewalk with my nose. If people saw me, I never saw them. And I wasn't aware of any cars going by. At that time, I was the only person in that part of the world, and I would never recover from the trembling and anger that possessed my body and mind.

After what seemed like hours of despair, I did hear a car, which slowed down. "Is that you, Jackie? My Lord, what in the world happened to you?"

Through my tears, I saw Debby, her head out of the car window.

"Get in, I'll give you a ride. My Lord what is the matter? Why are you down here and crying, are you hurt?"

Embarrassed, and touched by her compassion, I hurried around the car and pulled open the door, still sobbing so hard that she parked the car and reached for me.

"Jackie, what's wrong?"

The more concerned she seemed, the harder I cried. I couldn't stop.

"What's wrong, Jackie? Did someone hurt you?"

I shook my head, then cried out about the job. But that didn't seem like a good reason for me to carry on like that, so I did what I had not wanted to do all those years: I spilled out my problems with Frank's drinking.

That day I found out the importance of friendship. Debby had been on her way to the supermarket. Instead, she turned around and took me to her home, where we drank coffee, talked, cried, and laughed together. She told me about the kinds of problems she and her husband had had throughout the years, although none were as serious as Frank's drinking.

"It sounds like your husband is an alcoholic," she said. "There is help available. Alcoholics Anonymous can help. However, your husband has to go for help. In other words, there's nothing you can do if he refuses to go."

"He claims that he's not an alcoholic," I said.

"Every alcoholic says that, but eventually some decide to take control and get help. Your husband will, too. It just takes time. And about you getting a job . . . well, not all places require a highschool diploma, Jackie. You'll get a job, don't worry. Meanwhile, why don't you consider going to school? There are some evening classes you can take, if you want to go."

Three days later, Debby called me.

"My neighbor told me that Uni-Mart has an opening for help in their fabric department. I'll give you a ride if you want to check it out."

"What about the highschool diploma?"

"My neighbor thinks they will hire you, anyway. It's a low-paying job, but it'll be a good start for you."

Two hours later, I sat at a desk in a small room at Uni-Mart.

"Fill out this form and read this booklet, then come to my office across the hall," the manager had said.

I sat there staring at the blank spaces of the application form, my hands shaking, warm moisture coming out of my pores, and a loud pounding in my chest. *How am I going to explain my stupidity?*

I turned the pages of the booklet and tried to understand the words, comparing the sentences to the pictures of a woman waiting on a customer. There wasn't a door leading outside from the little room, and I could not escape.

Finally the door to the hallway opened slowly. "I thought you might need some help with the application," Debby whispered.

"I do, thank you. I'm too nervous. It's my first application ever."

She explained the questions and marked my answers, so all I had to do was sign my name.

"But they'll find out that my English isn't that good and send me away humiliated."

"No they won't. Just tell him the truth and ask him to give you a chance. Once he sees how you work, he'll keep you here for as long as you want the job. You don't need a large vocabulary to cut fabrics, and you know mathematics."

Unable to come up with anything better than Debby's suggestion, I took the papers to the office across the hall.

"So, you can cut fabrics?" Mr. Boon inquired, looking at the application. "What else can you do to benefit this store?"

This question caught me off guard. I had to come up with an answer before I panicked and ran out. "Well, I can rearrange all your fabrics so they appear pleasing to the eye. And I can translate for Mexican customers who do not understand much English. That would be great help, don't you think?"

Mr. Boon looked past the application at me and smiled. "Can you start tomorrow?"

"Yes. Thank you. I'll do a great job."

He wrote something on a folder. "Be here at nine. A trainer will show you what to do. After that, you'll work 9:30 to 2:30, four days a week."

I walked out of that office feeling like a person. I knew I could do the job, and the hours were perfect. I would go to work after the children left for school and get home at the same time with them. This was great!

Debby, who had waited for me outside the office, saw my wide smile and her arms opened wide. "You got the job. I knew it!"

"Thanks to you," I said, all choked up.

"You're going to do just fine," Debby said, and we started for home.

The next day, I left the house with my children. Four blocks away, they turned into the schoolyard, and I continued for six more blocks. I would do this walk four days a week, which allowed me to continue my volunteer work at the library. If I had been looking for that kind of work schedule, I would have probably never found it.

On that first day, walking to Uni-Mart, I felt complete. I was a real person, going to work on my first American job. Frank would have a fit, so I would not tell him about it for a long time.

A tall blonde lady named Lois showed me where everything was and stayed nearby during my first two hours on that job. I was surprised that I didn't get nervous while she watched me stock up some bolts of fabric. She showed me how to unlock the cash register, and how to put all the dollar bills so that the numbers and faces ran in the same direction.

Lois watched me cut the first few yards of fabric. "You're great with this stuff," she said, and walked away.

I busied myself, cutting fabrics and helping people find the items they were looking for. I felt like a new person, knowledgeable in my white jacket provided by Uni-Mart.

On the following Saturday, I suggested to Frank that we go on an all-day picnic at Balboa Park. The children could climb trees and run around, and he and I would talk on a blanket under a tree. We'd take time to play with the children, too, which they would enjoy.

The children cheered and clapped at the idea, and I saw Frank's bright smile and sparkling eyes. I felt so happy then, still hoping that we could make our marriage work.

I was stuffing the cooler with ham sandwiches, apples, grapes, and Kool-aid when Frank walked into the kitchen. "Mind if I put a couple of beers in there?"

"Yes I mind, Frank. It's not good to teach the children that drinking beer in the park is part of family fun."

"Okay, honey, you're right," he said, then carried the cooler to the car.

I let out a sigh and, with teary eyes, watched him walk away. A picnic without a beer would be a sacrifice for him. *What can I do to help him give up that habit?*

Once we chose a parking spot, the boys bolted out and ran to the nearest tree, and Lucinda ran behind them.

"You boys watch out for your sister," I yelled. "If anyone gets hurt, we'll have to go home. And Lucinda, don't you try to do everything your brothers do. They are older and bigger than you, okay?"

"Okay, Mommy."

Frank faked a laugh. "Two minutes, and she'll forget what you said."

"If she does, I'll remind her again. After the third reminder, we'll head for home."

"Right!" he said, giving his knee the old sweep with the palm of his hand. That little notion told me that he wasn't hurting for the beers I hadn't let him bring. I carried the bags of chips and cookies, and the blanket which I spread under the tree the boys were climbing. Frank came with the cooler, set it on a corner, and stretched himself out on the blanket.

"Frank . . . I really want us to talk seriously about our problems. It's not because I want you to feel bad, but because I love you and want our time together to be good always."

"I want that, too, honey." There was that look – the look that always made me feel like jumping into his arms as if we had no problems at all.

"I know you do. That's why I think it's so important for us to talk and fix whatever is wrong."

"That's the thing . . . I don't see that anything is wrong," he said with confidence. "And now with you working, things will get better. We'll have more money, and you won't feel trapped at home anymore."

"You don't see your drinking as a problem?" I tried to stay calm, which wasn't easy.

"No, I don't. There's nothing wrong with a guy having a few drinks every now and then. It's not like I drink every day or on the job. I don't miss work, and I do my job well. I'm at peace when I get home. I never lift a finger to you or the kids. That's more than I can say for some guys I know."

Just when I was ready to explode, Lucinda came running. "Daddy, can you help me climb that tree over there?" I watched her stretch out her arm, one soft little finger pointing. Frank got to his feet and hurried away, holding her by the hand. I waited on the blanket.

"It breaks my heart when I see you playing so lovingly with your little girl," I said when he returned.

"Why does it break your heart?" One eyebrow went up and the other down.

"Because I know that one day she'll see you drunk and will feel disappointed, like I felt about my father."

"What the hell are you talking about? I'm not going to disappoint my kids like your father did!"

"Maybe not, but I think you should get some help with your drinking. Do it for my sake, being that you love me so much."

Frank leaned back on an elbow. "If you're suggesting Alcoholics Anonymous, forget it. I am not an alcoholic. You can tell whoever put that idea in your head to go to hell. I am no damn drunk!" He sprang to his feet and ran to join the boys. Lucinda came down from her branch and ran after him.

I stayed on the blanket, astounded, but not crying, and I didn't even pray.

Chapter Fifty-Nine

A Ring in the Burger

I was working every day and doing my household chores, which kept me busy all the time, but I still managed some short visits with the neighbor ladies, and lunch with Debby every once in a while. As for the sewing at home, I did some for Amanda and Joanna in the evenings, but I told my other customers that I had gotten a job away from home and could no longer take in sewing.

So that part of my life was running smoothly. But the problem with Frank continued. He made his bar stops regularly, and at night we went through the same hassle. He wanted sex without a condom, and I didn't want more babies.

I finally realized that my struggle to get Frank to stop drinking was a losing battle. None of my dreams had been fulfilled so far: no flowers or candy when my babies were born, no anniversary gifts, no birthdays, or Mother's Day treats. I knew then that our marriage could not be saved.

So I decided that since I was earning money, I wanted to be taken out for a special dinner on Mother's Day. It would probably be a one-time thing, but I needed to know what that would feel like. Just once, it would be nice to get dressed up and go to a restaurant with my family on Mother's Day.

"It's something I want before the children grow up," I said to Frank. "While I can still dress them up the way I want. I'll make mother and daughter dresses for Lucinda and me, and a new shirt for each boy, which they can wear with their newest trousers. I'll buy them each a necktie. And you can wear your suit. Maybe we can even get someone to take our family picture."

"Where would you like to go for that occasion, honey?"

"To a steak house," I said, running the tip of my tongue over my lips. "I want a T-bone steak with a baked potato and whatever else comes with that, served on a table with a tablecloth and candlelight."

As I talked, I saw the sparkles in my children's eyes, especially in Troy's, who stated firmly, "You deserve it, Mommy, 'cause you're the best mommy in the whole wide world."

Lucinda jumped up on the sofa and took her place close to her father. "Yeah, Daddy, let's do it, okay?"

"Okay," he said, putting his arm around her. "We'll do it."

I noticed something about Rodney that was troublesome to me. He had waited to see his father's reaction before saying, "Yeah, great idea." I chose to believe that he was feeling too grown up to be going places with his parents.

Frank continued his stops at the bars, and could not walk straight when he got home. I still continued with my dream, making the dresses and the shirts for the boys. I just wanted that picture of a beautiful time to be in my mind for the rest of my life.

"A steak house on Mother's Day," Frank said a few times during his non- drinking days.

I always responded, "That's right."

However, on the first day of May, he walked into the kitchen with his cat- steps, looked down at the floor, and said matter-of-factly, "I think you'll have to settle for a cheaper dinner on Mother's Day, honey. I'm not going to have much money left once I pay all the bills."

I was rolling a pie crust at that moment, and I almost clobbered him over the head with the roller. But I really wanted to go out for that steak dinner.

"I can understand that, Frank. Why, with all your drinking, I'd be surprised if you'll even have enough money left for the house payment. But you know, I really want us to go to a steak house, so we'll use my paycheck. I'll get it on Friday, plus I have another five dollars coming from Amanda, so we'll be okay."

Frank stared at the floor. "Well, I'll feel like a piece of crap if my wife treats me to dinner on Mother's Day."

I thought for a minute, and swallowed a huge lump. "Oh, don't worry about that. I'll just give you the money and you pay for the dinner. No one will know where the money came from."

"Well . . . uh, thank you, honey, but I'll feel shitty anyway. I have let you down too many times."

"Don't worry about feeling shitty, as long as you don't smell like it."

He chuckled. "I have been a lucky man. Any other woman would have kicked me out a long time ago." He walked away scratching his head.

"It's not too late yet!" I replied, but he didn't answer.

We all got dressed up on Sunday at about two o'clock in the afternoon. It was the perfect day, a mild breeze, blue sky with clusters of white clouds here and there, and the temperature warm enough that we didn't have to cover our nice outfits with coats or sweaters. Lucinda and I were dressed in pink and white sandals and stood in front of the mirror, whirling our flared skirts. Frank snapped a picture of us, and would take the little camera with him to have someone take our family picture at the restaurant.

I gave him the money before walking out to the car, so he would not feel embarrassed at the restaurant. His hand shook as he took the bills. Arranging the money in his brown wallet, he whispered, "Fifty bucks for one meal?"

"It'll be worth it," I whispered back, and got into the car.

Two blocks away, he said, "Sure it's got to be a steak house?"

"Yes, the one in Coronado. I heard it's a nice place, and they use tablecloths."

The road from Chula Vista to Coronado was the same one Frank drove to and from work every day.

"You know, honey, I think it's foolish to take kids to a steak house. I've never known a kid that would rather have a steak than a hamburger."

"But this is for me, on Mother's Day, not kid's day."

"Is there such a thing as kid's day, Mommy?" Lucinda's chin rested on the back of my left shoulder.

"No, sweetheart, sit back."

Frank was quiet for about five minutes. Then: "Well, I wish you'd reconsider. Fifty dollars for one meal is a lot of money to dump at one time."

"It's for Mother's Day, Daddy." Troy's chin came forward.

"It's my money!" I added.

"Shut up, Troy, and sit back." Frank's voice was harsh. I knew he needed a drink. We had passed a couple of bars in Imperial Beach, and those fifty dollars were burning holes in his wallet.

"You know . . . Frank, I usually don't like to argue in front of the children . . . but if you keep that up, I'll forget they are here!" I looked back and saw the boys rolling their eyes. Lucinda looked startled, as if she had seen something coming full speed to crush her. My heart ached.

"You're right, Frank. We don't need steak dinners. McDonald's will be good enough, right guys?" None of the children answered. I looked back and smiled. "Right?"

"Right," three voices answered. But I didn't ask what they were thinking.

The golden arches appeared. "You made the right decision, honey," Frank said, turning into the driveway. No one else said a word.

"Okay, kids, what will you have?" Frank asked, getting out of the car.

"Hamburger, French fries, and a chocolate shake," Rodney said.

"Me, too," said Troy, and Lucinda followed.

"What about you?" he had the nerve to ask me.

I swallowed, and said, "The same as the children." I didn't look at him.

He turned and walked toward the entrance. I watched him, and the most bitter taste settled in my mouth. I would suffocate, holding this huge pain until we could be alone. Heart surgery without anesthesia would have hurt me less than that horrible experience.

Frank still treated me special on that Mother's Day. He handed me my meal before giving the children theirs. And from the corner of my eye, I watched him inhaling his hamburger and fries, then slurping his milkshake. I knew he was thinking about the drinks he would have later with *my* money.

I placed my fries and milkshake on the dashboard, unwrapped a corner of my burger, which smelled of onions, and brought it to my mouth. As I did this, the little diamond of my wedding band picked up the light just right, and I saw the blue sky and white clouds in it. Then I saw stars in my eyes, and felt a hot teardrop splatter on my right arm.

With the hand of that same arm, and with little movement, I wiggled my wedding ring off and pushed it into the half-moon mark my teeth had left on the burger. Then, ever so slowly and quietly, I wrapped the burger in its wrapper and squeezed it so hard my knuckles turned white.

The biggest hurt was that Frank never saw what was happening.

There was no doubt in my mind that he was thinking of the money in his pocket, and the many drinks he would have.

I avoided looking at him or the children. Keeping my sunglasses on, I collected my tears in a crumpled napkin.

He stepped out of the car once he swallowed his last mouthful, stuck his head through the back window and asked, "Are you kids finished?" They all handed him the trash. "How about you, honey? Aren't you going to eat the fries?"

I gathered my food with the ring in the burger, handed it to him, and turned to look out the other window. Then, as he walked to the dumpster, I watched his crooked legs, his wide shoulders, his bobbing head, and his hair plastered down with the greasy cream he used. I wanted to kick myself for having loved him for eleven miserable years. I had held on for the sake of my children, who probably guessed what I was feeling, but were afraid to speak.

"So, should we go for a drive?" Frank asked, getting back into the car and holding a cigarette with his teeth.

"No!" Three voices rang out from the back seat.

"Honey, what do you say? Wanna go for a drive?"

I inhaled deeply. "Hell, no!"

Epilogue

Frank didn't believe that I had filed for divorce even after the papers were served. While turning the pages, he said, "You can't be serious."

He put the papers on the coffee table and left.

The next day, he asked, "When did you stop wearing your wedding ring?"

"The day you threw it away," I said as I ironed his shirt.

"I did what?"

"Threw it away."

Frank gave me a cross look. "How in hell did I do that?"

"In the McDonald's hamburger, on Mother's Day."

He sprang from his overstuffed chair. "What was your wedding ring doing in a hamburger?"

"I put it there."

"Why?"

"Because I no longer felt married to you, that's why."

"It's about the damn steak dinner, isn't it?"

"It was my money, Frank. You had no right to keep it for your booze. It was my money, and all I wanted was to celebrate one Mother's Day, just once! But there are a lot more reasons, the most serious being your drinking, which you refuse to seek treatment for!"

Frank clenched his teeth. "I am not an alcoholic. Get that through your thick head!"

I kept ironing, one eye on him, the other on the blue shirt. Finally, he slapped his thigh and headed for the door on his way to the bars.

I made a bed on the floor in Lucinda's room, where I slept for the next six months. During those six months, Frank went around barking and trying to make me return to his bed.

"I don't know why in hell you're divorcing me. I have been loyal to our marriage and have never lifted a finger to you or the kids. I have told you time and again that I'll quit drinking one of these days!"

"Yes, you said that, but I'm not willing to grow old waiting for you to stop getting drunk!"

"All right, all right," he said. "You can have the bed. I'll sleep on the floor. Just forget about the damn divorce."

"I'm okay in Lucinda's room," I answered. "It's not like I have never left our bed before."

Frank even kicked the bathroom door open one day when I was in the shower. "It's time you stopped this foolishness about divorce. You promised to love me, and I'm claiming my marital rights!"

Only by pushing him into the bathtub was I able to get out. From then on, I took my showers while he was at work.

On his next try, Frank decided to use reverse psychology. "I don't blame you for divorcing me, 'cause you took a big beating."

Shocked, I asked, "Are you calling our time together a game? One of us trying to beat the other? If so, the game wasn't fair. You were bigger and smarter, and bound to win every time!"

"Oh, honey, stop fooling around and get back to normal." He reached for me, but I backed away.

"I don't want to get a court order to force you to move out, Frank, but legally you were supposed to leave upon receiving the divorce papers."

"No one's ever going to force me out of my own home! Get that straight in your head!"

We had those episodes at least once a week. On the day before our court hearing, Frank decided to try to save our marriage.

"I want to take you out to dinner," he said, sober, clean-shaven, and with his most tender smile. "I really want to save our marriage because I could never love anyone but you."

"You waited too long, Frank."

"That's because I didn't think you would go through with the stupid divorce."

"Where do you want to take me to dinner? It's not the steak house in Coronado, is it?" I was remembering the Tootsie Roll when Troy was born, and the five pounds of chocolate three months later.

"No. Not the steak house. But I cut out a coupon from the newspaper – buy one hamburger at Jack-in-the-Box and get one free."

It wasn't the cheapness of that proposal that made my blood boil, but the innocent look in Frank's face. I grabbed my head and screamed. I ran out the door, and kept running until I felt my feet burning.

Shortly after filing for the divorce, I had sat at the table and told our children why I was divorcing their father. That was my most painful experience, for I had wanted them to think highly of their daddy. "In spite of his drinking, your father is a good person," I told them. "And he loves you very much."

"Why are you doing it, then?" Rodney's question was loud and irritating. "What's wrong with drinking? Isn't he over twenty-one? You just want to leave him, that's all!"

"I heard Daddy talking mean to you, Mommy," said Lucinda.

"And I saw him puking in the toilet," added Troy.

Rodney gave his brother a mean look. "What's wrong with puking? Don't you puke sometimes?"

I explained to the children that my father had been a drunk, and I would not spend the rest of my life with a drunk husband.

"Please understand that I still love your father, and I adore you three, but our style of life is not what I wanted. Divorce is not a disgrace – it is a detour away from a marriage that isn't working. When two people can't work things out, they should part. Both married people have to compromise. In our case, your daddy chose booze over me. I can't live with that."

As I tried to explain to my children my reasons for breaking apart their safe haven, I noticed the look in Rodney's eyes. Like his father, he listened, but no one would talk him out of believing what he wanted to believe.

Frank did not contest the divorce, and did not show up in court the day of the hearing. Knowing that he would never let me stay at the house with the children, I had requested that we sell it and divide whatever money we got. We would divide the furniture, too. With my part of the money, I would buy myself a used car so I could attend school the next year.

I asked only for child support, for I didn't want Frank hating me over alimony payments. What I earned at Uni-Mart would be enough to pay the rent for a little cottage behind Debby's sister's house, which she had promised to me once the old tenant moved out. The three-room place was located between Uni-Mart and the school, making the walk for the children and me a lot shorter.

On the day Lucinda started second grade, I drove to the junior college suggested by Debby and registered to begin English One.

Driving there that day in my own car – a Chevy Impala, red with a white top – I felt free, but displaced. I had just legally given up my American name, which I would continue to use because it was convenient. Now I was no one's daughter, and no one's wife. There was something creepy about that thought.

Still, the morning was beautiful, and white and yellow daisies were blooming alongside the lonely road. Up on a hillside, a herd of cattle feasted on green grass, swinging their tails and moving gracefully past each other.

I turned left, following the signs to South Western College.

Frank, who had stated that he could never love another woman, married a young girl from the Philippines three months after the divorce. She gave him four children in five years, and if it hadn't been for an emergency hysterectomy, she would have ended up with a dozen or more.

All the children stayed with me, but a year later Rodney moved in with his father. He could not handle my repeated encouragements about education. I nagged too much, he claimed. His daddy was more lenient. Rodney dropped out of school at age sixteen to work as a mechanic in a garage.

Troy read anything that had to do with airplanes and engines, graduated from high school, then went on to college to study aviation.

Lucinda discovered boys, but made it through high school, and went on to become a nurse. She dropped out two years later to marry her highschool sweetheart and is now a stay-at-home mother of two boys.

Before leaving for college, Troy sat at the table with Lucinda and me for one of our long conversations. "This is important, Mom," he said, business-like. "So listen carefully. Now that you don't have to come running home from work or school to cook and clean for us, I want you to meet a nice man and get married again."

I almost fell off the chair. "Married again?" I had gone out with Debby and her sister Marie a few times, and had even danced with some young sailors and Naval officers, trying to experience the freedom I had not had as a teenager. But the thought of remarrying had not even entered my mind.

"Yes, Mom, married. You are still beautiful, and too young to end up alone. There is a nice man worthy of you out there somewhere. But you need to go out and find him. I don't want to think of you in a small apartment all by yourself."

"Yeah, Mom," said Lucinda, her beautiful hazel eyes sparkling. "You can still meet somebody good. How about it? Will you do it?"

I thought for a moment, admiring two of my beautiful teenage children. Then I said jokingly, "I'll marry again when I find a man younger than I, not an old tired one. He has to be a non-drinker, a non-smoker, and religious, for I want direction in life. And most importantly, he must be a professional with a high-paying job, for I do not need a man if I have to go to work to pay the rent. That's the only way I'll ever marry again."

"In that case, Mom," Lucinda said, raising her chin, "count on being alone for the rest of your life, 'cause there is no such man out there waiting for you."

"Ah," said Troy, armed with confidence, "but if there is such a man out there, Mom will be the one who finds him. Just wait and see." He winked at me. I stood up and hugged him.

Lucinda bolted out of her chair and joined us. "I guess you're right, Troy. Mom would be the one to find such a man."

I stretched my arms around both of them and held them tightly as our tears blurred our vision.

"So many years ago, I started out chasing a wild dream," I said. "And today I have treasures to hold in my arms."

"And I hold the biggest treasure in mine," Troy said.

"Me, too," Lucinda whispered.

This is very good, I thought, unable to say the words.